CW00968390

ONE WHO WALKED ALONE

ROBERT E.
HOWARD
THE FINAL YEARS

ONE WHO
WALKED
ALONE

By NOVALYNE PRICE ELLIS

Donald M. Grant, Publisher, Inc.
Hampton Falls, New Hampshire

ONE WHO WALKED ALONE
Copyright © 1986 by Novalyne Price Ellis

Jacket photographs © 1996 by
The Kushner Locke Company
Used with their kind permission

Now a Major Motion Picture:
THE WHOLE WIDE WORLD

Starring Vincent D'Onofrio and Reneé Zellweger
Directed by Dan Ireland
Screenplay by Michael Scott Myers
Distributed by Sony Pictures Classics
Available on videotape and DVD.

All right reserved under International
and Pan-American Copyright Conventions.
Printed in the United States of America

First Published 1986

7 9 8 6
ISBN 0-937986-78-X

DONALD M. GRANT, PUBLISHER, INC.
POB 187, HAMPTON FALLS, NH 03844

http://www.grantbooks.com

In Memory
of
Robert E. Howard

ACKNOWLEDGMENTS

No one writes alone anymore than one lives alone. I have had the help and encouragement of many people in this undertaking, and I would like to acknowledge my indebtedness and appreciation to them.

My special thanks and appreciation to Glenn Lord whose patience and interest helped keep me going. To Kirby McCauley for making valuable suggestions about the manuscript. To Clyde Smith for help and assistance; Clyde, a close friend of Robert Howard's, agreed to write the introduction. To Dr. Harley Smith, Dr. Hosea Phillips, Dr. Vaughn B. Baker and Mrs. Joan Fields for reading the manuscript and making valuable suggestions. Special thanks to Donald Grant for help and assistance in the final preparation of the manuscript.

My family also deserves special mention. To my son, Marvin D. Ellis, for help and advice with the photographs. Last and most important, my husband, William W. Ellis, who once again, as he always did when I was working, endured late meals and poor housekeeping, and, in this case, went even further to help. He helped type the manuscript! I am convinced that, without family and friends who help and advise, no manuscript would ever be completed.

NOVALYNE PRICE ELLIS

IN REGARD TO THIS BOOK AND THE AUTHOR

On Monday, June 15, 1981 Novalyne Price Ellis wrote from Salt Lake City to tell me that she had been elected to the National Forensic League Hall of Fame. She had received the honor the preceding evening. The trip to Utah came a short time after a week in New York City where she had gone at the request of her friends on the faculty of Cathedral Carmel High School. The New York City journey was also connected with the profession of speech, a profession which Novalyne has loved and followed all her life.

We didn't call it speech when I was a boy in Coggin Ward School. It was known as Expression in those days, and Novalyne held the attention of her classmates with a fiery rendition of Alfred Noyes's "The Highwayman." The teacher was Miss Bess Brown, and I was also one of her pupils. I carried "A Message to Garcia." I went on to other endeavors after the message was delivered, but Novalyne continued her dramatic training and is held in high regard by the hundreds of friends she has made among students, parents, and teachers throughout the years.

Novalyne is not only a success as a teacher of speech but will, in my opinion, become a well known writer after the publication of this book. She is a good writer and she has a valuable manuscript because she was a personal friend of Bob Howard and did not get the information she records second-hand. Her book is especially interesting to me because my last meeting with Bob was in January 1935, and her report fills a gap in Bob's life with which I have been mostly unacquainted.

Letters relative to Bob's death and burial reached me at the same time. I was in Pecos, Texas. My work plan called for me to spend the following week in the Carlsbad, New Mexico territory of Walker-Smith Company, the wholesale grocer handling the line of merchandise which I was selling. Though Bob had expressed his intention of dying before his mother passed away, with the statement that his father was a man and could take care of himself, it was very hard for me to understand how he could treat his father in this way. I wrote Dr. Howard on Sunday night from La Caverna Hotel with the hope that my letter would alleviate a fraction of his sorrow.

A local friend of mine, who grew up in Cross Plains, and was a pupil of Novalyne Price, stated, "Robert was so far ahead of most people that they didn't know what he was talking about." Another person commented on Bob's obsession with the mystery of death, concluding with the opinion: "Bob was so curious about the next world that he wanted to find out for himself just what is there and acted accordingly." Regardless, Bob Howard did his own thinking, and, like many a man and woman before him, knew that to disregard the lessons of history meant total collapse of the Western World. Certainly, in spite of all the optimists, the West appears to be galloping toward the complete chaos which Bob Howard, with his knowledge and wisdom, predicted, for he had the ability to recognize the good to be found in age old values and realized that his People could not survive without unity, knowing that nonentity is the alternative to the violation of custom.

So many years have gone by since Bob left us. Herbert Klatt was the first to go, and Bob was next. Dave Lee followed, and, of course Dr. and Mrs. Howard, The Reverend and Mrs. W. D. Vinson, and my parents, all gracious hosts and hostesses on the many visits to their homes, are dead. Truett Vinson, Harold Preece, Lindsey Tyson, and I remain to remember those days of long ago.

It is with pleasure that I have had the opportunity to read the original manuscript of ONE WHO WALKED ALONE and I appreciate the invitation to write the introduction to this account of the last years in the life of Robert E. Howard. I feel that the details which Novalyne recorded day by day present a vivid picture of Bob which will be eagerly received by her readers. This is her interpretation of the real man. If the reader is surprised at some of her statements that person should be assured that Bob was a very complex man and that Novalyne was well acquainted with him. This is another way of saying that there is a lot of Bob Howard in this book, for Novalyne saw Bob's devotion to his mother and his sense of duty to her. She also saw the true gentleman hidden behind his bluff exterior. She saw his brilliance and his genius. She experienced his dark moods, and her knowledge of him and of the things of which she writes came firsthand to add immensely to Howard lore. She has told her story and there is only one way I can describe it. It is a marvellous delineation.

Tevis Clyde Smith
Pearl Harbor Day
1981

When I began working on the old diaries and journals I had kept from 1934 to 1936, I became obsessed with the desire to go again to Brownwood to see and talk with Clyde Smith, one of Bob Howard's closest friends. I made the trip in December 1980. After that visit, Clyde, Rubye, his wife, and I kept in touch by telephone and by letters. In December 1984, I wrote to Clyde and Rubye concerning the history of Brown County, which Clyde had written. When I did not hear from them, I telephoned a former student of mine, J. H. Childs, who was a close friend of theirs. He told me that Clyde had died December 24, 1984, and that Rubye was ill.

Novalyne Price Ellis

AUTHOR'S PREFACE

Two names in the book, *One Who Walked Alone*, were changed in order not to embarrass anyone still living. Robert Howard disliked one of my students very much. That student is called "Mark" in the book. Dolores Dalton is not the name of the lovely young woman of whom Bob spoke so glowingly.

ONE WHO WALKED ALONE

I met Bob Howard today! I was sitting on the front porch with my physics book in my lap, trying to absorb some of the uninteresting facts in it, when I heard a car stop by the two big oak trees in our front yard. After a minute, I heard a car door slam. I didn't get up. I listened. On the farm, you don't have too many visitors.

Clyde Smith came down the walk to the porch. He was smiling; but he wasn't dressed up, and he didn't have a date.

I got up and said, "Hi."

He didn't answer at once. He turned his head and looked back toward the car and grinned even more. Clyde and I have known each other since we were in grade school, and we've always been friends. The last two or three years, we've dated steadily, not because we're in love; but because we like each other and like to talk about books and writing stories. Both of us try to write; he has sold a few things, and I'm still trying.

I shrugged my shoulders. "I don't care whether you speak or not," I said. It was easy to see that something was up that he thought would devastate me. Someone was in the car . . . someone he thought was special. I played along, pretending I didn't suspect a thing. I pushed a chair toward him. "Won't you sit down?"

"No thanks." He shook his head. "Didn't you say you wanted to meet Bob Howard?"

Bob Howard! I did want to meet him very much, but I didn't want to act too interested or too excited. You have to be in control of things.

"Oh, Bob Howard, the writer," I said.

"You've always said you wanted to meet him. You haven't talked about anything else for the past six months."

Clyde and I had *both* talked about Bob on Sunday when we had a date, and Clyde had told me that Bob was selling almost everything he wrote. Certainly, I wanted to meet a flesh-and-blood selling writer. I put my physics book on the edge of the pillar.

"Well, bring him in; I'll get another chair."

"We haven't got but about ten minutes," Clyde answered.

15

"I told you to bring him in and I'd get another chair."

"Would it hurt you to come out to the car for a minute?" Clyde asked. "Bob's scared of your grandmother, just like I am."

My grandmother is not a large woman, but she has very definite opinions about a lot of things. I smiled at the old joke.

It was probably better for me to go out to the car. If they came in the house, there was a chance that Clyde might open the door of the living room. That could be a catastrophe. As usual, I had books and journals on the floor. If he were to read even a line of some of the things I'd written, I'd never hear the last of it.

"Well, okay," I said, and I walked with him toward the car, feeling a little self-conscious. At our house, a young lady did not sit in a car with a young man. If you want to talk, come in the house. That's the rule.

Bob Howard was sitting in the front seat of the car! He got out as we came toward it. This man was a writer! Him? It was unbelievable. He was not dressed as I thought a writer should dress. His cap was pulled down low on his forehead. He had on a dingy white shirt and some loose-fitting brown pants that only came to his ankles and the top of his high-buttoned shoes. He took off his cap and I saw that his hair was dark brown, short, almost clipped. He ran his hand over his head.

The day seemed unreal, but I was making mental comments to preserve the moment. Bob's a big man. Not as tall as Clyde, but at least six feet tall. He looks so much larger than Clyde. He must weigh two hundred pounds. Maybe more.

We were beside the car now, and I was looking into his eyes and trying to read the expression in them. How do you describe a man's eyes? They were blue. Or gray. Deep. Shadowy. I couldn't tell from their expression whether he was happy or unhappy. He must be terribly shy, I thought. His eyes are so uncertain . . . filled with questions. I'll always remember his eyes and this meeting.

"This is Bob. Bob, this is Novalyne." Clyde was talking easily, freely. Introducing two of your friends is such a simple thing.

"Howdy," Bob said.

"Hi." I said. Just that. Nothing more.

"Bob's the greatest pulp writer in the world," Clyde said.

Bob glanced briefly at Clyde and smiled. "Yeah, that's right. I write for the pulps." I liked his voice. It was pleasant. Not too high. Not too deep. Pleasant. He looked back at me, and I looked him straight in the eyes and tried to think of something smart to say. He helped. "Clyde says you're interested in writing."

"I try." I managed to laugh. "But I haven't sold anything yet."

Bob opened the car door for me and I got into the front seat. He crawled into the back. Clyde sat behind the steering wheel. I sat with my back to my door so that I could easily see both of them.

"Want to ride around a little while?" Clyde asked.

I looked at him quickly. What about those ten minutes they had?

"Sure," Bob said cheerfully. "I've got the time."

"Why not?" I asked laconically.

And why not? It was spring. The mesquites had green fringe for leaves; in the background, the oaks were a darker green. Birds were singing. It was a nice time of year. I had reason to be excited! This had to be an important day in my life! We'd be sure to talk about Bob's writing, and maybe I'd learn something which would explain to me why I was not selling. And there was more to this than that too. When you're young, you think: Is Bob Howard the MAN I've been looking for all my life?

We didn't talk much until we got to the highway. Neither of us quite knew how to begin.

Finally, Clyde started things off. "What have you been doing?"

"Studying. That's all."

"Clyde says you're going to Daniel Baker College," Bob said. "When do you finish?"

"This spring," I answered. "I didn't have the money to go straight through college, and so I go every other year. I'll only be a hundred and a half when I graduate."

Bob laughed. "I was too dumb for college. They always wanted me to take a bunch of stuff I wasn't interested in."

I was beginning to relax. "It's like that everywhere. I argued with Dean McClelland and Dr. Chandler for years, telling them I didn't want to take math, biology, and physics because I'd never use them after I got out of college. Guess what?"

"What?" Bob smiled, and his eyes were less shy.

"My senior year I'm taking math, biology, and physics."

Bob laughed again, a low friendly laugh of interest and good humor. "I thought you'd major in English, public speaking, or drama."

"She doesn't have to major in drama," Clyde spoke up. "Any minute now she'll recite the whole damn *Merchant of Venice* for you."

"Not this afternoon." I felt really comfortable now. At ease. I could hold my own with these two. What I wanted to talk about was writing. I looked at Bob. "How did you get started writing?"

"I tried a lot of other jobs," he said, "and I didn't like 'em. I worked on a farm and that was not good at all, but clerking in a store is about the worst job you can have. So I decided the only way I could get out of working for a living was to start writing."

"That isn't work?" I asked.

"Well," he hesitated, "not by the sweat of your brow at any rate. You can stay home. All you have to contend with is a typewriter and it just puts down what you want it to. It doesn't swear at you when you do something wrong. If it does, you can whip it. What are you going to do when you finish school? Are you going to write? Teach? What do young ladies do when they finish college?"

"Teach," I said, "but maybe I'll find time to write too."

"No, you won't." Clyde winked at Bob. "You'll be directing plays. Doing something like that all the time. You can't stand not being around people."

"Writing is a lonely business." Bob shook his head.

"Yeah, and Novalyne can't stay by herself for a minute," Clyde went on. He ran his tongue around his lips in a way he does and smiled.

"Not true," I said. Sometimes that joke got a little old. "As an only child, I simply can't live without spending some time alone every day. Clyde knows that."

"What'll you teach?" Bob asked.

"Public speaking if I'm lucky. English," I said. "Maybe history."

"You like history?" Bob was genuinely interested.

"I like everything but math, physics, and biology," I said.

He laughed. "Same here. Do you have any idea where you'll teach?"

I shook my head. "Wherever I can find a job. They're pretty hard to get nowadays with the depression what it is. Last year, I applied for an English job at Early High School, but there were about seventy-five of us asking for the same job. So, I don't know where I'll find one."

"What kind of stories do you write?" Bob changed the subject.

I was a little embarrassed to talk about my own attempts at writing. "I've tried to write a few plays, but the amateur companies I might sell to only pay royalty on production. If a play is produced just once in a year, your royalty might not be more than five or ten dollars. That doesn't put any food on the table. The last few months, I've tried to write for the confession magazines, but I think the editor meets them at the post office and sends them back by return mail. I do better with the slicks."

"The confessions," Bob said. "I sold them a yarn or two."

"Trouble with Novalyne," Clyde said, "is that she goes to church, decides she wants to be a preacher and writes a sermon to bring in the unrighteous."

"Remind me to let you read some of them," I said. I turned back to Bob. "I really don't know what to do now. Usually, when I send a story to one of the slicks, I get a word or two written in pencil or ink on the rejection slip. I still get printed rejection slips all right, but most of them have a name or something on them, and so I figure more than one reader saw it—maybe even an editor."

"We live on words of encouragement," Bob said.

I nodded. "The other day I got a note from an editor, not a rejection slip. The main thing he said in the note was, 'Good irony. Please try us again.' "

"Send it to another magazine," Bob suggested.

"That was the second magazine," I said ruefully. "The first sent it back with just one word on the rejection slip: 'Sorry.' "

"That's better than a printed rejection slip without 'Sorry' on it. What's it about?"

I hesitated. One night when Clyde and I had a date, he had just read a book he wanted to tell me about. I didn't want to listen to that particular book, but he told the whole story anyway. While he was talking, I sat on my side of the car and planned a story about a man who always told the stories he read, and no one else had a chance to talk. When I got home that night, I wrote my story.

"It's called 'The Last of Henry's Stories,' " I said. "I'm not going to send it out again. I think I'd better learn to write before I try to sell any more stories, and so I practice."

Bob looked interested. "Practice?"

"I've been keeping diaries and writing journals since I was a senior in high school. Since I've studied plays so much, I write down conversations I have with people. Things like that. But it's practice. I've always thought that might help you learn to write."

"Sounds all right," Bob said.

"Damn," Clyde said, "I hope you don't write down everything I say."

Two can play at the teasing game. "Don't worry. I only write interesting conversations," I quipped.

"Well, damnation," Clyde said belligerently.

"I don't suppose a real, everyday conversation would go into a play, would it?" Bob said quickly, as if he were afraid Clyde and I would get into an argument. Bob seemed very kind and thoughtful of other people's feelings. Terribly shy. He doesn't know much about women.

"Not unless there was some conflict in the conversation, I suppose," I answered. "But a lot of conversations do have conflict in them."

Bob grinned at Clyde in the rear-view mirror. "If you were to write down some of the conversations ol' Clyde and I have, you sure wouldn't learn much about writing."

Clyde was clearly amused.

"What do you talk about?" I asked.

Bob took off his cap, ran his hand over his head and put his cap back low on his forehead. "Well, we talk about some nurses, and then . . . we talk about some nurses . . . and then we talk about some nurses . . . and then we . . . talk about some . . . nurses . . ."

"You talk about nurses," Clyde broke in, "I just talk about girls."

I thought maybe it would be a good idea to put a stop to that part of the conversation. "How did you get started as a writer?" I asked.

"Well, I agree with you that you have to practice," Bob said, "and so I practice too, but not the way you seem to. I read magazines I want to write for, and—"

"The pulps," Clyde put in.

"Yeah, the pulps. A lot of writers get their start there. They don't pay much, a half-cent a word, and so you have to stretch your yarns to the breaking point. You take a hundred words to say twenty-five. But that's okay with me. I'm verbose. I've got plenty of words."

"Do you try to write like the guys who write for the magazines you write for?" Clyde asked.

"Hell, no," Bob was emphatic about that. "I let them try to write like me."

Clyde nodded with appreciation.

"I thought you had to practice a style," I said.

"In a way," Bob agreed. "After I read a lot of issues of a magazine to get the feel of what the readers want and of the things the editors look for, I sit down at my old trusty typewriter and bang out a yarn I think fits the pattern. Then I send 'em off. Some of 'em come back. If they've been the rounds, I throw 'em in an old trunk I have. Someday, they'll sell, and I'll be rich and famous."

"Bob sometimes spends as much as eighteen hours a day at the typewriter." Clyde told me. "You call that pressing the seat of the pants to the seat of the chair."

"Do you begin with a character or with a description of a place or with a plot?" I asked.

Bob thought a minute. "Every way, but mostly with a character, I suppose. I've got a character going now—"

"Conan, the Barbarian," Clyde interrupted. "A ruthless barbarian who loves, fights, and battles the supernatural."

Bob took off his cap and twisted it in his hands. His eyes were smiling. "That Conan's the damndest bastard I ever saw. He gets himself into all kinds of scrapes. I sure don't try to give him advice when he tells me all that junk. I just sit back and listen."

"Do you know what he's telling you?" Clyde said to me. "He's telling you that a real character has a mind of his own, even in a story."

I didn't say anything to them, of course, and I certainly wouldn't want them to know what I was thinking. I thought: Who cares about barbarians or what a barbaric—bastard—does? It's real people—real live people—I want to write about.

"You wouldn't like Conan," Bob said to me.

"I might," I said. "I'd like to read some of your stories about him. Where can I find them?"

He looked pleased. "*Weird Tales* publishes most of my stuff."

I must have looked a little startled, for he grinned, ran his hand over his head and went on. "I guess you wouldn't want to walk into a store and buy a *Weird Tales* magazine, would you? What magazines do you read?"

"When I was in high school, I read *Cosmopolitan, Saturday Evening Post, Smart Set—*"

"H. L. Mencken's magazine when Novalyne read it," Clyde said. "But I'll bet she didn't follow him to the *American Mercury.*"

"H. L. Mencken, the man who looks in the mirror and thinks he's shaving God," Bob said.

He and Clyde laughed uproariously. They thoroughly enjoyed each other's jokes.

"I'd better be getting back," Bob said. "My mother will be ready to go by this time."

Clyde turned the car around, and we headed back toward my house. There were a lot more questions I wanted to ask Bob about his writing and about writing in general; however, even if I hadn't learned too much, it had been an afternoon when I had had the opportunity of being with a selling writer, and that opportunity doesn't come along every day in this part of Texas. Very few people are interested in the things I like and like to talk about. That's why I appreciate Clyde. We stopped at my house.

My grandmother was walking toward the chicken pens. We stood by the car and looked at her. I was proud of her, proud to be her granddaughter. She was in her seventies, but she walked straight and tall, not like an old woman, not like anyone else I knew. She was proud, proud of herself, proud to be capable of doing the things she did. She waved, and the three of us waved back.

"You know," Clyde said wonderingly. "I can stop smoking. I can go for days and never even want a cigarette, but the minute I see your grandmother, I want a cigarette."

We laughed, and Bob said, "She doesn't like smoking?"

"Doesn't like it!" Clyde grinned. "A breath of smoke comes her way and you have to swallow the cigarette, fire and all."

Bob laughed. "That's good for you."

"She's the greatest woman I've ever known," I said.

Bob seemed surprised. "Greater than your mother?"

"You love different people different ways," I tried to explain. "I love my mother. I admire her. She's a very beautiful and capable woman; but, there's something sort of special about my grandmother."

Clyde shrugged. "Bob, you'll learn that if her grandmother says white is black, Novalyne will swear that it's so."

"What do you call her?" Bob asked.

"Mammy," I answered.

"Mammy?"

His surprise amused me. "Old-fashioned, isn't it? That was a term of endearment in the part of the South she came from. She doesn't want to be called 'grandmother' because it makes her feel old."

Bob wanted to know how old she was, and when I told him she was seventy-five, he whistled softly. "She doesn't look it from here."

"Nor close to her either," Clyde said. "I think she could still whip you and me."

"I don't doubt it," Bob agreed. "I'm pretty weak."

"I'd better be going in." I turned to Bob. "I really have enjoyed meeting you, Bob. I'd looked forward to it."

"I've enjoyed it too," he said.

Clyde walked to the door with me. "I'll see you again in a few days."

At the steps, I turned around and looked back at Bob. He was still standing by the car; he had rolled up his cap and tucked it under his arm. He raised his hand, smiled, and waved. I waved back and smiled too. Clyde went back to the car and they drove away. I was still excited. I had met Bob Howard, a man who made his living writing stories!

I stood by the pillar where my physics book lay and looked after them until they were out of sight. I didn't want to study physics. After I finished helping with the night work and ate supper, I'd find one of my journals and write it all down. I'd try to describe exactly how I felt. When I could describe my feelings and what I saw and heard in such a way that someone else would be affected as I had been, I'd write a story and it would sell. I, too, would be a writer.

I wanted so much to be a writer.

INTRODUCTION TO THE
CROSS PLAINS
DIARIES AND JOURNALS

After I met Bob Howard in the spring of 1933, I finished college and tried to become a writer. Although I continued to get notes and letters from some editors, I was not making sales.

Clyde Smith told me that, when Bob finished school and decided to write full-time, he asked his parents to give him a year. If at the end of that year, he had not sold anything, he would give up his dream of being a writer. Clyde made the same bargain with his parents when he finished college.

I could not make a bargain like that with my mother and grandmother. Earning a living on a small Texas farm during the depression was too difficult. Besides, the prevailing attitude of the people throughout that section of Texas in the 1930s was discouraging to a beginning writer. When I told one of our neighbors, I was trying to write stories, she said, "Now, why don't you go to Brownwood and try to get a job at Woolworth's? Why, I know a girl working there who makes nearly nine dollars a week!" Sitting at a typewriter and writing stories indicated you were lazy, no-good, and were sponging off your poor old mother and grandmother!

During the spring and summer of 1933, I looked for a teaching job, but there were always sixty or seventy experienced teachers applying for the same one. In January of 1934, I did get a teaching position in a small town near Abilene. Though I was re-elected for the following year, I received a better position in Cross Plains, Texas, where my friendship with Bob Howard really began.

Teaching required so much time, I could write very few stories. But I kept trying to learn to write by keeping voluminous diaries and journals in which I recorded my views on life, conversations with Bob and other people, notes on the weather, descriptions of places and events, all in an effort to practice until the day I could write full-time.

When Bob killed himself in 1936, I planned to write a book about him. However, instead of becoming a writer, I became a full-time teacher, housewife, and mother. Finally, when the time came to write my book about Bob Howard, the man, I discovered that it was already written in the old diaries and journals I kept in those years.

To understand Bob, the things he said and did, and even, I think, the length of his life, one must see him in his own time and place. One must have some knowledge of his dreams, beliefs, and ambitions as he discussed them with persons who were close personal friends.

These diaries and journals, written with enthusiasm at the time of the happenings, present Bob Howard, the man, in his own milieu better than I could do it today. As I reread the journals, I was amazed at the relevance of his ideas to today's world and beliefs. But the end of the story, the predictions Bob made, the reason for his death, I leave to the reader to understand and reach his own conclusions.

And now . . . Bob Howard, the man behind the myth. The town . . . the people . . . the times in which he lived. . . .

My cousin Enid saved my life!

She came over last Sunday, and she was beaming. She had just heard from Cross Plains that they were going to hire another teacher, and this teacher, she went on excitedly, would teach public speaking, English, and maybe another subject. She didn't remember what, but it certainly wouldn't be home ec as I was going to have to teach in that little town near Abilene.

Teaching home ec really scared me! Sure. I was a home economics major in college. That was the only kind of scholarship available to women. But I was the despair of that department's professors. Two or three summers ago, when I walked across the Daniel Baker campus, Miss Peavey looked out the window and saw me. She stopped right in the middle of her class and said, "Oh, my God, there goes Novalyne Price. If she comes to school next year, she'll take home economics!"

But Cross Plains! Cross Plains, Texas. Bob Howard's home town. No home ec. Dear God, I prayed, if I must teach, let it be in Cross Plains.

Enid had made good in Cross Plains as a high school English teacher. Last year, her sister, Jimmie Lou, had taught second grade there, and she succeeded too. With the number of teachers out of work these days, it paid to have someone already established, like Enid, to recommend you.

"Get your things ready and go home with me," Enid said. "Tomorrow, I'll take you to Cross Plains and you can apply for the job."

Enid is so capable of telling you what to do, you don't even argue. Although the job sounded good, Enid scares me.

"Do you know Bob Howard?" I asked.

She looked straight through me.

"Listen," she said in that emphatic way she has of talking. "Before you apply for that job, I want you to know something. I expect you to do a fine job. Not a good job. You have to be better than that! I know you'll do well with the speech classes, but I want you to do well with the other two courses—English and . . . whatever . . . I'll help with the English. But you've got to work! You'd better stop fooling around, wasting time on something that won't get you anywhere."

She paused, and I began to wonder if you could teach sewing even if you didn't know how to do it yourself. With Enid after me constantly, my job would be rough. Even in Cross Plains.

"I want you to know about Nat Williams, too," Enid went on, as if I'd tried to interrupt her. "You won't ever have a better superintendent. There aren't many like him. He's an educator. That means he's interested in everything. He's just as interested in your classes and my classes as he is in football."

"Now, Enid, really—" I began.

She ignored me. Her voice was filled with scorn for lesser superintendents. "When he went to Cross Plains, the schools were nothing. I mean nothing! They just taught to the tenth grade. In less than two years—" That was so important she repeated it emphatically. "In less than two years, he had a four-year high school, fully accredited."

Stoically, I packed my suitcase.

Enid grew pensive. "Besides that," she added irrelevantly, "he's better looking than Clark Gable."

That, I thought, was heresy. Enid went on to explain about his wife and children, and I busied myself trying to find something to wear that would impress a good-looking, intellectual educator with my ability as a teacher.

We—Enid, her younger sister Georgia, and I—got to Cross Plains about the middle of the morning. I talked to Superintendent Williams. Enid had not underestimated either his looks or his competence; however, I was so nervous I couldn't appreciate him or the job.

Being nervous always affects me in one of two ways: I either go mad and talk all the time, or I go silent and can't think of a word to say. In Mr. William's office, I talked all the time.

He was quiet and dignified. He wanted to know how much experience I'd had. I told him in great detail about every job I'd ever had. I'd taught two years. I told him about each school, its size, its location, what I taught, what my room was like, how many students I had in each class, and I tried to tell him how much each student had learned. I *didn't* tell him how much I wanted to be a writer.

He smiled as if to make me feel at ease and nodded his head. Finally, he broke in. "I've heard you are a very good speaker yourself, but have you ever taught public speaking?"

"I began teaching speech when I was fourteen, a junior in high school," I said quickly. "Private lessons in expression to kids almost my own age. I gave them one thirty-minute private lesson and one one-hour class lesson a week. I had six students and made eighteen dollars a month. I paid for my own lessons in expression at Daniel Baker. I took speech there during my fours years in high school and also in college."

I sounded silly even to myself. I was glad when Mr. Williams got a chance to interrupt me.

"How many hours do you have in English?" he asked.

That question gave me a chance to tell him about every English course I'd ever taken, including Shakespeare. What I had taught in my English classes last year and how I'd gone back to Daniel Baker last summer to audit one of Mrs. Wright's advanced grammar classes.

"What about history?" he wanted to know.

I told him my whole history.

He asked me how I would like to teach two classes in English, two of ancient history and one of public speaking. The man asked me how I'd like it! Teaching was an honorable profession. Writing was not!

At that precise moment, I froze up and just stared at him. I couldn't think of a word to say.

"The Board of Trustees will meet this afternoon," Mr. Williams said uneasily. "If you can come back about four o'clock, we'll let you know what we've decided."

He got up, went to the door, called Enid and told her to take me to see a couple of Board members, and to be sure to talk to Mr. Walker at Higginbotham's.

It was almost lunch time, and so Enid thought we ought to drive around over the town so that I'd have some idea what it was like. Furthermore, it would give the Board members a chance to go home, eat lunch, and get back to work. Anything she said was fine with me.

On any other day, I would have loved Bob Howard's town. It was a typical southwest town. Quiet. Sprawling. Nice, well-kept yards with trees and a profusion of flowers. On any other day, I would have loved the rows of stores bordering the wide, wide main street that cut through the town and led straight to the school yard. Today, I didn't love anything.

We ate lunch at a little cafe next door to Smith's drugstore and across from the post office. After lunch, we crossed the street to Higginbotham's to talk with Mr. Walker.

"Listen," Enid said conspiratorially. "Mr. Walker is very active in church. He will be interested in the church programs you give. Tell him you memorized the 'Book of Job' from the Bible and read it in every church in Brownwood and . . . everywhere. He'll like that."

It hadn't dawned on Enid yet that I had been struck dumb while I was talking to Mr. Williams.

Enid introduced me. "This is my cousin, Mr. Walker," she said brightly. She explained that I was applying for a job here and mentioned the subjects I wanted to teach. She kept looking at me, her eyes getting sharper and sharper. I just stood there and looked at her and Mr. Walker.

She began on my church programs, explaining each one and how it had been received by the congregation. She finished with a glowing description of my rendition of the "Book of Job."

Mr. Walker seemed impressed. "That's fine. I'm glad to hear about those programs. Maybe we could get you to give us one some day."

"How do you do?" I said and avoided Enid's eyes.

On the way to Mr. Mitchell's office, Enid lectured me, told me to speak up, tell him my qualifications.

I couldn't think of any.

Enid glared at me and did the talking. I was beginning to get a headache. It was hot and my brown linen dress wasn't the coolest thing in the world. I wanted to take my hat and gloves off. I dared not. I had to look a proper teacher, for I was beginning to want this job very much, and not just because I might talk to Bob Howard about writing. I liked the town, the people I'd seen, and I liked Mr. Williams very much. I wanted to teach there.

I thought about the last story I'd gotten back from that woman's magazine. The editor had written me a letter saying that it was an awkward length. Then he went into detail about the length of stories in his magazine. At the end, he'd written: "You might tighten." That floored me.

Tighten what? If only I could talk with a professional writer! But I still had two confession stories out. If one or both sold, I just might tell people I was going to stay home and be a writer. If only I had the nerve!

We went back to the school in the afternoon. The Board met in Mr. William's office. Enid, Georgia, and I waited in the big study hall across from the office. There were a couple of other teachers there who had been told to come back that afternoon. One of the women had on a little voile dress, and a little soft, rolled brim hat. She looked cool and complacent. Maybe she had no dreams to suppress. I envied her.

In a few minutes, Mr. Williams and the Board came trooping into the study hall and sat down. My mouth was dry, and I tried to remember if there'd ever been a time in my life when I had been more scared. All of the Board were smiling. Ordinarily, I would have thought them nice, friendly gentlemen. At that moment, they could have been zombies, and I'd have been more at ease.

"Miss Price," Mr. Williams said, and I couldn't tell if that was a twinkle in his eyes, "we think we may want you for our public speaking teacher, but, first of all, we would like for you to give us a reading and then we'll decide whether you get the job or not."

I blinked, not sure what he'd said until I saw Enid smiling at me expectantly. "Read 'Betty at the Baseball Game,' " she whispered. I knew if I didn't get up, she'd hit me.

I put my purse down, took off my gloves, and went to the front of the room and gave my selection. They thought it was funny! They laughed so much I had to stop several times. After I finished, they said they still couldn't make up their minds and would I give them an encore?

By that time, my head was really hurting. When I finished the encore, Mr. Williams told me they had already decided they were going to hire me, but they just wanted to hear me read before I left!

I didn't know whether to laugh or cry, so I laughed.

Enid and Georgia brought me home. Well, now, I had a sensible job.

Mother gave me the mail. The two confessions were back! Printed rejection slips! Why do I get notes from *Harper's,* or *Collier's,* and even a letter from *Woman's Home Companion*, but I only get rejection slips from the confessions which are supposed to be easier to sell?

The day Bob Howard had come out to my house with Clyde, Bob had said, "The Confessions? I've sold them a yarn or two."

Why can't I confess something saleable?

Mother and Mammy were proud of my new job. I was too. As I kicked off my high heels, took off my brown linen dress that was too hot, I made up my mind about my future. I would go to Cross Plains, teach school, find a farmer, a shoe clerk, or some other man and marry him.

But the poet was right. "Hope springs eternal in the human breast." Maybe I'd learn something from Bob Howard about writing.

So this is Cross Plains, Texas . . .

We're here in Cross Plains now—Enid, Jimmie, and me—ready to begin school. One minute I'm all excited and can hardly wait to get started, but the next I'm scared stiff.

Mother brought me and my things over—my typewriter, of course, and my books and clothes. I got things straightened around in my room and met my roommate. She's nice and, they tell me, the best in her field, but I wish I didn't have to room with anybody. Roommates cramp your free style. Ethel, that's her name, is a first-grade teacher. She says things like, "Oh, my, my, a typewriter! Well, where will we put it? Where will we find room for all our clothes? Oh, my, my, what nice clothes!"

I didn't tell her that Mother makes all my clothes and that I can get a dress out of a very small amount of material.

I like Ethel, but even if I didn't, it's easy to remember what Enid told me. To Nat Williams, one teacher is as important as another. I could reason, then, that first-grade teachers are as important as speech teachers. Oh, my, my.

We have a room with Mrs. Hemphill, who has a lovely new brick house. Real pretty. It sets off by itself and is about a sandy block from school. It faces west, and we have the front bedroom. With the hot afternoon sun bearing down on it, it isn't very cool.

It's a nice bedroom, though. A large room with plenty of closet space, a vanity dresser, a chest of drawers, a bed, and a table where we put the typewriter and books. Ethel has her books at one end of the table, and I have mine at the other. I have more books than she has. It appears that I have more books than anybody.

We ate supper with the Hemphills. They're very nice. I couldn't eat much because my stomach was turning round and round saying—Tomorrow school begins . . . school begins . . . school begins. We'll have a faculty meeting, of course. Oh, God.

After supper, Ethel asked me if I wanted to go to church. I thought it was a good idea to begin the year with a prayer, and so we went to the Methodist Church. It's only about three or four blocks from us, but there aren't many sidewalks, so it's a little difficult to get to.

Tomorrow, at the faculty meeting, I suppose our handsome superintendent, Nat Williams, will tell us what he expects from teachers. I'll try very hard to please him. Not just because I'm afraid of Enid, but because a good school man is really hard to find.

I want this to be a wonderful year, and I want to do a lot of things. I want to be a good teacher. To write. And I definitely want to direct a few plays.

I have a lot of fears about going into the teaching situation. Sometimes, I'm afraid I'll never get out of it! I wish that my stories would start selling so that I wouldn't have to teach! But I can imagine what my friends, and even my family, would say if I stayed home to write! They'd say to my mother, as some people have, "Are you going to let that lazy Novalyne sit around all day and bang on a typewriter? She ought to be out trying to earn a living. She's lazy. That's all. Lazy!"

I wonder if this has happened to Bob Howard.

This is the real *Cross Plains* . . .
The first faculty meeting . . .

It's here! The first faculty meeting and all the preliminaries are taken care of.

I met all the teachers and got to see Mr. Williams again. He looked even more handsome than he did the day he hired me. Undoubtedly, he is the best-looking man I have ever seen. Average height—about five-eleven, I'd say. Dark complexion. Been in the sun a lot. Dark brown hair. Not cut too short either, the way Bob Howard cuts his hair. Mr. Williams's is long enough to run your fingers through. Maybe he, too, has a few extra pounds around the middle, but on Nat Williams it looks good.

I like Lewis Norman too. He's the principal. He's not good-looking the way Nat is; he's not talkative, the way Nat is, but if you need him, I think he'll be there. A good man.

The other teachers are people with whom I'll work all year. As they came in alone or in two's and three's, they stopped to talk to friends, greeted each other like long-lost relatives, visited with someone a few seconds, found a chair, dropped into it, saw someone else, smiled, and waved.

New teachers were not part of the "family" yet, and they were envious of those who were. They sat at their desks, staring at the old teachers as they came in. New teachers smiled too much. They were too eager to please. They wanted to be liked.

The women were not dressed up, or maybe since there's a depression, they have on their best. Some had on gingham dresses. Cool maybe, but faded from too many washings. It's hot, but I dressed up. I had on a slim, close-fitting, black-silk dress, a silly little perky hat with a black veil. I'm the only one with a hat on. I had on white gloves and black patent shoes with the highest heels I could find. Enid said it was silly to wear gloves and to dress up like that. I put my gloves in my purse.

Ethel and I came together, but we didn't sit together. I sat down one seat back and across the aisle from Enid. She's bossy. I'll admit that, but she's a lovely person. She'll let you know what she thinks and why. She's like Mammy that way. Her hair is dark brown, her skin fair, and her eyes large and blue. They can cut through you better than any knife would. She wears glasses and looks like a school teacher. She doesn't have many dates, not nearly as many as Jimmie does, not even as many as I do. Men look at her, see that school-teacher look and shy away. She was only fourteen when her mother died, and she literally took over her four younger sisters, two brothers, and her dad. She cooked, washed, sewed for the family, bossed them around, nagged when they didn't do their part of the work, and still went to school! She's finished college and now is a fine English teacher. Why can't men appreciate that?

Jimmie Lou is on my left, two aisles over, talking with Anna May, the grammar school principal. "Divinely tall and divinely fair" is an apt description of Jimmie. Her hair is light brown, her skin fair, her eyes hazel. But it's her figure that counts. She has a figure that's nothing short of great! On her, a cotton dress looks expensive.

Some of the other teachers look nice too. Louise, the beautiful one, teaches Spanish and math and directs the chorus.

I didn't try to talk with anybody. I sat still and tried to imagine how these teachers and Cross Plains would affect my life.

We had our meeting in the large study hall so that we'd have desks to write on. It must seat about a hundred kids. It's rectangular, wider than it is long. It has four large tables in the front of the room, one of which has a

Mary Enid Gwathmey

Miss Gwathmey, head of the English department in Cross Plains High School, was instrumental in getting her cousin, Novalyne Price, employment at the high school. Miss Gwathmey was an outstanding English teacher, planning her course upon the needs of the students. She gave up teaching to become a librarian, a position she held in San Marcos, Texas, until her death in 1970.

battered unabridged dictionary on it. Battered but probably not from use. The windows are open because it's so hot. The shades are pulled half-way down. Every one is exactly even with the one next to it. A soft wind slides in and fans us now and then.

Outside about a block away, some children are playing, laughing and shouting. You can hear them when you aren't concentrating on something inside. On the football field closer to the school, the coach has some high school boys in overalls working, laying off lines and things.

But my *real* introduction to Cross Plains was about to begin!

Mr. Williams took his place behind one of the tables at the front of the room. Teachers stopped talking instantly, moved heavily or lightly in their chairs and the women looked at him adoringly. I did too. I've joined the group of his admirers.

Suddenly, for one frantic moment, I wanted to jump up and run out of the room. A premonition, maybe.

I knew that Nat Williams was going to make a good speech. He had the poise as well as the knowledge. It certainly wasn't Nat Williams, the speaker, that bothered me. It was the small town teaching situation itself that I suddenly wanted to swear about. Does a town own its teachers? Does it own all the people who live in it? Does it tell a man what he can do with his life?

If it hadn't been for Enid, I know I would have lost my job right then and there!

And it all began so innocently. Simply with Mr. Williams getting up and making a speech to us, the faculty. He looked at us with that personality smile of his, and, of course, we smiled back.

He started off the way speech books list as a good attention-getting device—compliment the audience. "We've got a great school here and a great faculty." Smiles, head noddings, self-conscious grins from all the faculty.

"We're going to have a great school year." He looked at the coach. "We're going to have a winning football team." Everybody clapped. Coach tried to look self-conscious and humble and succeeded only in looking stupid.

Mr. Williams talked about basketball and track. Enid is right. Everything about a school is important to Nat Williams. Other things were important, too. He said we were going to win the Interscholastic League this year. I sat there thinking: There are a lot of declamations, poetry, and one-act plays in league contests. I'll practice . . . I'll practice . . . I may kill the kids practicing, but I'll win the Interscholastic League for you, Mr. Williams.

If I thought he was interested in athletics and Interscholastic League, I should have waited. When he began on the aims and objectives of academic achievement, I was amazed. He wants the kids to get a college education while they're still in high school!

"Every teacher is an English teacher," he said. "We can't expect to have our students write correct papers and speak correctly, unless every teacher stresses good grammar, good writing, and good speaking."

I saw Enid smile, and I knew that was another reason she thought he was wonderful. He had talked fewer than seven minutes, and he had set goals for us, made us enthusiastic about our school and jobs, and made us feel the success of the school depended on each of us, yet we knew in our hearts that he was the one who made it a success.

I suppose he thought we couldn't take any more of the high-minded stuff right then, and so he changed pace. Every public speaker should be that smart!

He said that we had some new members on the faculty and that we were offering a new course this year. "Public speaking, and we have Miss Novalyne Price to teach it. If you know her or have heard of her, you know she's good. The day we hired her, we had her give a couple of readings for us, and we knew we'd given the job to the right person."

I was too thrilled for words.

But soon I gathered myself together. Mr. Williams introduced all the new teachers, saying how lucky we were to get each one, and I realized, then, that *I* was no exception. Every teacher, new and old, was great as far as Nat Williams was concerned. He said that a successful school depended on other things too, and so he talked of teamwork and teachers getting along with one another. As I listened, I thought that was no problem, for anybody can get along with me if he tries hard enough.

"Since we want the best for every single child in this school," he said, "you will not criticize one of your fellow teachers to any child. Any faculty member who cannot get along peacefully with every other teacher will be looking for a job next year."

Then he dropped his eyes to the table and waited a minute. He drew his lips into a thin, straight line. Enid had told me about that. "When he draws his lips down into a straight line," she'd said, "and they turn a little white, keep your mouth shut and let him alone."

Something was coming. Something important to us and to the town. Everything was quiet. Only the free wind blew the window shades, and they made small, soft little knocks on the window. You wouldn't notice it if you weren't listening to the stillness.

Mr. Williams raised his head and looked at us. "At a meeting of the School Board about a week ago, they decided to take action on an old policy but one which has not been necessary to remind you of until this year." He paused. "I must agree with them that actions by some faculty members have made this necessary."

He looked as if what he had to say was not only necessary but also hard to say, and that was the quietest school room that I will ever see again in my whole life. Somewhere out on the street, a car chugged by, and you could hear it.

Somewhere, some kids laughed and shouted, and you could hear them. But in that school room it was still.

"There will be no drinking, smoking, dancing, Sunday picture shows, or playing bridge by any member of this faculty."

I jerked against the desk and looked at Enid. Those sharp blue eyes of hers cut right through me. They said, "Shut your mouth and don't open it!" I settled back in my chair and looked at Mr. Williams.

"Remember. We are responsible not only for the education of the children entrusted to our care, but we are also responsible for their spiritual welfare. We want them to grow up to be fine men and women. We want them to have good examples to live by. The teachers are their examples." He paused.

My God, with all I've got to do, I have to be an example too!

"You should not plan to go home every weekend either," Mr. Williams went on. "You will be expected to stay here where your work is and attend church here. I want to make it clear that there will be no drinking by any member of this faculty." He cleared his throat. "Furthermore, we want to keep the children from smoking if we can. No smoking on the school grounds or in the buildings. If they see you smoke, they will want to smoke, too. And this applies to the lady faculty members; we more or less accept the fact that men smoke, even if we don't quite approve of it, but lady faculty members are not to smoke anytime, anywhere."

I made an inarticulate gurgle in my throat. These rules and regulations were as strict on the teachers as they were on the students! I got control of myself and wondered why I had thought it might be different here in Cross Plains. Because this town harbored a free spirit—a writer—did I imagine it different from other Texas towns I knew about? The same rules and regulations applied everywhere around here—perhaps even in Brownwood.

Be an example to the children? Do their mothers, their older sisters, or their aunts smoke? Why, then, can't a teacher smoke in her own room? I don't smoke. I don't even want to smoke, but suddenly I want a cigarette. I thought about Clyde's saying that being around Mammy made him want a cigarette, and I understood him for the first time.

I got another one of Enid's looks and settled back in my chair. I want a cigarette, and I want a glass of beer. I can't stand the stuff. I hate it as much as the Board of Trustees do, but I want a cigarette, and I want a beer.

If Mr. Williams had had a glass of water, I think he would have drunk it then. "It has come to my attention that some teachers play bridge so late at night they cannot do their work the next day. You are not to play bridge, not even in your rooms at your boarding places."

Again, I gurgled softly. I'm the worst bridge player in the world, but this was the most unfair thing I ever heard of! Everybody there knew what it was all about. Rumors get around. Most of the lady faculty members—among them Enid, Jimmie, Anna May—played bridge a lot, and they played until midnight every time they played. Sometimes, perhaps, later. I'd heard them talk about their bridge games.

But there was another side to the story. Enid, for example, didn't play bridge every night because on many, many nights she sat up grading English papers. She never neglected grading English papers, even if she had to stay up until one or two o'clock in the morning. Who complained about that? Who would complain if you sat up all night every night studying your lessons in order to teach English, history, or math?

Go to bed early every night? I was in for it. At home, I rarely went to bed before twelve o'clock, and I would rarely go to bed before twelve if I stayed in this town for a hundred years. The Board, good men trying to do the right thing for the students, had no right to tell teachers what they could do and what they could not do with their free time. You can't tell a grown man whether to write or dig ditches!

I wanted desperately to walk out the door. You think that when you grow up, you will be your own boss. You'll decide for yourself what is right and what is wrong.

"Another thing," Mr. Williams said, "you are not to attend nightclubs or go any place where there is dancing. You can't dance all night and teach school the next day."

I stopped listening. No dancing! I loved to dance. I especially loved to dance with Bert Wright. He's the best dancer in the country, and I am next to best. Whenever I go to a party and Bert is there, we dance . . . and dance . . . and dance. We are not Vernon and Irene Castle, but in our own little world . . . in our own small way . . . we are. I will dance with Bert again!

Mr. Williams explained the basic rules . . . the time school would begin each morning . . . when we had to be there . . . noon duty . . . how long we had to stay after school . . . How did we want our salaries? In nine months or in twelve? In some schools you were paid in script, but when Mr. Williams organized a school's finances, you got paid in cash.

When the paper came by me, I took the twelve-month plan. It means that my salary will be divided into twelve monthly payments of sixty-seven dollars and a half. I will try my best to be a good teacher, but the Board of Trustees will treat me like a child; they will not allow me to decide what I will do or not do!

The day ended. Ethel and I came home to Mrs. Hemphill's. Ethel agreed with everything Mr. Williams said. "Oh, my, my. The Board is right. The way some teachers behave! You just don't know. It's the right thing. Put a stop to sin."

I didn't answer. When she finished her bath, I brought my books into the bathroom and sat down to write it all down.

As I write, I'm beginning to cry. I can't see the book, the tears are coming so fast.

I'm crying because I'm going to stay with it. I'm not going home. I can't. I can't give up a good job and a good salary. . . . Writing is too uncertain, and even if I sold something, people would still think I was lazy. Mother worked too hard and gave up too many things to help me get through college. She doesn't think a college education is for staying home on the farm . . . not even to write. . . .

You're a girl . . . you get a good education . . . then you get a nice, easy job teaching school. . . .

Wednesday . . . A lovely Wednesday . . .

Several of us went to town after school today: Enid, Jimmie Lou, Louise, Anna May, one of the elementary teachers whose name I never seem to be able to remember, and I.

Really, though we didn't say it even to each other, we were going to town to look for men. Sure enough, just before we got to Smith's drugstore, we could see a group of young men on the sidewalk.

Jimmie Lou said, "All right, girls. Look hot but keep cool."

Then, of course, the girls began to giggle and sort of hop around, trying to be cute. They laughed over nothing at all, the way girls act when they see a bunch of unattached young men.

The young men were aware of us too. We knew it, though they didn't want us to know it. They wanted to show off for our benefit. They threw their heads back and laughed loudly. Funny. Everybody knew we had come to town to find them and they wanted us to find them, but nobody admitted it.

I didn't jump, and I didn't laugh. I held my head up straight, put my feet down as if I owned the world. I pretended to ignore the men. However, I admit I did look them over very coolly, surreptitiously, to see if Bob Howard might be among them. He wasn't.

We got to the drugstore and there was some whistling and loud guffaws on the men's part and silly giggles from all the girls but me. Louise and Jimmie Lou spoke to one or two of the men.

Mrs. Smith, who owns the drugstore, is very friendly and nice. Everyone likes to talk with her, especially Enid, who is a close friend of hers. Mrs. Smith laughed one day and told Enid that people must need a friendly ear to talk into, for if you bought a person a ten-cent cup of coffee, he'd tell you his life history while he drank it. Today, Mrs. Smith and the girls were talking about things I didn't know anything about. It made me feel more lonesome then ever.

An elderly man came out from a little room in the back of the drugstore and walked toward the front. He was a big man, and he walked with a sort of loping gait, a little shy, as if the bevy of females in the store cramped his style. He tipped his hat and said, "Good evening." Everybody but me said "good evening" back to him. He went out of the drugstore, spoke to the men, stood for a minute, said a word or two, and walked down the street out of sight.

For some reason, I was curious. I walked over to Mrs. Smith and Enid and said, "Who was that?"

"That's Dr. Howard," Mrs. Smith said, as if everybody ought to know who Dr. Howard was.

"Oh, Dr. Howard," I said.

Jimmie Lou and Anna May moved closer to Mrs. Smith and Enid.

I looked at Mrs. Smith, thinking how nice she looked, not like a typical small town woman. Her short, almost black hair was carefully marcelled and parted neatly on the side. I was sure that she liked Dr. Howard. Did it extend to the rest of his family?

"Do you know Bob Howard?"

She stared at me a moment. Enid looked alarmed. "I know a Robert Howard," Mrs. Smith said.

"That's the one," I said eagerly. "Bob—Robert Howard, the writer."

"Oh," Mrs. Smith was completely uninterested. "That was his daddy— his father who just went out the door."

"Yes. But do you ever see Bob?"

Everybody looked at me as if I'd lost my mind or something. I ignored their stares, even Enid's. I was not being out of line. Girls—nice girls—asked about men they thought they wanted to date. Why, the way those girls had pranced around, giggling, and silly when they passed those men on the sidewalk! And, now to stare at me! Ridiculous!

"Bob Howard. He writes stories. That's how he makes his living."

They looked briefly at each other and back at me. Then Jimmie Lou spoke up, "Well, I think he's kind of a freak."

"Yeah," Louise said. "I've heard he's crazy."

Crazy! Well, why not? This is a town that tells teachers what they can and cannot do! Let no man dare to walk alone! If he does, he's crazy.

I began to get a little angry. I looked back at Mrs. Smith. "What about Bob? Does he ever hang out around the drugstore?"

"Oh, Lord, no," she said. "Sure. I see him go across the street to the post office. Sometimes, he comes downtown with his mother, but, Lord, no, I never see him hanging around town."

For some reason, I felt I had to explain things to them. "I've met Bob. He's nice. I want to get better acquainted with him."

Blank stares! I could not believe their reaction to those simple words.

Mrs. Smith shrugged her shoulders. "He's not very friendly. I don't see him talking to many people other than Dave Lee and Lindsey Tyson."

"Don't hold that against him," I said, belligerent now. " 'A prophet is not without honor, save in his own country.' "

From the look in everyone's eyes, I had an idea I was saying the wrong thing, but I couldn't stop. There was something else involved here! A matter of principle. Do you condemn a man because he doesn't live his life the way you want him to? But, of course, if I asked them, they would say they were not condemning him.

"I don't think he's crazy," Mrs. Smith said, "but he is a little peculiar. Personally, I don't care much for the things he writes either. Dr. Howard brought one of his stories to the store once, and I read it. It was all about men fighting and killing each other. I didn't enjoy it too much."

I tried to interrupt. "But just because you didn't like—"

She ignored me. "He goes around by himself or with his mother most of the time."

"Other people in other places like him," I said.

"I've heard he goes to see somebody in Brownwood," Mrs. Smith admitted. "And maybe he's a different person over there. I'm sure I don't know. Dr. Howard says he has friends there."

"I know one of his friends," I said. I had to make them understand that Bob's an artist. Different, but not crazy. "Clyde Smith is a friend of his. He's brilliant too. Bob has another friend there—one that he and Clyde both know—Truett Vinson. He's a very nice person too."

I might have been speaking a foreign language from the look on everyone's face. And what about me? Would they call me a freak if I dated Bob? I had a lot to lose.

I looked at Enid. She was the one whose opinion would matter the most to me. She wouldn't want to date one of those boys out front either. She was too serious. But she wouldn't try to find a Bob Howard, no matter how brilliant he was. She'd sit alone night after night, grading papers. Not me. Friday and Saturday nights are long . . . long . . . long. . . .

"Have you got a telephone?" I asked Mrs. Smith.

She nodded. "Right over there. Help yourself."

I found the Howard number and called it. Maybe I'd have a date with him Friday . . . AND . . . Saturday . . . AND . . . Sunday.

His mother answered the telephone.

"Is Bob there?" I asked.

"Who is this?" Her voice was quiet. Precise.

"I'm Novalyne Price." I tried to sound cheerful. "I'm one of the new teachers here, and I met Bob a couple of years ago in Brownwood. I was with

Clyde Smith. I just wanted to talk with Bob. Is he home?"

She waited a minute. I was almost ready to ask about him again when she finally spoke. "No. Robert isn't here."

"Where is he?"

She seemed to be thinking. "Wel-l-l, I believe he went to Brownwood."

"Oh." I was genuinely disappointed. "Do you expect him back today?"

She hesitated. "Really, he didn't say when he was coming back. Perhaps tomorrow or the next day, or he may decide to stay the entire weekend."

"Well, when he comes back, would you have him call me?"

Again, she hesitated before she answered. "Oh, yes."

"I'm staying at Mrs. Hemphill's," I said. "He can call me there."

"Oh, yes, Mrs. Hemphill's. Yes, I'll tell him you called."

I wasn't ready to give up yet. "Is he still writing?"

"Of course, he's still writing." She sounded shocked.

"I'm interested in writing, too," I said.

"That's nice." Her voice was cool, indifferent.

"I want to talk to Bob about writing."

"I'm sure he'll be very glad to talk with you."

I sighed. "I suppose if he's not there, there's nothing I can do."

"No."

"Be sure to tell him to call me," I said and hung up.

Feeling blue and unhappy, I walked back to Enid and Mrs. Smith.

"Whom were you calling?" Enid asked.

"Bob Howard," I said.

She made some kind of sound and gave me a scornful look.

Sunday night . . . Late . . .

Last Wednesday, after I talked with his mother, I didn't really expect Bob to call that night. If he were out of town, I couldn't expect him to call unless he got back home early, and she didn't sound as if she expected that. Even though she said he might be gone all weekend, I waited Thursday, Friday, and Saturday nights for him to call. Every time I heard the phone ring, I listened. Hoping.

Last night was probably the dullest Saturday night I ever spent in my life. When I got up this morning, I didn't feel well. I went to breakfast, hating everybody. I didn't want anything but toast and coffee which caused Mrs. Hemphill to worry and say that I wasn't eating enough. If the rest of my life is to be spent in small towns, I might as well starve to death.

After breakfast, Ethel fluttered around with "Oh, my, my are you going to

Sunday School and church?"

I looked at her hard. "Ethel," I said morosely, "what else do you do on Sunday in Cross Plains, Texas, but go to church and Sunday School?"

I had no intention of doing anything else, but this morning there was more to it then just going to church and Sunday School. It wasn't simple. I was going under protest, and I wasn't sure what kind of mood I'd be in when I got there. The reason you go to church is to be quiet and to meditate on God's will and to pray that He will save your soul. It's a hollow mockery to go because the Board of Trustees tells you to go in order to be an example for the children. You say to yourself, "Lord, am I here to worship you or to be seen by the Board of Trustees?"

I put on my nice black dress that I had worn to the faculty meeting. I must admit it was more appropriate for this occasion than it had been for the last one. This was a cool September morning, so I looked appropriately dressed. I put on my hat and gloves, picked up my purse and looked into the mirror.

Suppose Bob Howard had telephoned me. Suppose he were here this morning. He is a writer. How would he describe my eyes? Would he say simply they were large, brown, eager for life, or would he see them with a touch of unhappiness at a time when you wanted to be happy? Funny how just a plain, simple date with a man could add a sparkle to a woman's eyes!

Ethel came in. I stopped looking at myself in the mirror, and we started down the street to church. Whether it was the high heels or not, walking seemed a little harder to do this morning. Once I stopped and said, "Wait a minute, Ethel."

I took off my shoe and poured sand out of it.

"Damn," I said.

"Oh, my, my," Ethel gasped. "Oh, my, my!"

It aggravated me. "Good heavens, Ethel. Don't you ever say 'damn' on Sunday?"

"Oh, my, my. Think of the children."

"There aren't any children around here," I snapped. I wiped my shoe out with my handkerchief. "Do you know what I'd like to do with this sand, Ethel? I'd like to take every shoeful and pour it on the Board of Trustees."

"Oh, my, my." Ethel was plainly agitated. Then she went on talking about the necessity of teachers being the right kind of teachers, especially in a small town where everybody knew everybody. She talked about being good examples for the children.

Someday, I'm going to listen to Ethel.

In my heart, I knew I had to change my way of thinking. Everything in the world was wrong. Why? I had looked forward to seeing Bob Howard, and he hadn't called. I was mad! Mad at the whole dern world!

When we got to church, we saw the preacher at the top of the steps near the door, waiting to greet people as they arrived. Ethel introduced him to me. It was the second time she'd introduced him to me, but it didn't matter. He just looked at me a little bit longer this morning and seemed very, very interested in the fact that I was teaching public speaking. He said, over and over, that public speaking was a very necessary subject which everybody ought to have. I agreed. After all, that was the very reason I was teaching the dern course.

He kept on talking. I began to wonder, the way he kept looking at me, if he was interested in my soul or in the public speaking class.

He looked a little drawn. Worried. But, then, he didn't just have the Board of Trustees to worry about. He had a whole congregation. Different sizes. Different ages. Different beliefs. A cross section of a small-town world, and he had to please them all. Poor man.

I can't worry about the preacher's problems, I have too many of my own to worry about. The Sunday School class began. Immediately, I loved and hated it—and I hated it much more than I loved it. Especially the teacher.

At the end of her second sentence, we knew the teacher was one hundred per cent behind the Board of Trustees. She began talking about teachers, how glad she was to have them in her class, and what an awesome responsibility teachers have setting good examples for kids. Then I knew that if I heard that one more time, I'd scream. She talked on, saying the same thing over and over. I began to twist and turn in my chair, hoping she'd get off the subject before I decided to set her straight.

Finally, she began the lesson. She didn't know any more about the Bible than I knew; she didn't know any more about teaching a Sunday School class than I did, and she made statements that I could argue with, not because I actually disagreed with what she said, but for the main and simple reason there were two sides to the question, and I was spoiling for a fight.

I didn't keep quiet. I got her into an argument. I asked questions, and she went on the defensive. She fumbled around trying over and over to explain something she didn't understand. I knew she didn't understand it. The class knew she didn't know what she was talking about. Why can't people simply say, "I don't know."

I was glad when the class was over, and I was sincerely sorry for what I had done and wished I had kept my mouth shut.

On my way into church, I saw Mark, the kid who is already my favorite student. He was dressed up with a coat and tie, and he looked very grown up. He surprised me. "Gee, Miss Price, you sure do look pretty today," he said.

My heart suddenly sang. I smiled, pleased, thanked him, and went on. I felt better—a thousand times better.

In church, I sang in the choir, listened to the preacher, and repented for my ugliness to the Sunday School teacher.

Sunday afternoon is a long time when you're hoping the phone will ring, and, somehow, knowing by that time that it will not. Ethel could find things to do. She read a book which she is going to review for her study club; then she took a nap.

I thought surely Bob would come home by Sunday night. He'd call. I didn't go to church with Ethel. I just sat. Kept the door open so that I could hear the phone ring. It didn't.

Thursday . . . half-past two a.m.

If the mountain won't come to Mahomet, then let Mahomet go to the mountain!

Last night, I called the Howards, but Mrs. Howard said that Bob wasn't there. She didn't know where he was. Yes, she'd tell him to call. Thirty minutes later, I called again. Not there. Thirty minutes later, I called again. Still not there. I called four or five times today when I could sneak out of class. He was never there! Never available! When does the guy have time to write?

I decided it was time for Mahomet to go to the mountain! But how does he get there?

Luck! Pure and simple, luck.

Jimmie and Enid brought their car back last weekend when they were home. Tonight, they asked Anna May and me to go riding with them, and all of a sudden, I had a bright idea!

"Do you know where Bob Howard lives?" I asked.

Anna May said that she did.

"Take me by his house," I said. "I have a question I want to ask Bob."

They looked as if people never asked each other questions.

"I want to ask him about writing stories," I added.

Enid spoke up. "You don't have time to write stories if you do your job the way you ought to do it. Besides, I don't think you ought to go running over to a man's house."

"No," I insisted. "I'm going to go see him."

I was beginning to get the idea that Bob had not got any of my messages.

"Why don't you call him?" Anna May asked.

"Call him!" I exploded. "I have called him. I've called him about a dozen times, but he's never there."

"Why didn't you tell whoever answers to have him call you back?"

"I did everything but write her a letter," I said. "His mother always answers the phone, and I told her a jillion times to have him call me."

"Well," Enid said sharply and logically, "that proves it. If he wanted to get in touch with you, he would have. It means he doesn't want to."

"Take me by," I said. "I'm going to go see him. I'll ask him a question about a story if it kills me."

As we rode down the street, I tried to think of a question that would sound reasonable to Bob. I couldn't think of one that sounded reasonable, even to me. What did I want him to tell me? I'd have to depend on a spur of the moment question.

Jimmie stopped the car in front of his house. I got out, my heart was pounding furiously.

"We'll wait for you," Enid said disapprovingly.

A thousand impressions impinged on my mind as I went down the walk. The house was average. A white frame house in need of paint. The walk was average. The yard was average, no better kept than the yards next door. Nobody here had done anything spectacular about the place he lived in. I went up the steps and across the porch. I could hear the sound of a typewriter and someone talking at the very top of his voice. It sounded as if somebody were reading from a book while someone else typed. I stood still at the door, listening. Bob was writing and talking at the top of his voice as he wrote.

The hall I was looking into was dark, but to my right, a light from an inner room shone out. I could hear people talking in that room but Bob was louder.

I took a deep breath and knocked on the door. The talking in the room next to me stopped. I knocked again and waited . . . and again and waited.

A chair was pushed back. A woman's voice asked, "Are you expecting someone?" A man grunted, "No." Bob's voice still accompanied the typewriter.

Footsteps. Dr. Howard lunged out of the living room into the hall to answer the door. He glared at me in the semi-darkness.

"Yeah?" he grunted.

I was a little perturbed. "I'd like to see Bob, please."

"Bob?" He made no move to open the door.

The typewriter and the talking in the room beyond stopped.

"Yes," I said in my best school-teacher voice. "I want to speak to Bob."

He hesitated. He made a move as if to open the door but changed his mind and stopped. He stepped back. "Mamma," he called. "There's somebody here to see Robert. She can't see him, can she?"

"Who is it?" came the still, quiet voice I'd listened to on the phone.

"I'm Novalyne Price," I raised my voice so that she could hear me.

"Well, Robert is bu—"

Then Bob Howard came from the living room into the hall and to the door.

"Hello," he said in a charming, friendly way. "Come in."

He opened the screen door for me. "Come in and sit down," he said. "I want you to meet my folks."

I went in. Dr. Howard was standing behind a big armchair; Mrs. Howard was sitting on the end of a divan.

"Mother, this is Novalyne Price," Bob said.

I said, "How do you do?"

Her hair was nearly white, short, and parted on one side, not stylish. It looked as if she just combed it quickly to get it over with, not to make her look better. She got up with a great effort and stood leaning slightly to one side.

"How do you do?" she said stiffly. Women don't really like each other.

"This is my father," Bob said, and I turned and spoke to Dr. Howard. He grunted out a brusk "howdy do." The man was more painfully shy than Bob.

"Well," Mrs. Howard said and paused. "Well, we'll go . . . in another room." She looked at Dr. Howard. They left the room together.

Bob motioned toward the divan. "Have a seat."

Again tonight, I was impressed by his bigness. His hair was longer too. It was standing straight up as if he had run his fingers through it many times and forgot to comb it. His eyes were asking questions again, but this time I knew the questions: What's this all about? Why are you here?

I knew without being told that no other woman had ever stood face to face with Robert Ervin Howard in his own house. I knew I was the first woman ever to sit there in that living room just to talk with him. How do women know these things? They know.

"I don't have but a minute," I said. "There are some people waiting for me outside in the car."

"Well," he said, "why don't you tell them to leave, and I'll take you home?"

"Oh, would you?" I said, very pleased. This was going better than I had dared to hope.

"Sure thing," he said cheerfully.

"Good," I purred, very feminine. "Well, let me go tell them." I also needed more time to think of that question I wanted to ask him.

He came with me down the steps where he stopped and waited. I ran down to the car and told the girls to go ahead.

"No, we'll wait," Jimmie said. "Don't be too long."

"Look," I said. "Be reasonable. Who wants to ride home with a bunch of women when a man will take her home?"

Cars were going and coming down the street. I hoped that none of my pupils were in them. A woman teacher in front of a man's house!

But I would not give up my chance for a pleasant, happy evening! I took a deep breath and said again. "Bob is going to bring me home."

Enid was angry. "I suppose if you've made up your mind, there's not much we can do."

They drove on. I turned and went back to the porch where Bob was waiting. He held out his hand, and I put mine in his.

"Were they afraid to leave you in my tender care?" he asked.

I laughed. "Heavens, no. They didn't want you to have to go to any trouble for me."

The moon was shining, and the crickets in the grass were singing. It was a beautiful night.

"Trouble?" he said lightly. "No trouble. A man doesn't get a chance to take a pretty girl home every moonlit night. It's the harvest moon, you know, a time of great rejoicing and honor to Ceres."

"You do have a gift for using words," I said. "Do you dance in the moonlight to Ceres?"

"With much grace and dexterity. You should see me." He laughed, and so did I—easily, freely. The words of one of Robert Burn's poems were beating in my mind:

> *The rank is but the guinea-stamp,*
> *The man's the gowd, for a' that.*

I liked Bob Howard, and I didn't care what some people said about him. We went back into the living room and sat down.

"What did you want to talk to me about?" he asked.

"About writing in general," I said. "I'm still trying to write stories, and I'm still getting notes and also rejection slips."

He ran his fingers through his hair and smiled, but his eyes didn't seem as happy as his smile. "I think everybody gets them. Some of my friends tell me they still get them after years of writing and selling. I get them myself, too."

"Yes, but you do sell?" It was half-question and half-statement.

He nodded. "A man's got to make a living some way."

The rest of the house was as still and quiet as if we were alone, but I felt that someone was listening somewhere, that if you spoke in this room, you could be heard all over the house. I looked toward the hall door and then back at Bob. He was sitting in a high-backed rocker, his arms on the chair arms. I was sitting on the divan, on the end opposite to the one where his mother had been sitting when I came in.

"You're still writing full-time?" I asked.

"Yeah. I was writing when you came in. Didn't you hear me?"

We both laughed. "Do you always tell your stories as you write them?"

Again, he ran his fingers through his hair. "A hell of a noise, wasn't it? Well, yeah, I do. I find that if I talk them out—hear the words as I put them down, the yarn goes a little smoother. Sounds better when you read it."

"I know what you mean," I said eagerly. "The voice brings words to life."

"That's right," he said. "You're absolutely right. And back to this selling bit, and you don't write unless you sell, I'm working on a Conan yarn now. I don't know whether it will sell or not, but I'm working on it. I figure the law of averages will give you sales if you keep pounding them out."

"I write slowly. It takes me more than a month to 'pound out' one and another couple of weeks to get it typed."

"You'll have to learn to write faster than that. Maybe even two or three a week, depending on the length."

Across the hall someone coughed. Bob jerked his head toward the door. All was still again, and he settled back in his chair.

"Listen," he said. "Why don't I take you home now? Maybe we can ride around a while. My car is just outside."

"Fine," I agreed.

"Just a minute. Wait here. I'll tell my folks."

He went across the hall into another room, and I heard a low mumble of voices. I looked around the room. It wasn't impressive, but it was the feeling it gave me that was important. It was an ordinary room that people had lived in a long time without seeing it, their minds engrossed with other things . . . the state of their health . . . their more pressing jobs . . . their private loves and hates. This was the kind of unfashionable living room you might find in a house where there wasn't much money and people were more concerned with their feelings than with beauty.

The divan was old, and the side where Mrs. Howard had sat didn't stand up as high as the middle. The other furniture was nondescript too. A rocker or two and a straight chair, a table or two. A double door led into a dining room. A white cloth was on the table and books and papers.

Bob was coming back down the hall toward the door. I could see him now as he came, his faded blue shirt open at the collar, his brown, floppy, short pants coming just to the top of his high-buttoned shoes. As he came smiling through the door toward me, I heard her voice calling, "Honey . . . Honey. . . ."

He stopped abruptly, jerked his head toward the room from which he had come, whirled, and went back.

"Ma'am?" he called. "Yes, ma'am?"

She said something that I couldn't understand, and then he said, "I'm going to take Miss Price home. I won't be gone very long. I'll come back when it's time for your medicine."

Then I heard her voice, very clear, very distinct. "That's all right, honey. You go right ahead. Forget about me if you can!"

I did a slow burn. "Forget about me if you can!" Was that to make sure he wouldn't forget about her? I may not know much about men, but, boy, I know women inside and out, and I know a possessive woman when I see one.

Certainly, she hadn't told him I had called. No woman who would say "Forget about me if you can" would have told her son that a woman wanted him to call her.

Bob came back and said, "Let's go."

He was very nice, very attentive. Going out the door, he took my hand and pulled it through his arm. We walked down the steps close together. I felt very happy, comfortable, very much at ease. It was easy to forget that woman in the other room, even though I could still hear her voice saying, "Forget about me if you can."

"How was Brownwood?" I asked him, as he opened the car door for me.

"Brownwood? Hell, I haven't been to Brownwood in months."

"Oh?" I said innocently. "You haven't?"

"No. I was going to ask you how everything was." He was getting in the car now, ready to start the engine. "You've seen Brownwood since I have."

I pressed my point. "That's funny. I called you about a week ago, and your mother told me you'd gone to Brownwood."

"Oh," he said. "Oh." He ran his hand through his hair, looking uncertain, confused. I felt sorry for him.

"I could have misunderstood her," I said. "I thought she said you'd gone to Brownwood."

"That's what happened." He sounded relieved. "I think you must have misunderstood her because . . . because I haven't been to Brownwood lately. She may have said I was working on something I couldn't leave right then."

"I see," I said, and I saw a lot more than I was telling him.

As he headed the car away from town, Bob kept on talking. "My family . . . They're damn good to put up with me staying around home writing all the time. Everybody in this town thinks I ought to be out working at some kind of job. That's hard on my family. And so I just tell them to hell with what people think. When I'm writing, I'm working. You know I'm working. To hell with everybody else. So when I get going on a yarn and somebody calls me, just tell them I'm working, or something like that. But I think you must have misunderstood her."

"I'm sure I did." But I was sure I had not misunderstood her. Still, I knew how people in this part of the country felt about writers.

I wanted to drop the subject. After all, it didn't really matter. I had gotten to see him and be with him. *She* hadn't been able to stop that even if she wanted to. And she wouldn't be able to stop me from seeing him again if I wanted to. *"Youth to youth since the world began,"* sang the poet.

I began to reason in my own mind about it. I could see that his concern for his mother could be a good thing. I'd heard Mammy say, "If a man is good to his mother, he'll be good to a wife." To me, that meant he would be nice to a girl friend. His love, devotion, and concern for mother meant he would have the same concern for me. No fighting this man off! No need to worry about his getting fresh. He was too nice a man.

Clyde had said, "Bob is attached to his mother." And that was something you could admire. He was a brilliant man; he'd been trained to respect and admire women. He hadn't been around young women very much, and so what could I do to interest him? Follow William James's psychology: Give him honest, sincere appreciation. He is shy. Build him up. Don't worry about the future.

We talked about the moonlight.

"It's a pretty night," I said.

"Beautiful," he agreed. "That's a beautiful harvest moon, if I do say so myself."

I laughed. "I suppose you're responsible for the moon."

"By all means. That moon was designed especially for you."

"You knew I was coming?"

"Oh, yes. I was going along with ol' Conan and all that bunch of cr—stuff, and, all of a sudden, you popped up out of the typewriter." He reached over, took one of my hands and held it in his. "Yes, sir. You popped up out of the typewriter, and I said, 'Now, Bob Howard, you big, ugly lummox, there's a girl who's going to appreciate your moonlight.'"

I was amused. "I think you're a poet."

"Well, now, you know, girl, not many women can appreciate a thing like that. Here I am, pounding out words and poems and singing to high heaven and looking up and ordering moons, and do you know anybody who can appreciate them . . . and me?"

"Me," I laughed. "I can."

He held my hand tighter. "Good. You're one in a million, girl. One in a million."

We both laughed, not because it was funny but because life was funny. The moon was funny. The world was funny. And I laughed because I realized he would never call me by my name. To him, I'd be *girl.* I wondered if he referred to women that way in his stories.

He talked then about his character Conan and the scrapes he'd gotten himself into. "That's the damndest bastard . . . the damndest bastard who ever was." Then he asked me about teaching school. "Any of those kids give you any trouble?"

Immediately, I told him about Mark, the tall, lanky, brown-haired, brown-eyed kid with the devil shining in his eyes, and the cute little smart aleck way he'd acted the first day of school by coming to class late and saying, "Howdy, teacher," as he came in the door. It hadn't been anything, really, but a new teacher had to be careful and not let the other kids think he was getting by with something, and so I'd said, "Now that all of us know you're here, sit down and listen." As I explained to Bob, that turned the tables on him; the kids laughed at him and were more on my side, which I thought was the secret of good discipline.

Bob laughed heartily. "You turned the laughter on him and away from you. That's smart. Now, when I went to school, the teacher wouldn't have done that. She'd just hauled me into the office and said, 'Here, take this sassy oaf and straighten him out with a board.' I think your way was better."

Bob made me feel awfully smart for the way I'd handled that. I glowed. A woman likes sincere appreciation too. But, then, I almost ruined things. I said, "But you know that kid—Mark? He's my favorite."

Bob jerked around to face me. "You have favorites?"

I shrugged my shoulders. "Oh, every teacher has favorites. That's normal. Teachers are human, too, you know. You just naturally like some people better than you do others, that's all."

"How old is he?"

"About seventeen or eighteen." It wasn't important to me.

Bob didn't say anything for a minute. "I always hated teachers who had favorites. I guess it was because I was never the favorite."

Something in his tone caused me to look at him. I wanted things back the way they were when he thought I was smart.

He began to turn the car around. I was a little chagrined. Was he taking me home because I had a favorite student? Well! If he wanted to get upset with me because I am human, okay! I could live without him. I looked out the car window, thinking how pretty the moonlight looked on that bare, open field beside the road. Weeds had grown up along the fence. A big, round weed dislodged itself from the rest and rolled across the field, looking silver in the moonlight. It was a time for romance, not anger.

We headed back toward town. I looked at my watch. Heavens! It was early, not even ten o'clock! I wondered why talking about a smart-aleck kid was wrong. Couldn't I talk about a high school kid if he talked about Conan? He hadn't understood how I felt about that brash, lanky kid who had more on the ball than almost anyone else in the class. Besides, you can always tell a good mule by its friskiness.

After Bob turned the car around, he became friendly again, and I decided I'd been too quick to become upset.

We talked more about his writing, more about the kind of stories I wrote, and the kind we liked. When we got back to town, it was too soon to suit me. I'd put aside my concern and was having a good time.

"You know," he said, and paused a minute. "I—I've got to give my mother a dose of medicine. It's time for it now. Do you mind if I stop and run in and give it to her? Then I'll take you home."

Well, blow me down!

Tevis Clyde Smith

Clyde Smith was a good friend of both Robert E. Howard
and Novalyne Price. It was Smith who introduced them in
1933. Smith was the author of a history of Brown County,
Frontier's Generation. The book was based upon a series
of interviews with old settlers of the county.

"Sure," I said hastily. "That'll be all right. Sure."

He stopped the car, got out, and went down the walk to the house. I wanted to laugh, but couldn't. I had heard him tell his mother he would be home in time for her medicine, but it just didn't make sense to me. But he had come home at ten o'clock on the dot to give her a dose of medicine!

A car rattled by and I watched it while I sat and waited for my boy friend to give his mother a dose of medicine! In a few minutes, he came back down the walk with the loping gait that reminded me of the way his father walked.

"Okay," he said. "Do you want to ride around a little longer? Or should I take you home? What time do teachers have to go to bed?"

"This teacher goes to bed any time she feels like it. Sometimes ten o'clock and sometimes one or two or three. No special time. Say, isn't your father a doctor?"

"The best doctor in this part of West Texas. Why?"

"I just wondered why he couldn't give your mother her medicine."

"Well," Bob said, shaking it off. "It's my job. My dad is gone a lot of the time. When he's home, he has to try to get some sleep. No telling when somebody will knock on the door for him to get up and go take care of a sick baby, man, or woman. How about driving out toward Cisco?"

" 'Fraid not," I said. "I'd better be going in. I don't have things ready to teach tomorrow. By-the-way, I taught a little while at Rising Star—private classes in expression."

I told him a little about it, and life was fun again. We drove a little while longer. I forgot he had to go home to give his mother a dose of medicine. I wanted to forget that.

He took me home and walked up to the door with me. Everything in the house was still. I stood on the top step, and he stood on the bottom one, but he was almost as tall as I.

"I've got a question I'd like to ask you," he said. He looked a little shy and uncertain. "This may not be any of my business, and if it's not, you tell me so pretty damn quick."

"Don't worry," I said lightly. "If it's not, I'll tell you pretty damn quick."

"I want to know about you and Clyde. Clyde's my best friend, you know."

"About Clyde and me?" I was dumbfounded. "Clyde is a great guy. He's married now."

"Yeah. I'd heard that, but I was wondering if you might be carrying the torch for him."

I didn't answer at once. It took me a minute to think of something light and frivolous to say. "I don't think I'd look very good holding a torch," I said finally. "Miss Liberty, maybe, but me . . . no. Clyde was a good friend. I enjoyed being with him, and I will admit that since he got married, I've missed him. Sure."

"But you're not heartbroken?" He hesitated. "I want to make sure."

"I've got a strong heart. It's not only not broken, it's not even dented."

"That makes a difference, you know."

"But Clyde's married." I repeated, still unbelieving. I certainly didn't want to lose a good prospect for a Cross Plains friend for one that was married! "I'm free to go with anybody I want to go with; however, I would have gone with anybody I wanted to go with whether Clyde was married or not. You don't think he was the only person I went with for four years, for heavens sake!"

"So you're not tied to any man . . . or ghost?"

"No," I said, and I meant it. It was also in my mind that I was not going to be tied to him either.

"I wanted to make sure I didn't have to fight any ghosts. Now . . . that's settled. How about tomorrow night?"

For the first time since school started, Friday night in Cross Plains looked great. "Fine. I don't have a date tomorrow night."

"Well, you've got one now," he said. "Girl, I want to tell you, you've got one now." He turned slightly. "And about that moon. That's a beautiful moon, if I do say so myself. I'll order another one tomorrow night."

"Great," I laughed. "I do appreciate your moons."

He turned and looked at me. He didn't offer to kiss me, and I was glad because I didn't want to kiss him.

He left then. I stayed by the door until he started the car and drove away. The moonlight was beautiful, and I hated to go inside. Down the street, in the block below me, there was a house with a light in the window. Across on the next street, I heard a car, driving fast. The crickets were beginning to sing. Everything was nice and peaceful. I thought: I won't be lonesome in Cross Plains any more. I'll have a friend to talk to. A friend I'll enjoy talking to.

> *"The hope I dreamed of was a dream"*
> *Friday night. Our first real date . . .*

It was an exciting day. At school, to get ready for the football game, we had a big pep rally. I made a rousing talk and the kids cheered like mad! But all during the day, when I wasn't too busy, I thought about Bob. What a pleasure it would be to have a date with a man who, on the way to the show, would talk about books and writing.

Home. Supper. Time to get dressed.

Getting dressed for a date is a ritual, especially when it's a new date.

Would Bob be THE ONE? I'm twenty-six. It's time I thought about that. Maybe my trouble was I wanted too much. I frowned. While I want my man to be a good conversationalist, I also enjoy useless talk, teasing, harmless gossip. There's a place for that kind of talk, but I wanted to talk about other things too—what Roosevelt was doing to end the depression. Religion. The textbooks say it's not a good idea to talk about religion, but textbooks don't know everything. I like to talk about religion.

I had other requirements too. One Bob really qualified in, for I wanted my man to have work that he enjoys and makes a success in. But I wasn't sure that he met the next one. My man didn't have *to have* a million. That's not important. He just has *to look* as if he has it. The two times I'd seen Bob he was dressed in everyday clothes, but I reasoned that since he has pride in his work, he'd have pride in himself. He'd dress up.

I took my bath, reached for my blue and pink flowered bathrobe and went back into my room to make up my face.

"Oh, my, my," Ethel said. "A date tonight?"

Ethel is nice. I like her. She's pleasant to room with. Tonight, I felt silly, giggly, and excited. "Oh, yes, yes. A big, big date. He is huge, you know." Both of us laughed.

"Going to the picture show?" She was sitting, hunched up in bed, a magazine on her knees. She settled herself against the pillows. Her sensible, high-necked blue gown had a perky little white bow at the neck.

"Sure. Maybe to Brownwood or Cisco." I almost sang the words.

"Nice." She nodded. "They have a good show on in Cisco. Is it farther to Brownwood than to Cisco?"

"I don't know." I let my pretty black silk dress slide over my shoulders. Around the waist it clung like a glove. I draped the towel around my shoulders and carefully combed my hair. Every hair in place, I put on my black and white hat and picked up my gloves.

"Oh, my, my!" Ethel gasped. "You're going to wear a hat and gloves tonight?"

I laughed exultantly. "A lady is never without her gloves and hat."

"I hate gloves," Ethel said.

The door-bell rang. He was here. Ethel and I froze, staring at each other. We listened to Mrs. Hemphill's footsteps padding to the door. He's here! I almost stopped breathing.

A murmur of voices came from the living room. In a few seconds, Mrs. Hemphill would call me. I'd pretend not to be ready, of course. You didn't just rush madly out to meet a man! You pretended you had a lot more to do, as if you'd been so busy you'd forgotten he was coming until the very last minute.

Mrs. Hemphill's footsteps clunked toward our door. "Miss Price." I couldn't answer. She called a little louder and knocked on the door. "Miss Price."

I looked at Ethel for confidence. "Just a minute, Mrs. Hemphill. Just tell him to sit down and wait. I'll be there in a minute."

Ethel giggled. "Oh, my, my," she whispered.

The whole thing was funny to both of us. But Mrs. Hemphill ruined it! Do you lose all your sense of romance when you get married and have five kids? She stuck her head in the door and blurted out, "Oh, goodness. You're already dressed!"

Back to the mundane world! "Yes," I said acidly. "At least I am now."

She seemed amazed. "Well," she said, slowly, unbelievingly, "you're all dress—You're all dressed—"

I did the only thing left for me to do. I got my purse, touched my hat to make sure it was exactly where I wanted it, held my head up, and my heels tapped lightly as I walked into the living room. I almost had to push Mrs. Hemphill aside. Couldn't she do anything but stand there looking as if she'd had a dose of ether? Ordinarily, she's a very sensible woman. What had got into her? Then I knew!

A big gorilla of a man dislodged himself from his chair and leaped up. There he stood in those ankle-high brown pants, high-buttoned shoes that looked like something out of the ark. No coat! No tie! A dingy white shirt, open at the collar! His hands were clutching an old floppy cap, turning it round and round.

What do you do when you hear a soft snap and know that a dream has died? What do you say? You don't say anything. You just stand there. You think: a date is a special occasion. You dress up for special occasions!

He looked embarrassed. It had evidently just dawned on him that I had expected him to be better dressed than he was. For a minute, we just stood there, staring at each other. There he was looking like something the cats had dragged in, but here I was dressed fit to kill in my very best! I was disappointed. Angry. He was too embarrassed to say anything. I could tell that by looking into his eyes.

"Oh," I gulped, because that was all I could manage.

His neck bulged as if he'd swallowed something big. "Well—Well— I—I didn't know—" he stammered and stopped.

Words I couldn't stop came tumbling out. "I expected you to have on a coat and tie!"

His face turned red. "Well—well, by God, I've got on a clean shirt."

I took a deep breath. "Okay," I said slowly. "Okay."

I heard Mrs. Hemphill clump out of the room, and, suddenly, I wanted to shoot somebody. Anybody. Him. Her. Mostly him.

Bob recovered a little faster than I did. He turned, reached down in the chair and picked up a magazine. "You said you'd like to read some of my stuff, and so I—I brought a copy of this magazine that's just come out . . . It's—it's got a yarn of mine in it. I—I thought you might like to look at it."

My eyes bulged. I'd never looked at a magazine like that before! That cover! A big, handsome man, except for his very short hair, was standing there with a big, green snake wrapped around him. A blonde girl sat on the ground staring at him. She was something! All she had on was a wispy scarf that didn't quite cover her up front. Between her legs was another wisp of cloth fastened to a red and gold belt.

"It's—it's 'The Devil in Iron.' " Bob's voice was unnecessarily loud.

I gulped. What did I say now? Some part of my mind tried to reason with me. After all, he brought the magazine because I had said I wanted to read some of his stories. For heaven's sake. Appreciate that!

"Thank you for bringing it," I managed. "I—I really appreciate your bringing it. I surely do want to read it." I hate myself when I say the same thing over and over.

"Well, okay," he said. "There it is."

While I stared at the magazine cover, he shifted around uneasily in front of me. Should I ask him to sit down? Should I send him home for a coat and tie? What do you do in a situation like this?

"I—I thought," Bob stammered, "that we'd just ride around for a while. My mother—I've got to be there around ten o'clock—She's got— I mean— that's what time her medicine—Well—I just thought we'd ride around for a while."

"Okay." My mind was made up. Clutching the magazine in my hands to keep them from shaking, I turned around. "I'll be back in a minute." My heels clicked into my bedroom. With every click, I got hold of myself, and I knew I would see it through. I put the magazine in my suitcase so that Ethel wouldn't see it. I took off my hat and gloves.

Ethel was staring at me over her magazine. "Oh—" she began, but I cast one look in her direction and she shut up.

I went back into the living room without the magazine, without the gloves, without the purse, without the hat. "Okay," I said a little stiffly. "Let's ride . . . around . . . a while. I left the magazine here. I'll read it tonight when I get home."

He didn't say anything. His confusion irritated and bothered me. He didn't know what to do, and I was beginning to feel a little mean. But if I got dressed up for a date with him, the least he could do was get dressed up too. That bit about his mother! Baloney! THE ONE? Again, baloney.

He opened the car door for me, and I crawled into the seat. He closed the door and loped around the car and got in behind the steering wheel. He jerked his cap on. I reminded myself: Good conversation. Remember! You like that. Better enjoy this conversation!

"I'm sorry," he said. "I'm sorry I'm not dressed up."

"Perfectly all right." I was a little cool. "I guess I misunderstood you last night."

"I didn't think about going to a show or anything," he said. "I just thought maybe we'd drive around a little while, and—well—I'd shoot my mouth off. If there's one thing I like to do, it's ride around and shoot my mouth off . . . Ride around with a pretty girl, that is."

I melted. Just tell me I'm pretty, and I eat out of your hand.

He turned the car toward Rising Star. I settled back in my place. I don't give up a dream easily. I studied him silently. He certainly wasn't suave and polished, but you never know. A delicate perfume could be put into an ungainly bottle.

The everlasting Texas wind blew sharply tonight, but we rolled up the windows to shut out its keen fall nip. The live oaks and post oaks were mysterious in the moonlight. Here and there a little house, set back from the road, spoke of people, busy with each other, unaware that we passed, so intent on themselves. I wondered about them and . . . about us.

Bob started talking about Conan and one of the stories he had written. He mentioned Kline, his agent. He was getting warmed up. So was I. I moved so that I wouldn't fall out of the door on my side of the car.

"Is Kline a good agent?" I asked.

"So-so." Bob jerked his cap off and threw it in the back seat. "Sometimes I think he might work a little harder for me. Chances are that I could sell my stuff as well as he can, but selling things myself takes too much time. I'm thinking about trying someone else though. I'm working on a yarn now that will go straight to Wright."

"Another Conan story?" I asked.

"Yeah," he answered. "He's my bread and butter. I do bang out a western or adventure yarn now and then, but, mostly, I go along with Conan."

"What's that story about—the one you brought me to read?"

" 'The Devil in Iron.' " He seemed a little defensive about it. "I don't guess you'll like it."

"Oh, yes, I will." I couldn't understand his being defensive about a story that had sold and been published. "I'm sure I'll like it." For some reason I was getting on the defensive too. I hoped he wouldn't begin that "you're educated, I'm not" bit that he had used the first time I met him.

He turned and looked at me, and I wondered if we'd run into the ditch beside the road. "You're a writer, too," he said. "What kind of stories do you write? Adventure? Love? About teaching school."

I shrugged my shoulders. "Certainly not about teaching school." I hesitated, wondering how much I ought to say about my stories. But if you were trying to learn, why not talk about it? "I write love stories. As I told you before, I try a few confessions—"

"You got a lot to confess?" he interrupted, smiling.

I thought that was a silly question. "Depends on whether I confess what I *do* or what I *think* about doing." I answered laconically. He whirled and looked at me again.

He's not the best driver in the world; he gets too interested in what he's talking about. I glanced at the ditch, took a deep breath and started over. "I still don't have any luck with the confessions. They send them back by return mail."

"I know what you mean." He sounded sympathetic. "What's your last one about?"

That was a little hard to explain to a prospective boy friend—even a writer. "The title was 'I Gave My Daughter Movie Fame.' "

"What?" Bob barked. "What did you say?"

I hadn't expected him to be so shocked. Hadn't he written for the confessions? Besides, with that more than half-naked woman on the cover of the magazine he brought me, what right did he have to be shocked? I was not only on the defensive; I was downright mad! "It's for the confessions. Aren't those stories a little bizarre?"

He was literally bouncing around all over the side of the car. He doesn't move quietly and slowly like other men. He's vital. Big and vital. He lurches, lunges, and rolls even when he's driving a car. "Wha—wha—what?"

I repeated the title. "I . . . Gave . . . My . . . Daughter . . . Movie . . . Fame."

He laughed, quickly and abruptly, then seemed to get control of himself. "I—uh—What's it about?"

It had not occurred to me that I'd written a funny story. I explained slowly. "A woman has an illegitimate child, a daughter, and she tries to make it up to her. The child is adopted by this aunt of hers. But the woman can't give up. She keeps doing things for the girl. Finally, she helps the girl become a movie star and very famous."

While I was talking, I could see that Bob was trying very hard to keep from laughing. But what was even stranger to me was that the more I talked, the more it became sort of cock-eyed even to me. I didn't know what it took to win movie fame. True, I read movie success stories in magazines. I went to the movies once in awhile. I knew when the acting was good or bad. Did that qualify me to write about movie fame? As for illegitimate children—Well, when I was growing up, two girls whom I knew had illegitimate children. Did that qualify me to know about things like that?

I was beginning to see why my story had been a dud, but why did Bob think it was so funny? Finally, he snorted and began to laugh, a deep belly laugh of a man enjoying a good joke.

All I could do was sit and stare at him, slowly realizing that my feelings weren't hurt. Usually, if someone laughs at me, I am devastated. This time I was just interested . . . not hurt.

"Hell," he said, running his hand through his hair and swiping at his eyes. "I'm sorry. Don't pay any attention to me. I don't know a damn thing about illegitimate daughters and movie fame."

I didn't answer. I just sat and looked at him. We'd passed Rising Star. The roads toward Cisco were better, and more cars were coming our way.

He waited a minute. "Now, you know, come to think of it, I guess you do know what you're talking about. That's part of your job, ain't it? Plays, I mean. Hell, I guess that's what you're the most interested in."

Know what you're talking about? I had assumed I did. But it was too complicated to think about now. I had something else on my mind. Why wasn't I hurt by Bob's laughter? He was nice looking, but could I ever love a man who dressed like a slob? Who didn't mix and mingle with people? Dressing up was very important to me because it said something about you. It was part of Mammy's belief that you always tried to look your best; furthermore, it was part of my speech training. A man or woman facing an audience needed to look his or her best. That made the audience want to listen to you. But, in life, other things were important too. Having brains and being able to talk was important.

He was waiting for me to answer.

"I know a little bit about drama. Not much really," I said ruefully. "I read a few plays when I can get hold of them. I read about plays being produced in Dallas and in New York. And the illegitimate child seemed like a good idea at the time."

"Don't let me discourage you," Bob laughed again. "I don't know why, but it just struck me kinda funny that you—of all people—should write about giving an illegitimate daughter movie fame from way out here on these west Texas hills."

In Cisco, he stopped the car near a drugstore, and we went in. At first, I felt a little self-conscious. People looked at him curiously, then at me, glanced at him again, but their eyes came back to me. I touched my hair and glanced into the mirror behind the fountain. We sat down at a table, and the soda jerk took our order.

"I've tried confessions a little," Bob said, smiling at me. "I always thought there was a kind of formula to them. I thought you sinned, suffered, and repented."

The soda jerk put the cokes in front of us. I sipped mine before I answered. "It seems to me that when a woman has an illegitimate child, she's sinned a little. As for suffering, she clasped and unclasped her hands and emoted all over the show. I think if you hurt that bad, it must be repentance. I honestly think it followed the formula, but the editors didn't know it."

He laughed. "I see what you mean. But did the woman suffer because the child would never know who her mother was or did she suffer because—well, because of the man . . . because she did what it took to get the illegitimate child? I think that'd make a difference to the editors . . . if I know editors."

I stared at him. I was aware, then, of all the things about us: the night, the sounds in the drugstore, the fizz of other cokes being made, a murmur of conversation, the soft sound of people's footsteps down the aisles among the tables. A young girl's high laughter. The sound of a car horn outside.

"Am I making myself clear?" He leaned across the table and put his hand over mine.

"Perfectly," I nodded, a little self-conscious about his hand on mine in public that way, but it held a world of understanding. "I was just trying to write about ordinary people and their ordinary problems."

"A woman from the hills of Texas who could give her illegitimate daughter movie fame wouldn't be an ordinary girl with an ordinary problem, would she?" He smiled and took his hand off mine.

I hesitated. "You don't care for ordinary people stories?"

"No, that's where we're different," he said. "But maybe you're right. Illegitimate children are the product of civilization with its myriad problems, its rules and regulations. Civilized man makes rules against his nature, then beats his damn brains out because he can't live up to them. I write a lot of my yarns about a different age, a different way of life."

"Like 'The Devil in Iron' where a man fights an enormous snake?"

He nodded emphatically. "And against a strange pagan god. But that's my formula—man struggling to survive in an elemental way. Life and death in a new world."

I frowned, not sure I could ever be interested in that elemental life. Would Bob like me if I didn't like his stories? He pushed his chair back from the table and reached his hand to me. We went outside into the fresh night air. We decided to drive on past Cisco toward Abilene. Along this road, too, the houses with lamps burning in the windows were set back from the road.

"Bob," I interrupted the history of Conan's world. "See those houses we pass now and then?"

"I wasn't noticing," he admitted, driving onto the shoulder of the road so that he could turn the car around. "Civilization is crowding in on us. This is mighty poor farming country same as that around Rising Star, Cross Plains and down into parts of Brown County. The people in those houses have a hard time just staying alive."

"I know," I said. "I grew up on a farm and I love it. It's people like that I want to write about. Real people with real problems. People who live in small houses but who keep a lamp burning in the window."

Bob lurched against the steering wheel in his enthusiasm. "Not me. I don't want to write about men struggling along on a sandy farm, getting drunk, coming in the house at night and beating up a small, frail woman who can't fight back. I don't want the hate and—"

"Hate!" I exploded. "Sure. We struggled on our farm. Right now, I'm teaching because making a living on the farm is such a struggle—cotton just five cents a pound; and the hail last spring knocked the wheat down on the ground and now it's not worth much. But we don't hate! Why should you think there's hate in those houses?"

"You're a dreamer, girl," he said, turning to face me again. "You come from a good home. You don't know these people out here. I do. You think they're nice and sweet and loving. That's not true. You said it, though. Trying to dig out a living on the farm in spite of the hail, the wind, and the dust is hard. No rain at the right time. That fills men with hate. That's what you get with civilization."

"Just because you're poor and have to work hard doesn't mean you're filled with hate," I insisted. Emotion made me move around on my side of the car as vigorously as he moved. I was going to argue with him about that, even if I never had another date with him. "Besides, I *do* know these people out here. I grew up with them."

"No, girl, I think you've lived a sheltered life." He shifted his weight around as if bothered about something. After a minute, he turned to face me again. "I don't think you're going to like ol' Conan. His struggle is big, uncomplicated with civilized standards. The people who read my stuff want to get away from this modern, complicated world with its hypocrisy, its cruelty, its dog-eat-dog life. They want to go back to the origin of the human race. The civilization we live in is a hell of a lot more sinister than the time I write about. In those days, girl, men were men and women were women. They struggled to stay alive, but the struggle was worth it."

Maybe a lot of people read his stories for the reasons he said they did. Maybe people like to read about big men who struggled against the supernatural, against huge snakes, using a scimitar to strike and kill, and girls with big bosoms not doing a dern thing but sitting there, staring at the man struggling. Why would a story like that sell better than mine where a woman couldn't forgive herself for having sinned against a child? It didn't really make sense, but I could accept it, and I could learn.

I moved closer to Bob and put my hand on his shoulder. "I don't agree with a word you say about civilization, and unknown gods, and houses that appear and disappear and fall into ruin and suddenly build up again. But you've helped me more than anybody else who ever talked to me about writing."

His laugh was warm, exultant. He grabbed my hand and held it so tight I almost groaned. "You stick with me, girl. I'll teach you a lot about civilization, about men, and about writing. You stick with me, girl."

As we drove back through Cisco, its main street with its dim, yellow street lights, looked wide and empty. The wind blew, and our car slipped silently through the town.

To make conversation, I said, "I really have to study my lessons for next week."

"What subjects did you tell me you teach?"

"I have one class in public speaking, two in freshman English, and two in ancient history."

"Ancient history? Now, there's a subject I'd like to teach. Do you study about Jenghiz Khan? A great man, Jenghiz Khan. My favorite barbarian."

"Not in ancient history, but I've heard about him. An uncivilized barbarian, wasn't he?"

"Aha!" he said jubilantly. "That's where you're wrong. That's the tomfoolery they teach you in school. He was just as civilized, if you like the word, as the people he lived among. But what he wanted was different. The Mongols were warriors. Give a Mongol a good horse, and he'll conquer the world."

I was inclined to argue. "When they conquered a city or state, didn't they destroy all the beautiful works of art?"

He shrugged that aside and went on with his story. "When his father died, he was just a kid, but his mother saw to it that he fulfilled his destiny. Any man who reaches greatness reaches it because of his mother."

I resented that statement.

Jenghiz Khan was a subject in which he seemed passionately interested. As he talked, with so much enthusiasm, I could think of him as a man whose eyes looked upon a time long since passed and forgotten by other men.

He described the land, the colors of Jenghiz Khan's robes, the horse he rode. As I listened, I knew what Jenghiz Khan experienced and thought. But I understood as one who plays a part in a play; you study the man . . . you study the role . . . you try to understand and experience him; then you try to reveal him to an audience. But in the final analysis, on stage, you create the illusion of reality. Bob was not acting. He was there. At that moment, he *was* Jenghiz Khan, the barbarian, conqueror of an empire.

It overwhelmed me. "How do you know so much about him—Jenghiz Khan? History books don't tell you these things. History books don't describe. They recount."

"I was there, girl." Exultantly. "I rode with Jenghiz Khan."

At first, I didn't know what to think. Then I reasoned about it. I thought: We must talk about reincarnation someday. I don't believe it, of course, but we must talk about it. He probably doesn't believe it either. No wonder a few people in Cross Plains don't like him. They don't understand him. His preoccupation with history and with writing instead of the price of corn and cotton is something they could not understand.

Could I? I liked to talk about books. . . history. . . writing. Well, this was an opportunity to listen to a very interesting storyteller! Did I want this?

I listened to the saga of Jenghiz Khan.

I watched Bob's face in the dim light. He was a good-looking man . . . aloof . . . accustomed to being alone a lot, but now enjoying immensely the pleasure of a good listener. His voice was vibrant, full, pleasant, rising and falling with the excitement of battle, or racing across changing terrain. He spoke with authority. His descriptions were vivid. I listened avidly. Amused. Fascinated. Uncertain.

In college, Mrs. Trapp's classes had held me spellbound, but no one had ever made history so alive and glowing. I felt every emotion Jenghiz Khan felt. I reacted with intense feeling toward things he did. I was repelled when he took his sword and ripped open a man's belly, spilling his guts in the dust and heat of the desert. But I saw another side to Jenghiz Khan, too. I saw his gentleness with his horse. I marveled at his respect and admiration for his mother. I saw him cross verdant valleys with no fences.

"Bob," I interrupted, finally, "don't you ever write about modern times? Modern heroes? Do you always write about barbarians—about past history?"

"Sure," he said. "I write about several other characters. Stephen Costigan, John—"

"What kind of problems do they face?"

He laughed. "Magic. Voodoo. Oriental magic."

I shivered. "Why problems like that? Why not just a plain, ordinary problem like: 'When the cotton's picked this fall, I'll get a new car. But, then, cotton's just five cents a pound. How can I get the car?' You know what I mean—the kind of problem a man would face in 1934?"

"You don't like to read about magic? Voodoo? Why, girl, that's one of man's oldest problems."

I wondered if he were teasing or serious.

We were back in Cross Plains. I sighed and looked out the window. It had been a fantastic day. The football game. My excitement getting dressed for this date. Talking about history. About writing. Jenghiz Khan.

At my door, he told me it had been a wonderful evening, and that he liked nothing better than riding around with a pretty girl and shooting his mouth off. He did not ask for another date, and I was glad. He made quick decisions. I needed time.

I leaned against the door and watched the lights of his car until they turned into the next street. I stood for a long time just thinking.

It was after twelve o'clock. Nearly one. I wondered if he had forgotten his mother's medicine.

Saturday is a long, long day . . .

This morning, early, Mrs. Jackson called me to tell me they were going to Abilene to do some shopping, and they might see a show. Would I like to go with them? I thanked her profusely and got ready in a hurry. I like the Jacksons and both their kids—Jennie Laura and S. R.

Actually, we had very little time in Abilene. Not enough time to find a bookstore where I could have looked for a book about Jenghiz Khan.

Jennie Laura, a romantic senior, asked me if I were dating Bob. I was tempted to say, "No. I'm dating Jenghiz Khan." But I didn't. Mrs. Jackson looked sharply at Jennie Laura and said, "Robert is a fine man. Good to his mother." Mr. Jackson spoke up. "Yeah. He's a mighty good boy."

I agreed, and added that he was a great storyteller, a man who was fascinating; one who had new and different ideas.

The subject was dropped.

Another lonesome Sunday afternoon . . .

This afternoon, I told Ethel about Bob.

"Bob swears an awful lot," I said slowly. "Every other word is either 'damn,' or 'hell,' or 'goddamn,' or some other swear word."

Ethel shook her head. "You can stop him," she said crisply. "I've heard he's a nice person, and not just from you."

I sighed. "I can stop him from swearing, if I can yank his tongue out by the roots."

Ethel looked at me if his swearing were my fault.

"What I'm afraid of," I added, "is that I'll start swearing, too. My father swore a lot. At the age of two, I was pretty good myself. Mother gave me lessons in how *not* to swear, and it's one reason she left my father. She didn't think girls ought to use man-sized words."

"Oh, my, my!" Ethel said. "Your mother was right."

I went into detail about Bob's ability to make history vivid and interesting. I told her how he talked about Jenghiz Khan and how I could listen fascinated.

Ethel said, "Do you like him? Much . . . I mean?"

I stared at her. "No. Yes. I don't know."

It doesn't have to be in the paper . . .

News does get around in a small town! You say "Good morning" and soon everybody knows about it, but the worst part of it all is that they *think* they know what you were *thinking* about when you said it. If you *do* something, they manage to get the whole story before you've even finished doing it. It's a thing I don't like about small towns.

This morning a little before eight, I walked into the office at school. The usual little group was there—Mr. Williams, Louise, Lewis Norman, and Coach. The minute I walked in, I knew they'd been talking about me. I could feel the words and laughter still hanging in the air.

Everybody said, "Hi."

And I said, "Hi."

They asked me how I was and I said that I was fine and how were they?

Lewis said, "Do you think it will rain?"

The sun was shining.

I said that I didn't think it would rain, but that it might hail—or whichever came first.

Coach smiled his slightly scornful smile toward anyone who didn't play football and left the room. I glanced at Louise. She looked very pretty in that black and white dress of hers. But I didn't look so bad myself, I thought, as I sat down in a chair beside Nat's desk.

Then they began their teasing. Lewis and Nat talked good humoredly through the whole story of my date with Bob. But they knew the outline, not the content. They knew Bob had come to see me Friday night without a coat . . . without a tie . . . without a hat . . . They knew I'd been dressed up, but the meaning they had was wrong, I thought. It seemed to me they thought Bob was a big, clumsy slob, not the kind of man for a school teacher to date. I tried to keep smiling, thinking frantically: His brains . . . his accomplishments . . . Don't they matter? Don't they matter to anybody but me?

Louise said, "Did he kiss you?"

"No, damn it," I said, and left the room.

In the hall, I could hear Nat and Lewis still laughing.

Some of the students came into my room, and we talked about the play we were going to have. The bell rang, and my first class straggled in.

I taught a good class, but some part of my mind kept asking me funny questions. Was I so afraid of the world's laughter I could not cling to a beautiful friend? I liked to hear Bob Howard talk. If he ever asked me for another date, what would I say?

Some incredible things happen on Thursdays . . .

Bob hasn't called me for another date, and I am not sure whether I care or not.

After school today, I went to the drugstore with Enid and Jimmie. While they talked with Mrs. Smith, I stood at the counter and thought about Bob and wondered if he were home banging out a yarn about Conan. I had no more excuses to call him; but if I didn't see him again unless I called him, I would never see him again. It was as simple as that. Still, he had had an effect on my life. All week I'd tried to make my history lessons come alive the way he made history come alive for me.

So much for history.

Enid and Jimmie wanted to eat supper. Enid said, "You're sure you won't have something to eat—a piece of pie or something?"

I shook my head and said that Mrs. Hemphill would probably have supper ready by the time I got home.

"Might as well go by the post office," I thought when I started home, "I'm not expecting anything from anybody, but it won't hurt to go by."

No one was in the post office, and my footsteps echoed. The loneliness was depressing. But a letter was in my box! The return address: R. E. Howard, L. B. 313, Cross Plains, Texas. I held it in my hand and stared at it. A letter. I don't believe it! Not a telephone call. A letter.

Someone came in the door and said, "Hi." I glanced up, said, "Hi," and looked back at my letter. The door closed, and I was alone again.

Carefully, I tore open the envelope. Two and a half lines!

> Dear Novalyne,
> How about going to the show in Brownwood Sunday afternoon? I'll be over about 1:30 p.m. Let me know by return mail.
> Your friend,
> Bob

Now what? Teachers are not supposed to go to Sunday picture shows! But that was only one of my worries. Bob and I were different in a lot of ways. Could we be friends and be so different? I liked to dress up in my best clothes, whether they were expensive or not. Bob doesn't give a damn about the way he dresses. Suppose he comes over Sunday dressed in those floppy, too short pants. He says he wears them like that so that if he gets in a fight, his pants won't be in his way! And that dingy white shirt—even if it is clean! We are so different! A date with him was something to think about . . . something to decide.

I put the letter back in the envelope and went out the door. The sun had gone down, but it was still so light people had not yet turned on their car lights. I almost broke into a run, but stopped quickly. Teachers are not supposed to run like young kids!

A town sets its standards. Teachers don't run. Don't go to picture shows on Sunday. Don't do this or that. If you break those standards, the town thinks you're crazy. The town had definite standards for teachers and for other people to live by. You dress the way *they* think you should. You get the kind of job *they* think you should have. You can clerk in a store. Or you can work on a farm. You can keep books for some store. What about being a writer? No. You can't be a writer. You can't sit at a typewriter all day pounding out pulp yarns. If you do, you're lazy and good-for-nothing. That most all writers began by pounding out yarns for the pulps they didn't stop to think about.

Not even Enid could accept the pulp and confession magazines as legitimate starting places for writers. Good stories had stood the test of time. Examples of good writing were put into literature books. They had always been good. They probably did not start at the bottom! What would Enid say if I dated Bob—someone she thought was crazy? Her opinion mattered more than anybody else's to me. She was the one I worried about. What will Enid say?

Other people . . . relatives . . . friends . . . those who don't like you . . . those who do . . . people in general . . . have their say about the things you do. And it is something I resent. Bob doesn't fit the pattern people have cut out for Dr. Howard's son. A lot of people laugh and say he's crazy, but that doesn't make him crazy. By whose standards do you judge a man?

If I date Bob, some people will tease me. Others will think I'm crazy or peculiar. So what?

You pay a price for everything in this life. You have to decide for yourself whether the price is reasonable or too high.

Ethel was getting ready to go to supper when I came in. I put my letter on the table inside a book. By the time supper was over, my mind was made up. I knew the score. I went to the bathroom and looked at myself in the mirror. "Listen," I said to my stormy image, "you thought he *might* be THE ONE. Now, you're pretty sure he's not. But remember this: You enjoyed talking with him. He's a good man, and a good friend. Who has a right to control your life? You, girl. That's who."

I went to my room, sat down at the typewriter and wrote three lines to Bob to tell him I'd be glad to go to Brownwood to see a show and that one-thirty would be fine. I took the letter out of the typewriter, got up, and told Ethel I was going to the post office to mail it. She thought she ought to go with me, but I insisted on going alone.

Outside, the stars were dim and far away. A soft wind touched my face. I ran most of the way to the post office.

Sunday . . .
My horoscope promises an unexpected pleasure . . .

Fall slipped in softly and unobtrusively with beautiful crisp chilly nights and warm, dreamy days. The grass was turning brown and the leaves were falling. One sipped coffee slowly, dreaming of fur coats and velvet dresses.

Today, one refrain haunted my thoughts: Bob is coming. Bob is coming.

Sunday morning was clear and beautiful. The wind brisk. The day was too pretty for bothersome questions to nag me. Do you really want to see a picture show? Suppose he comes dressed—

When I told Mrs. Hemphill I had a date and that I'd answer the door, she wanted to know with whom. But as soon as I told her, she raised her eyebrows, shook her head, and asked the inevitable question: "What do you see in him?"

And I said, belligerently. "He's one of the most interesting men I've ever known."

She shrugged her shoulders.

At one-thirty on the dot, Bob's car stopped in front of the house. I peeped out the window of my room and nearly fainted! I honestly didn't know that good-looking man who got out of his car and started toward the house. He had on a nice brown suit with a vest and tie, a tan hat settled debonairly over his right eye. I was so excited when I opened the door, it was all I could do not to throw my arms around his neck and hug him.

He was beaming, as proud of himself as I was of him. He couldn't keep the good humor out of his voice. "Well, how's my best girl! Ready to go?"

"Come in," I said. "I'll get my hat and gloves."

Dressed up, he was good-looking in a substantial, successful way. I settled myself on my side of the car, thinking: Funny how dressing up makes everybody feel good!

He headed the car toward Brownwood.

"You look swell!" I was enthusiastic and glad for him to know it.

He grinned, pleased. "This fool hat kinda bothers me. It's not the kind of hat I ought to be wearing."

"What kind of hat should you be wearing?"

"Well, you take these hats the Mexicans wear—sombreros. Now, there's a hat for you. It's the kind of hat you need in this part of the country. Keeps the sun off real good."

I laughed because the world looked so beautiful I could laugh about anything. "Isn't it a pretty day?" I said.

"For a fall day," he admitted. "This is a bad time of year, girl. A dying time of year. Things are in their sere and yellow leaf."

"Sere and yellow leaf." I tried to think where I'd heard that before.

"It was cold this morning when I got up," I said. People are funny. When they are interested in something else, they talk about the weather.

He nodded. "Yeah. It got down in the fifties last night, but it must be nearly ninety by this time."

"And I've got on a wool dress."

"You women!" He looked at me approvingly. "You women. Here it is summertime, and you're coming out in fall dresses; but you look mighty good, and I like that perfume you're wearing."

I said thank you about the perfume; then I said, "I hope you'll have your picture made for me in that outfit."

"You mean with my hat on! Now, what kind of a looking guy am I going to be in a picture with my hat on?"

"Very handsome," I said sincerely.

"You want my profile?"

"Oh, yes. It's a very good profile."

He looked pleased but shook his head. "I've got a weak chin. A very weak chin. See how it recedes into my neck? I've got a weak chin."

"You do not have a weak chin," I protested.

"Yes, I do. But I'm not the only one. Do you know Truett Vinson?"

"I've met him, but I don't know him very well."

"Well, he's really got a weak chin, a pointed chin," he said whimsically. "Man hit him on the chin and it'd knock him out till he'd never be able to come to. One little tap on the chin, and he'd be out cold. Weak chin. Mine's weak, but it'd take a hell of a blow to knock me out."

We laughed. I changed the subject. "Who do you know in Brownwood? A lot of people?"

"No, not many." He grinned. "I know some girls there."

"Naturally. Who are they? Name one. Maybe I know her too."

He hesitated, enjoying himself immensely. I didn't know whether I'd get the truth or a fiction. "Oh . . . one of them looks kinda foreign. I don't know. She may be."

I frowned, thinking of a Mexican girl I had known in high school. "What was her name?"

He looked at me, grinning, pushed his hat back on his head. "I think her name was Yasmina Devi."

"I never heard of her," I said.

He lifted his hat and scratched his head. "You've never heard of the

Devis?"

Something in his manner made me a little suspicious, but maybe I didn't know the right people. "I never heard of them," I said.

"I'm sure surprised." He sounded sincere, but his eyes were dancing.

I shrugged my shoulders. "Try me on somebody else. I'm almost certain to know someone else in Brownwood besides Clyde that you know."

He thought a minute. "Oh, yes," he said enthusiastically. "I do know someone else. One of the most beautiful girls I've ever seen."

Well, that was a come down. "What's her name?" I asked gamely.

He made a sweeping gesture with his hand and raised his voice as if he were announcing royalty. "Miss Dolores of the House of Dalton."

I wasn't very enthusiastic. "I've heard of her."

"Well, let me tell you about her." He was ready to become eloquent. "One day ol' Clyde and I were in Woolworth's, trying to get our shopping done. Clyde was looking down at the counter, and I was just standing there. Then I looked up and right across the counter was this tall, beautiful girl with blonde hair, clear eyes, and flawless skin. It was Dolores Dalton. I couldn't say a word. I just fainted dead away. Ol' Clyde brought me to, and I got up. 'What in the hell's wrong with you . . . fainting like that?' he wanted to know. But I couldn't talk. I just mumbled and pointed. And so we went out the door. Dolores had already gone down the street. I recognized her. Now, you won't believe this, but I recognized that girl from her back. Her back! I'll tell you she walked like a queen . . . shoulders back . . . golden hair bouncing around her shoulders."

I was taking it all in and getting more and more perturbed. He didn't have to rave about her! Besides, Clyde had told me the same story.

"A man got in my way, and I had to fool around, shoving him aside. I looked around and ol' Clyde was lying there on the sidewalk—fainted dead away. He'd got a glimpse of her profile, and I don't mean her nose. I mean that big—Well, I had to spend some time there on the sidewalk bringing him to. When he got up, he couldn't talk. He just pointed and we walked on down the street trying to catch her."

"I've heard she's very pretty," I said grudgingly.

"Most beautiful girl I think I ever saw." He was really enthusiastic now. "Beautiful skin. Beautiful body. Oh, what a beautiful body! Beautiful big— Beautiful big bosom."

That didn't set well with me. I'm a small medium. He raved on about Dolores Dalton and how beautiful she was. I quit listening and looked out the side of the car.

During the show, I forgot about his raving over Dolores Dalton and just enjoyed the music . . . dancing . . . the love story. After the show, we found a place where we could get cokes. At a table he chose, his hands were on my arms, lightly, as he helped me into my chair . . . a soft fleeting second his arms were around me, and I was thrilled.

It was a beautiful day, and, dressed up as he was, any woman would be proud to be with him. He was nice. Talented. He had taught himself to write stories that sold.

He wanted to know how far our farm was from town, and I told him it was about seven miles. Then he asked if I wanted to go by to see Mother and Mammy, but I said I needed to be in Cross Plains early in order to look over some school work for tomorrow. I didn't tell him I had to study my history lesson. I didn't want to spoil the day talking about history.

On the way to Cross Plains, he wanted to know if I could dance like Ruby Keeler. I said, "If I could dance like her, I'd be in the movies, and she'd be teaching school." Then I looked at him sitting there with a smug, complacent grin on his face. "Can you sing like Dick Powell?"

He sang a few bars of "Blue Moon" in a nice baritone that was pleasant but would never make the movies. That was my answer. I thought: We certainly are not talking about serious things, and it's fun. There's a great comfort in knowing that if you wanted to, the man you were with *could* talk of more serious things, or he could be whimsical and lighted-hearted too.

Then I did a curious thing for which there was no reason whatever. I reached down and opened the glove compartment of his car. In it was a big thirty-eight revolver. I took it out before Bob realized what I was doing. He caught his breath and reached for the gun. "Hey, girl, what the hell are you doing? You'll kill us all. Be careful of that. It's loaded."

He kept reaching for it, but I kept it beyond his reach. "Why have you got a gun?" I asked curiously.

"You never know who you're going to run into in this part of the country. Put it up."

I put it back in the glove compartment. "Don't be so scared," I laughed. "I've seen guns before."

Bob pulled out his handkerchief and wiped his face. "Well, you sure can't tell it from the way you handled that one. I guess you've never had one in your hands before."

I shrugged my shoulders. "Certainly I have. Do you carry it all the time?"

He laughed. "Of course, I carry it all the time. Do you think it's just for Sundays?" He settled himself more comfortably and began to be philosophical. "Now, look here. See how dressed up I am. I look like I've got a lot of money. Right?"

"You look like a million," I said approvingly.

He grinned, pleased. "Suppose we have a flat. I get out to fix it, and some half-baked gunman comes along and sees me. He'll think to himself, 'See how dressed up that feller is? He's got money.' Then if he can't figure how to take it away from me, he'll try to shoot me. I've got to have a gun, so that I can shoot first."

I laughed, for he wanted me to. "I've known some men who carry guns."

He dismissed the idea with a jaunty wave of his hand. "Sure. Out in this part of Texas, you never know who you're going to meet. You might run into some Indians."

I looked out the window at the clouds drifting across the sky, and said, idly, simply to make conversation, "My cousin carries a gun, but not to shoot Indians with."

"Why does he carry one?"

"He carries a twenty-two in the back of his car because if he's out after cattle and comes upon a den of rattlesnakes, he can grab his twenty-two and shoot."

Bob leaned against his door and looked up at the sky. "He comes up on a den of rattlesnakes, he'd need to get the hell out of there. Don't stay around to try to shoot 'em."

I brushed that aside. "I've got a gun."

He whirled to look at me. "You've got a gun! What the hell are you doing with a gun? You got it with you?"

"Don't be silly," I said. "Of course I don't have it with me."

"I'm glad to hear that. I'd hate to try to kiss you and get shot."

"I've got a gun for the same reason you have," I said. "You never know who you'll run into. The railroad runs across our farm about a hundred yards from the house. It cuts about ten acres off the land, dividing it from the rest of the farm. Big freight trains have to go slow past the house because it is upgrade all the way from Brownwood. Since the trains move slowly, tramps riding the rails sometimes get off and come to the house to ask for a handout. Some are white; some are black; and some are Mexican. Tramps. You don't know where they came from or where they're going. You have to be careful. A cousin of mine, my father's nephew, is on the police force in Brownwood. I asked him to get me a gun to make us feel a little safer. He did. A little pearl-handled revolver."

"Well, hell, I can see you need a gun on the farm, all right," he agreed, "but you'd better be careful, girl. You'll shoot yourself instead of the tramp. Where do you keep it at night? Under your pillow?"

"Oh, no. I keep it in the bottom drawer of the dresser."

Bob grinned. "Mighty interesting. Tramp comes in the house, and you say, 'Wait a minute, Mr. Tramp, until I get my gun. I want to shoot you.' You think he's going to say, 'Yes, ma'am, I'll be glad to oblige?'"

I laughed. "You're crazy."

"Yeah," he said, and his voice was light and pleasant, bantering. "Now, I do know this: Any time you have hold of a gun, derned if you wouldn't be more dangerous than any desperado who ever trod these western trails. A man would be a damn fool to stick around to see whether you were going to shoot him or yourself. Three women on a farm by yourselves with no man around certainly do need a gun, but I don't think you're a Calamity Jane." He stopped talking for a minute and looked at me, smiling. "You need a gun, all right. I can see that, but, honey, you be careful. Don't shoot yourself instead of the tramp."

I pretended not to notice that he called me "honey," but it pleased me. I decided to change the subject. "Mammy can shoot a gun as straight as any man who ever lived."

"I'll bet on that," Bob said. "I'll bet Mammy can do nearly anything she wants to. I sure want to meet Mammy some time."

"I'm going home next weekend; I'll introduce you. You'll like her, I think. She's wonderful. She throws a rock straight too. She can throw a rock straighter than some people can shoot a gun."

He nodded and looked at the sky again. "I'd expect it. Yessir, I'd expect it."

I like to talk about Mammy. "Last summer, she went outside to chop down mesquite trees, and she saw a rabbit. She thought to herself: 'I wouldn't mind having a little cotton-tail rabbit like that for supper.' So she picked up a rock real slow and easy and aimed it at him, and she hit that rabbit in the head and killed it instantly, just like that." I snapped my fingers.

"God," he said, admiringly. "Remind me to be mighty careful around Mammy. I don't want to get in her way when she's got a rock or a gun."

It was almost sundown, and the sky was beautiful with color. We reached the top of a little hill. Bob stopped the car, and put his arm around me, pulled me close to him. The last rays of the sun cast a gold tint as the drifting clouds changed from crimson to rose . . . to pink.

"Look, girl," he whispered softly, awestruck. "Look at that sunset. Just you look at that sunset! Only in Texas do you ever see a sunset like that."

I didn't want words to spoil the moment. It was enough to be suspended there at the top of a small, insignificant hill made luminous and beautiful in the glow of the late afternoon. We were still, in space, for there is great space on the semi-prairie where we live. I moved away from him, back to my side of the car, to think about it . . . to look at the things around us: the scrub oaks turning dark in the soft dusk, the gaunt trees, the spindly brown grass creeping out of the thin, sandy soil among the rocks.

No other man I'd ever known had stopped to look at a beautiful sunset. But here was this big man, awkward, ungainly, who wrote and talked so knowledgeably of barbarians, of killings, wars, fighting, and death, stopping to look at the sunset. I didn't try to talk. I watched him. I think he was deep into a story and had forgotten me.

He brought himself back to the moment with a light laugh. "Girl, I hope you appreciate all I've done for you today," he said. "Now there . . . there's a beautiful sunset . . . if I do say so myself."

Monday evening . . .
After a long day at school . . .

When I got to school this morning, I knew there must be problems. The office door was locked and Lewis, Mr. Williams, and Coach seemed to be in conference about something.

Truthfully, I was relieved. No teasing today. No teasing at all.

During the noon hour, I went to the rest room to touch up my face. Another teacher was there for the same reason. She held her lipstick in her hand and pressed her lips together to get the lipstick evenly on both lips. She looked at me while I used my own lipstick. "Who was that good-looking man I saw you with yesterday?" she asked.

I told her, and she looked surprised. "Well," she said. "He's a lot better looking than I thought he was."

That was all. But I was pleased.

Wednesday evening after ten p.m . . .

I had a date with Bob tonight. This wasn't really a date. Last Sunday, he asked me if it would be all right for him just to come by some evening after I got home from school or after supper. We would ride around and he would shoot his mouth off about life and the world in general. When I said I'd like that, he wanted to know if he had to wear a coat and tie, or would it be all right to come comfortably attired without the tie and coat as long as his shirt was clean. I thought that, since we'd just be riding around with no place in particular to go, it would be all right.

I said that any time after Monday night would be fine, for on Monday nights I had to meet with my dramatics club at school. He wanted to know, then, if I taught school day and night. I told him I did, but I loved the night work better because that was directing plays.

The date with Bob tonight was like having a date with an entirely different man. Sunday, he was full of fun, pleasant. Tonight, he was quiet. Aloof. Distant. When he got in the car, the old bounce, knocking the steering wheel this way and that, was simply not there.

"Which way do you want to drive?" There was a melancholy tone in his voice.

"Any place except toward Brownwood," I said. "I know how things look in that direction."

He smiled faintly. "How about toward Baird? That's not bad country."

"Okay." I was determined to be cheerful and good-humored. "What have you been doing?"

He hesitated. "You really care?"

"Of course," I said, surprised.

"I've been trying to pound out another yarn."

"Another Conan story?"

"Yeah, but this may be my last one. I'm getting a little tired of Conan." He made a sweeping gesture with his arm. "This country needs to be written about. There are all kinds of stories around here." He turned to look at me for the first time tonight. "What have you been doing besides teaching school . . . as if that wasn't enough?"

I laughed. "I started a story last night." What I didn't tell him about it was that I had thought about him and his mother, and I'd wondered how much she had influenced what he did in school. Besides that, I wanted to get him started talking about writing.

It worked. He looked interested. "Another confession?"

"No," I said. "This one is about a high school boy . . . uh . . . he's tied to his mother apron—"

"Don't tell me about it," he interrupted quickly, "unless you've got it completely written."

"Why not?" I asked, baffled.

"When you tell a story and someone listens to it, you are really publishing it. Then when you sit down to write, it just doesn't come. You're not excited about it anymore. You're not trying to discover something new. I mean, of course, that's the way it works for me. Maybe it wouldn't work that way with you. No two people write exactly alike. But I don't usually give advice. If you want to tell me your story, go ahead."

"I know what you mean," I said. "When you tell somebody something, the creativeness flows out in the telling."

He was smiling now. More good-humored. More the way I liked him to be. "Don't get me wrong. I've done exactly what I'm telling you not to do, but when I do it, the yarn always comes out wooden. Not easy, flowing, light."

I could understand what he was saying. I told him about an experience I had had in college. I had gotten what I thought was a great idea for a one-act play. It was so exciting to me, I told a friend of mine about it. My friend thought it was a great idea too.

Bob seemed very interested. "What happened?"

"I never did write it," I admitted chagrined. "My listening audience gave me a great response, and so it didn't work when I tried to put it on paper."

Bob nodded sympathetically. "That's how it works for me."

"Didn't you and Clyde write some stories together?"

"Yeah. But it's not the same thing as telling your story to someone," he said. "With another person, you exchange ideas. Bounce them back and forth. Plan them."

"Do you always outline your stories?"

"Absolutely." He paused, thinking. "Oh, once in a while, I put a sheet of paper in my typewriter and start out and get where I'm going with no outline at all. But the way I explain such things is that it's either been gestating in my mind, or I have lived it or knew about it in some other life."

On a dark, lonely road with the stars dim and far away, reincarnation was not a topic I wanted to explore.

He settled back in his seat. "I don't want to leave the wrong impression. Most of the yarns I write are planned very carefully, and they're complete with a detailed outline."

I asked him what he meant by a detailed outline, and I gathered from what he said that he made notes and arranged them in order. But it was not the way I outlined history or one of my speeches. He said his outline helped him to know his characters, what they wanted, and where they were going. The outline helped for it made the yarn stick in his mind. Then when he sat down at the typewriter, he went straight through the story. Even so, it took a big wastebasket to hold the pages he threw away.

I was quiet for a while, looking at the road and at the stars. I worried. Maybe I'm not a writer after all. I had not written an outline, but I had thought about it. I knew the characters and what they would say to each other. I knew how the story would end. It had been on my mind a lot the last few days; even when I was teaching a class, I would think of it. I could get emotional about it. I wanted to hit the boy's mother on the head with a hammer.

We rode for a long time without talking, and it was very pleasant. With Bob you can be silent and it's nice. Each of us was concerned with his own thoughts. I was thinking of my story and of him, and I supposed he was thinking of Conan. He was sitting, haunched over the wheel, his eyes intent on the road. If I were to speak to him, I would be intruding.

Suddenly, he turned toward me. "You're writing a story about a high school boy? Is it one of your students this happened to?"

"Oh, no," I said quickly, "Not one of my students." Then I asked him if he thought I should have a particular boy in mind as I wrote.

His answer was interesting. He laughed. "No, but if somebody asks you where you get your characters . . . and they're sure to do that . . . you always say, 'He's a combination of a lot of people I have known.' That way, if your character is a damn fool, nobody will want to identify with him." He stopped talking for a minute and ran his hand through his hair. "To tell the truth, I don't know how a man gets a character for a story, anymore than I know how he falls in love. I don't know if his characters spring full-blown from his head, or if he sees a man walking down the street and recognizes him instantly." He looked at me, frowning. "I doubt any writer knows for sure where his characters come from."

A lovely night, not too cold but not at all warm. A good friend. A subject I liked to talk about. I became talkative. I told him how I chose characters to play certain roles in a play. In the play, I was getting ready to direct, there were four characters—a country boy and his sister, and a city boy and his sister.

"While I was reading the script," I explained, "I began to see the characters as real people, but I couldn't point to a real live pupil and say, 'You're the country boy I was reading about,' though there are plenty of boys in school who were born and reared on the farm. After football practice, they go home and milk cows, chop wood, and help out about the farm. But not any particular boy is the one I picture as the character in my mind."

Bob was listening with an interest that was flattering. I took a deep breath and went on. "As I read, I endow my characters with mannerisms I observe in people around me. One character may pull his ear as a boy in my high school class used to do. He may scratch his head, stroke his chin, run his fingers through his hair—" I broke off and looked at Bob.

He wanted to know if, as I directed the play, the boy I chose for a certain role became the character for me.

"To a certain extent," I said. "You see, Bob, it only becomes a play when it's acted out. Up until the time it goes into rehearsals, it's just a script and the characters are only in the director's head. As I direct the boy to whom I assign a part, he begins to develop mannerisms to portray the character. If he's any good at all, he becomes the character. When I give a dramatic reading or play a character in a play, I always see the character I imagined as I read the script. Never myself. To me, they are real people in actual situations. In a limited way, I become that person."

"It seems to me you know how to get characters for a story, and nobody needs to tell you anything," he said. He moved about, lurching against the steering wheel, knocking against his door, running his fingers through his hair, as he always does when he is in a good humor and interested in something. "It seems to me your play directing is very similar to writing. I think it'll help you a lot with writing. Have you ever directed any of Shakespeare's plays?"

I shook my head dolefully. "I've only directed scenes in class. I'd love to direct *Midsummer Night's Dream,* but I can't visualize it on our stage."

"I mean, how would you treat a historical play?"

I watched the car lights play upon the fence beside the road before I answered. "When I read one of Shakespeare's plays, I can't see that men's hearts have changed much since the late 1500s and early 1600s. Men still hate other men—Jews, Negroes, anybody who is different. I guess men are just men, whatever century they live in."

That gave Bob a chance to go to town on a subject he liked to talk about. "You're right. Unfortunately, men are men. In this civilization we live in, they get more depraved and demonic all the time. I'll tell you, girl, it's a hell of a world we live in."

I protested that. "I don't think it's such a bad world. Sure there are men who are bad, but there are also men who are good. There are men who hate, but there are also men who love. There—"

"Damn it, girl." He interrupted me. "You talk like a dreamer." He turned the car around, and we headed back toward Cross Plains. He went on. "I tell you that you don't know the things that go on round you. There in Cross Plains, when they discovered oil, you wouldn't believe the kind of scum who moved in, drinking, whoring, carousing all night long. Not a decent man in the whole lot of them. Scavengers! Bastards!"

"And I expect there were some good men, decent men who came in too, but you don't talk about them." I pulled my leg up under me, so I could face him. I'd had enough of his condemning civilization! "Good men don't get the publicity. They—"

"That's because there are so damn few of them." He raised his voice. "You Sunday School people hide your heads in the sand. You refuse to—"

I decided to set him straight. "Your father is a good man, isn't he?"

"You're damn right he's a good man." He glared at me. "He's the only one I know. He's—"

"What about Clyde? Dave Lee? Lindsey Tyson? They're good men, aren't they?"

He lunged at the steering wheel. "Hell, yes. What's that got to do with it?"

"Everything," I insisted. "You do know four or five good men. You can't tell me that out of all the universe, God only created four or five good men."

He banged against the steering wheel. "You don't stick to the subject." He was talking loudly, almost yelling. "You bring up a bunch of irrelevant nonsense to keep you from seeing things as they are. Decay. Maggots of corruption are all around you, and you prate platitudes to hide the truth from yourself. Greed. Corruption. Selfishness. That's our civilization."

I couldn't let him get by with that. "Didn't you tell me you might have to take your mother to the hospital?"

That seemed so irrelevant to him he was unable to answer. I went on. "Hospitals. Schools. These are the products of civilization. They didn't exist in that Hybo—wherever it was Conan lived. Hospitals try to heal people's bodies to make their lives worth living again. You use them, but you don't give civilization credit for them."

He didn't answer. I didn't say anything else either. I tell my kids in the public speaking class that a speaker has to have something to say, say it, and shut up. But I felt lonely and dejected. I needed a friend to talk to more than anything else in the world, and something in me makes me argue and lose them.

Outside the car window, the houses with lamps in the windows began to look familiar. We were almost back in Cross Plains. Then without warning, Bob put his arm around me. "We men made a hell of a mistake when we sent you women to college and gave you the vote."

The world was good again. Impulsively, I put my arms around his neck and kissed him on the cheek. He laughed softly. I felt better and moved away from him, back to my side of the car, so that he could drive.

After a minute, as the houses became more numerous and we were home, he said, "What time do you want me to come over to take you home Friday?"

"After the football game," I said. "The season's almost over, and I'd like to see this one. It's real important." He didn't say anything. "You like football, don't you? I thought maybe you might go to the game with me." I wanted him to go to the game with me, dressed up as he had been last Sunday. Then everyone would know what a nice person he could be.

He stopped the car in front of the house but made no move to get out. "I do like football," he said, finally, "but not high school games. Besides, I've got a lot to do Friday afternoon. How about seven or seven-thirty? That will be about the right time, won't it?"

I said it would be fine. He walked to the door with me. It was not ten o'clock yet, and a light in the Hemphill's dining room told me the boys were still up, studying. At the steps, I said, "It's early."

"Yes," he agreed. "My mother isn't doing well. I have to hurry home. I'll see you Friday."

He turned and left. I took hold of the door handle as if I were coming inside, but when he turned the car around in the street, I sat down on the steps, holding my arms close to me to shut out the cold nip of the night air.

The stars blinked far away in the dark sky. In a little while, the dining room light was turned off and still I sat, thinking about Bob, thinking about his mother. I thought of the way he did things for her, always putting her interests ahead of his own. How had she bound him so close to her? Most young men his age would demand their freedom. How great a sense of duty!

He was a strange man. Did being alone so much . . . having only a few friends . . . being criticized by the town . . . do this to him? Is he the dutiful son he appears?

Something was wrong somewhere I didn't understand. Sometimes . . . I got a fleeting glimpse of something deep inside him. Something he could not think.

We are not sure of sorrow;
And joy was never sure.

I will never understand Bob's mother.

After school today, I helped Mary select a declamation. After we found one she liked and wanted to memorize, we talked a long time about the part she wants in the play. When we finished our conversation, I went to town to see whether or not I had any mail. It's a good walk, and it gave me time to plan some news stories to give to Jack Scott for the paper. Teachers have a lot to do, and I love every minute of it.

The drugstore was almost empty, and Mrs. Smith was standing at the counter by herself. As I went through the door, I almost ran smack into Dr. Howard. He grunted, made an ineffectual pass at his hat and lumbered on down the street as if he were scared.

Mrs. Smith laughed. "You'd better watch out," she said. "I'd be afraid to get in Doc's way."

I pushed some boxes out of my way and rested my arms on the counter as she was doing. "He can look pretty fierce," I admitted.

"His bark is worse than his bite." She looked at me closely, smiling to herself. "I'll tell you something if you won't tell," she said.

"I won't breathe a word of it," I promised.

"Do you remember the night you went over to their house to see Robert?"

I nodded. Would I never hear the last of it?

Mrs. Smith straightened her collar, patted her hair and smiled. "Dr. Howard told me that when you and Robert left for him to bring you home, that he looked at Mrs. Howard and said, 'Mother, are we going to lose our boy?' " She paused. "And I guess you know what she said?"

"I haven't the faintest idea," I said.

Mrs. Smith waved at someone passing the drugstore, and then looked back at me. "Doc said she said, 'No. Don't worry about that. We're not going to lose him.' "

She looked at me as if she expected me to say something, but if I had said what I was thinking, Nat Williams would have fired me without blinking an eye.

We talked about other things and I came on home. I forgot to go by the post office.

Friday—bad day with a happy ending . . .

For a while today, I thought this Friday just shouldn't happen! I didn't even enjoy the football game because I was in a hurry to get back to Cross Plains, so that I could be ready for Bob to take me home.

I was not in too happy a frame of mind, for something unexplainable that had nagged at me all week was still bothering me. I kept saying, "Maybe this—" "Maybe that—" The truth was that I was still wondering why Bob was so willing to take me to Brownwood, but he wouldn't go anywhere in Cross Plains with me, not even to a high school football game.

Bob says I worry too much about the "whys" and "wherefores" of things, and he may be right. He says it's better to take life the way Conan does. Conan fights bigness, ugliness, badness because it's there, but he can shake off his involvement and go on to new fights and new adventures without worrying about *why* things were as they were. I said that sometimes bad things were just below the surface and that they might determine life or death . . . as it sometimes does in a Henry James novel. Bob said, "To hell with Henry James."

Usually, I have no trouble concentrating on a football game. Not today. One of our players was shoved out of bounds by someone on the opposing team, and I was almost hit. It scared me!

This same thing had happened at another of our football games recently. A boy was shoved out of bounds, and a spectator had been injured; he was still in a very serious condition.

The incident was not only something to think about, but it had also led to a philosophic discussion between Bob and me. When I told Bob about it, I said it was an innocent, unavoidable accident, but a man's life was at stake! Such innocent acts with their portentous effects were, I thought, an ingredient of Henry James's "Daisy Miller."

Bob said he didn't like that sort of philosophic wondering in the things he wrote. His readers wanted action. Don't stop. Don't analyze. Don't philosophize. Act. Feel. Act.

There were so many things to worry about today. In the north, the sky was a dark blue. A norther was going to blow in, and I wasn't dressed for it. Texas northers hit sudden and soon; your only warning is a dark blue, angry sky.

Just about the time the game was over and we were starting toward the car, it struck. We hugged ourselves and ran. We quickly rolled up the car windows, glad for the warmth inside. There were four of us in the car: Anna May, Enid, Jimmie, and me. I sighed. It would have been so much nicer to have gotten in the car with Bob rather than with a bunch of women.

It bothers me, puzzles me, and makes me very angry, because I can't get

Bob to go anywhere with me in Cross Plains!

On the way back to Cross Plains, somebody asked me what I was going to do this weekend, and I said, innocently, I was going home. A simple statement that led to an argument with Enid.

She looked surprised. "When are you going?"

"Tonight. Bob's taking me." Instantly, I was on the defensive.

Enid rasped out. "That crazy guy! I don't see what you see in him."

I mumbled that he was one of the most interesting men that I'd ever seen, or words to that effect. Then it irritated me. I said, bluntly, "He's a writer. You're an English teacher; you ought to appreciate that."

"Not the kind of things he writes," she said positively. "I wouldn't touch his stories, or one of those magazines he writes for."

"You don't know anything about them," I said quickly. It wasn't easy to talk back to Enid. "You read Edgar Allan Poe, don't you? I heard you talking about him to your class the other day."

She looked at me as if I had the measles. "Poe is a good writer," she said. "I was pointing out what a wonderful choice of words he had; I was trying to get my students to enjoy using words carefully to improve their writing."

"Bob has a wonderful choice of words, too," I insisted, "and as far as the content of his stories and of Poe's, they write the same kind of nightmarish stuff. The main difference is that Poe's works are in the literature books and Bob's aren't . . . yet. Someday, some English teacher will be telling kids to try to write like Bob."

"I will have to see that to believe it," Enid said. "I will certainly have to see that to believe it."

I settled back in the car and only half-listened to the talk inside while I wondered what kind of mood Bob would be in tonight. I could defend him all I wanted to, but I knew he wasn't perfect . . . that he couldn't be perfect with the mother he had. Everything was so damnably mixed up.

But when he came, Bob was in such a good mood that the whole idea of talking about problems and writing went completely out of my mind.

"Did you ever make a fool of yourself, then want to cut your throat?" he asked when we got to the car.

"Definitely," I said, falling into the spirit of the occasion. "I'm very good at making a fool of myself. Why? What did you do?"

He laughed and threw his cap into the back seat of the car, chuckling and embarrassed at the same time. "I was out working on my car this morning, trying to get it cleaned up for tonight. While I was working, like a fool, I was talking, trying to figure out something about a yarn I was stuck on. I wasn't talking too loud, but I got to a place where ol' Conan was fighting, and I said, 'Fool. Dog of hell. Die!' About that time, a timid little voice said, 'Robert, is your mother home?' I turned around and there was your friend, Mrs. Jackson, looking as if she didn't know whether to run or stay there. I wanted to go through the ground or grab my gun out of the car and shoot myself." He shook his head, laughing ruefully.

I laughed appreciatively. "I know how you feel," I said. "I'm always doing things like that."

He ran his hand through his hair, leaving it standing straight up. "God," he said. "What can you say when you do a thing like that? All I could do was stand there and look at the woman, and I guess the way I looked scared her half to death. She had a little cake or something she'd baked for Mother. I suggested she go on in the house, and I got real busy around the car and kept my mouth shut." He laughed again. "I sure as hell felt like a fool all day."

"I can sympathize," I said. "After I saw the Mantel company do the *Merchant of Venice*, I memorized a forty-five minute cutting of it and gave it at various literary societies—college literary societies and women's study clubs."

"I didn't know women's literary societies were interested in anything but what their neighbors were doing," Bob said, still good humored.

"Well, they are," I said.

Then I told him about being invited to give the selection to a group of high school students. On my way to school, I was rehearsing, gesturing, waving my hands around, only to look up and see a school bus with a bunch of kids watching me out the back window. That reminded him of something he had done almost like that. He was particularly impressed with a fighter we had in Brownwood, Kid Dula. One day as he went home from the post office, Bob was thinking about Kid Dula, and, all of a sudden, he got an idea for a whopping fight yarn and began shadow boxing as he walked down the street, and even accompanied the shadow boxing with words!

While we laughed about what we'd done, our reactions to the situations had been different. When I saw that somebody was watching me, I stopped rehearsing immediately and turned my car in the opposite direction. Bob kept on shadow boxing, telling himself that he didn't care what people thought of him. I knew he did care, very much, but was just too stubborn to admit it. However, the important thing right then was that each of us knew how the other felt when he makes a fool of himself.

I changed the subject. "I want to ask you a question."

"Shoot," he said, still laughing. "I probably haven't got any more sense than to try to answer it."

"I heard that you and some other boys got drunk one night and threw beer bottles at the clock in Cisco or . . . somewhere."

Bob laughed heartily. "Talk about making a fool of yourself!" he said. "That would be a good one, wouldn't it?"

"Did you?" I persisted.

"Do you believe every thing you hear?"

"I wouldn't be asking you if I did."

"Well," he said cryptically, "I wouldn't say it wasn't possible. And I would point out that a town clock would make about the best target you could find."

"It would kill you to answer with a simple 'yes' or 'no,' wouldn't it?" I said. "If the cops had come along, what then?"

"That would have been a very bad bust," Bob guffawed.

"Okay," I said. "Since we're telling each other some of the bad breaks or busts we've made, I might as well tell you my prize bust when I said the wrong thing at the right time."

"Go ahead," he said. "I can probably top you, for if there's one thing I've done well in my life, it's make one mistake after another. Then I've spent hours wanting to jerk my tongue out."

I took a deep breath. "Well, one semester while I was going to college, I worked for a doctor. A little cafe opened up across the street from the doctor's office. The best looking boy started working there. He was my dream man. He had dark brown, nearly black hair, and blue eyes. One day, Loyce, that's Enid's and Jimmie's sister, came to town to see me. I said, 'Loyce, the best looking man in this world works over there in that cafe. Let's go have a cup of coffee.' When we started out the door, I made some sort of bust. I don't remember what it was that I said, but when we got into the cafe, we were both laughing like crazy. The young man came up and said, 'What's so funny?' I said, 'Oh, I made a bust.' He said, 'And you can laugh about it?' Then Loyce spoke up. 'Oh, Novalyne's the craziest thing in the world. When she makes a bust, she laughs like an idiot. Anybody else would be embarrassed to death.' I threw back my head, and said, 'Well, it's a good thing my busts tickle me; they don't tickle anybody else.' "

Bob started laughing. He even stopped the car in the middle of the road and leaned against the steering wheel and laughed. Finally, he gasped out, "I can't top that one."

A car was coming, and he got hold of himself. We rode on down the highway. He was still laughing when we got to my house.

I loved the way he was at ease when I introduced him to Mother and Mammy. He hadn't been that much at ease when I was introduced to him. With them, he seemed sure of himself. Poised. I thought how nice it would be to introduce him to my friends in Brownwood, and also how nice it would be to have him go places with me. Anybody who saw him tonight would like him—even Enid. People who said nasty things about him did not know him and had never seen him as he was tonight. The Jacksons probably had. They knew him and liked him.

I liked the way he gave his attention to Mother and Mammy. He was like a poised movie star at his best among an admiring public. He talked to them the way I liked to hear him talk. Quietly. Intent on their answers to his questions. In a few minutes, Mammy was telling him about the things that happened in Alabama when she was young. I didn't know how he'd got her started, but he gave her his undivided, flattering attention; and Mammy bloomed. She loved a good audience. She told him about Alabama in the 1860s. He asked about the Civil War and if she could remember it.

She remembered many things that happened, for she was about four or five years old when it got really bad. She said that it was not only the soldiers who came through their area that they were afraid of. They were also robbed and harassed by the riff-raff who followed after the soldiers. The riff-raff were worse than the soldiers. True, the soldiers took cattle, chickens, turkeys, and your money; the riff-raff took everything they left. They took the sheets off your beds, the quilts you'd quilted, the food in your pantry, and the milk in the spring house.

Mammy took a deep breath. "They'd come in when we were ready to sit down to the table to eat a meal; they'd make us stay away while they ate everything on the table. The children cried." Mammy paused, remembering. "We were always hungry."

Bob lunged forward in his chair. He'd hung on every word, and now he reacted physically. It is one thing to read history, but it's altogether different to talk with someone who remembered. "And there was nothing you could do about it?" His voice was venomous against the injustice.

"Well," Mammy mused, "yes and no. There was a little bit of help."

"Help?" Bob picked up the word quickly. And though I'd heard the story many times, tonight, it was new again. Bob's interest, his emotion, his deepest attention to Mammy while she talked, made me participate in the story.

"There was a man we called the 'safety man,' " Mammy said slowly. "The people were starving, and Mr. Lincoln and the government sent in 'safe men' to help you. When the safety man came, the riff-raff ran off. When they came in to harass and bother you, somebody had to go get the safety man."

Bob's eyes were intent on Mammy's face, and his voice was soft. "This is the first I ever heard of the safety man."

"Safety men travelled around the country. Sometimes they were there when you needed them, but most of the time they stayed in town," Mammy went on. "We tried to keep a horse and a cow or two hidden down in the woods, or on the hills, but the riff-raff or the soldiers nearly always found them. If they found your horse before you could get away, then a man or boy had to run all the way to town to get the safety man. We lived several miles from town. It took time. Then, too, the safety man might not be there because someone else had got him first."

"What could the safety man do?" Bob wanted to know.

"If he got there before the riff-raff left, he could make them put the things

Mary Emmaline Reed

Novalyne Price's grandmother—referred to as "Mammy" in the book. This photograph was made on her 79th birthday. She was especially fond of Robert E. Howard for he was fascinated by the stories she loved to tell of the Civil War and the witches she'd heard about during her childhood in Alabama.

back and leave you alone. Sometimes, if they were already gone, he followed them to get your things back, but he couldn't always get all of it. Still, if it hadn't been for the safety man, things would have been much worse."

"You said 'Mr. Lincoln and the government,' " Bob said. "I suppose you hated Lincoln?"

Mammy shook her head. "No. Not in my family. He was on the other side, but we thought he was a good man and that he helped all he could. There's not much anybody can do with the riff-raff that follows an army."

Bob shook his head violently, as if to clear his mind of a horrible experience. "I guess I can see how you'd feel—even about Lincoln."

He rose awkwardly to his feet, shrugged his shoulders, and made an attempt at levity. "I want to talk with you more about that someday," he said. "I'm coming over Sunday afternoon, if that's all right with you."

Everybody laughed, and somehow I felt his ignoring me was a compliment. At times, Bob can do that to me . . . laugh at me . . . tell me I'm wrong . . . even ignore me, yet I'm as pleased as if he'd complimented me. On the other hand, he sometimes acts like a barbarian, and I hate him. Tonight, I just stood there grinning, pleased.

Mammy said, "Come back any time, and I'll tell you more about the Civil War and Alabama witches and ghosts. We'll send Novalyne off down in the pasture somewhere. She'd rather be down there anyway than in the house."

The world looked better to me right then than it had all week. After Bob was gone, Mammy and Mother said that he was a nice, pleasant man.

I'd enjoyed Bob tonight, too. I was glad to know Bob Howard, the real man.

I went outside the door into the cold, night air, and looked up at the sky and thought about Bob. I could love him, I thought if he were always as he was tonight. But I'm not going to try to take him away from his mother or anybody else. I am going to act strictly the way I feel. If he likes me the way I am, okay. If not, okay.

It was a beautiful cold night. I wanted to stand on the porch in the cold and feel happiness deep within me, but I couldn't. If I let myself look too deeply inside him, or myself, I might find something to fear. Questions. Eternal questions.

Fear? What is there to fear in any human being?

Sunday night . . .
"Lo, the bird is on the wing . . ."

It was still cold today, but not as cold as it was Friday when the norther blew in. Bob came at the appointed time, and there was more light talk and laughter. More kidding with Mammy about how they should get rid of me so they could talk about important things that happened years ago in Alabama.

"It's not the here and now that matters," Bob said. "It's what happened long ago that's important."

He asked Mammy if she had ever known of any magic—black magic—or voodoo or other such happenings back in Alabama.

Mammy loves to talk, but today was not the day for stories. "No. No magic that I knew of. Some strange things did happen . . . things you couldn't explain rationally. When I was a child, there was an awful lot of talk of witches, schools for witches, and ghosts. I heard such talk until I grew up, married, and moved away."

Bob listened intently. "I want to hear about that someday."

Mammy laughed. "Get Novalyne to tell you. She knows all my old stories backwards and frontwards."

"You don't write about those things?" Bob was incredulous.

I was on the spot, and I didn't like it. I couldn't say, in front of Mammy, that I changed them around to where the witch girls were good, sweet girls who always got their man. "They're not scary when I write them," I said, lamely. "You can write them scary."

Everyone laughed, and we got ready to leave. Bob commented on the large number of books I had to take back with me and the fact that my suitcase no longer held all my clothes.

He said, "Ain't that a new dress you're wearing?"

I looked at mother and she was smiling. "It is," I said.

"Pretty," Bob said. "Real pretty. I like that kind of dress."

If he tried, I think he could be a real ladies' man. He knows how to say things women like to hear. It would have been hard to tell which of us was more pleased—Mother, Mammy, or I.

We were late getting into the show, and, somehow, I could never seem to get into the magic of it. When it ended, I was ready to go.

Outside, things looked better. I wasn't in such a rush, and so when Bob said he'd like to go down the street to Dublin's to see what books they had in the window, I went gladly enough.

Bob said that he really needed to pick up a book or to order one—another history. And I said, "For heaven's sake, haven't you got enough histories?"

Bob shook his head, and held my hand tight in his. "No. You never have too many histories. They pay off. About a year ago, I bought a history—paid twenty-five dollars for it. Sounds like a lot, but I sold five or six hundred dollars worth of yarns based on what I learned from it."

"I can understand it," I agreed. "Several years ago, I bought *The American Songbag* by Carl Sandburg. I paid twenty-five dollars for it, because I could use it on some of my programs. You know—programs of songs and poetry."

The love of books was something we shared. Bob said that if you used a book to make more money or to add something to your profession, it was worth it, no matter if you had to pay fifty dollars for it. We looked in the window, saying which books we would like to have. I pointed out a history and said that it would probably help me with my history classes.

Bob's attention was centered on a copy of *The Rubáiyat*. He already had a copy, but he said he might come back next week and pick up that book and another one—that one by Cabell.

We stopped to look in another store window. There were a number of pretty rings—diamonds and plain rings—in it. One, I thought, was very pretty. Bob squeezed my hand and said that maybe we ought to take a really good look at it, because someday we just might want to buy one like it for our best girl. He was being breezy and cute.

I laughed and tried to get my fingers out of his hand so that he couldn't break them. The restlessness inside me was beginning to subside, and I was feeling more cheerful, and then—

Well, it's funny how conversations can get started. All is peaceful and calm one minute and the next an argument breaks out and threatens the most peaceful couple in the world, and love takes to wing.

As we crossed the street we met a man, whose name I couldn't remember. He tipped his hat and spoke to me. I said, "Hello," thinking nothing about it.

"Who was that?" Bob asked.

"I don't know his name," I said casually. "I knew him when I was a kid and Mother and I lived here in Brownwood. She worked in a tailor shop. He came there to—"

"He knew you," Bob said. "Why don't you want to tell me his name?"

I looked at him quickly. Was he pretending to be jealous or just teasing me because of the man I'd spoken to? I said again that I didn't know who he was but rumor had it that he was the illegitimate son of a white doctor . . . or dentist . . . or rancher . . . or some other big shot here in town.

"What do you mean *white* man? That wasn't a mulatto, was it?"

"As far as I know," I said. "Everybody seems to know him. You don't mention the fact that he's the son of a white man except in hushed tones, but it's said that some of the best white blood in the State of Texas flows in his veins."

We walked slowly to the car and Bob opened the door for me. I got in and sat waiting, amused, for him to get in before I said anything else. When he got in the car, he pushed his hat on the back of his head and sat looking at me. "How does it happen you speak to him as if you're a friend of his?"

That shocked me. "I knew the man when I was a kid," I said. "He bought me an ice cream cone once. Of course I speak to him. What's wrong with that?"

Bob shook his head doubtfully. "Nothing, the way you tell it. The thing that got me is that you spoke as if he were a damn good friend."

At that moment, I forgot all the cute, nice things Bob said and did, and I was furious. I took off my gloves and put them in my purse and said crisply, "I've never thought about being a good friend of his or not being one. But now that you mention it, I say, 'Why not?' Besides, you thought he was a white man until I told you he wasn't, and that's something that really bothers me."

Bob made no move to start the car. He stared at me. "I'd like to know what it is."

I reached up to brush my hair out of my eyes. "At the end of the day when work is over, that man's white father, whoever he is, can go to the best restaurants in town, sit down, drink coffee, eat his supper, but that mulatto, his own son, can't go in there by himself and sit down at a table and eat."

"Hell, I should say not," Bob blurted out.

That made me even more angry! And I thought Bob was so broad-minded! "Look," I said sharply. "I think the man has a right to go any place his father goes."

Bob started the engine and put the car in gear, but he jerked his foot off the gas and the engine coughed and stopped. He made no move to start it again. "My God, girl. Do you know what you're saying? If he's part Negro—"

"I don't care if he's nine-tenths Negro." I raised my voice. "He's as good as the white man who sired him."

"Girl!" Bob exclaimed, "I've never heard a woman talk like that before. What in the world do you mean? I never heard a woman say things like that." He was so disturbed he was repeating himself.

He started the engine again, and I kept quiet until he had the car in the street. He took a deep breath and sounded much calmer when he spoke. "I suppose on the face of it, it looks right, but that's just on the face of it. Hell, there's more to it than that."

I saw someone I knew, waved at him, and pulled one leg up under me and looked at Bob. "No, there's not." I was calmer too. "If a white man goes to the flat, and that's what we call the part of town where the Negroes live, and leaves a half-white, half-black child down there, then that kid has every right in the world he has."

We almost hit the car that was stopped in front of us. Bob busied himself a moment, starting the engine again, and driving on with his eyes on the road instead of on me.

"I know Sunday School twaddle like that sounds good," he said, "but I'll swear that if we listened to you, the world would be in absolute chaos." He whirled toward me again. "Where did you get any such ideas as that?"

Where do we get our ideas? I had to think about that for a minute. "Maybe I was influenced by something that happened a long time ago," I said. "Do you know anything about raising turkeys?"

That completely floored him. For a minute, it looked as if the man of words was suddenly dumb. He lunged at the steering wheel and door. "I don't know a damn thing about it, and I don't see how raising turkeys could give you ideas like that."

"It's important since it led to my first contact with Negroes," I said, preparing myself for a long argument. "It happened right after my father and mother separated, and my mother and I went back to Mammy's to live. Mammy was raising turkeys, trying to make the farm pay."

Bob didn't interrupt. He turned slightly so that he could look at me part of the time and at the road part of the time.

"Turkeys are still half wild," I explained. "As long as they're small, the mother hens keep them pretty close to home, but when they get older, they begin to go to the wild. Every afternoon, you hunt them and drive them home, the way you would cattle, except that you don't ride a horse. You walk miles and miles through—"

"And you begin to wish you had slaves to hunt them for you," Bob said.

I tapped him on the shoulder. "I'm trying to tell you something. Just shut up and listen."

I told him about the turkey drives and how tired we'd get. When we came to a neighbor's house, we'd sit for a while, visit with the people there, and then go on again.

"One afternoon, we came to a house where a Negro family lived." I paused. "People called him 'Nigger George,' and so I thought 'nigger' was his first name."

Bob laughed heartily. "You were young."

I said that when we came to the George's house, we sat on the porch and talked, just the way we did with other neighbors. Mrs. George sent the children to the cistern to draw fresh, cool water for us to drink. Two little girls about my age took me out to play in their playhouse while the grown folks talked. "They had the same kind of playhouse I had—a circle of rocks under a tree and pieces of broken glass for dishes."

"This is responsible for your wild ideas?" Bob laughed indulgently.

"Maybe," I said. "When we were ready to leave, I kept waiting for Mammy to say, 'You all come to see us sometime.' I expected Mrs. George to say what the other ladies said, 'We sure will, Mrs. Reed. You all come back again when you've got longer to stay.' Only that day, they didn't say it. What could I do? I liked those little girls, and so I said to them, 'You all come to see me sometime, and we'll play in my playhouse.' "

Bob shook his head. "What happened then?"

"Everything got very quiet," I said, remembering. "Then Mammy and Mrs. George started laughing. Then everybody laughed. The little girls said, 'All right,' but they were smarter than I was, and they laughed too. I didn't know what was funny, and I felt like a fool. Stupid. Dumb."

"I know," Bob nodded sympathetically.

His understanding encouraged me, and I went on. "When we left, Aunt Georgia, who was almost fourteen and not given to much patience with a four-year-old kid, said, 'You crazy thing. You asked those little girls to come to see you.' Mother said, 'She didn't know any better.' Then Mammy said something which may have influenced me forever. She said—"

"I don't know whether I'm going to like this or not," Bob interrupted. "I like your grandmother, and I don't know whether I want to hear this or not."

I looked at him leaning against his side of the car, his hat pushed back on his head, watching me, but not condemning me yet.

"Mammy said, 'Mr. George is a good man. He pays his debts, works hard, and keeps his place looking clean and nice. I've never heard a word against him. I'd rather be around him and his family than around some white man who doesn't pay his debts, doesn't keep his place up, runs around, gets drunk, and things like that.' I've kept her words in my heart all these years. It meant to me that the way you judged a man was by what he *is,* and not by the color of his skin."

Bob whistled softly. "Well, by damn, you and Mammy make a good case. But I guess you know that if a Negro is found on the streets after dark in Coleman, Santa Anna, and several other towns around here, they run him out of town. Chances are they might tar and feather him."

"I think it's terrible," I said.

"Hell, no, wait a minute," Bob said, trying hard to be reasonable. "Let me tell you something, girl, that you don't seem to know. Those people come from a different line. They have different blood—"

He stopped, took a deep, audible breath and exhaled slowly. Then, making an effort to be calm, he went on, "Now, girl, I can see what your grandmother was trying to say. She was trying to tell her children and grandchild to keep themselves pure and not to associate with any person who'd pull them down—white or not. She was right. A sensible man has got to go this far with her: a good man, even a black one, ought to have certain standards."

He talked, then, about slaves who ran away from their masters and came out west and made good hands on ranches and who fought side by side with white men . . . maybe just to be free. He said that it was important for a man to have certain standards to live by. He certainly agreed with Mammy there.

"Every man has to uphold his race and protect his women and children," Bob said earnestly. "He has to build the best damn world he can. You mix and mingle the races, and what do you get? You get a mongrel race—a race that's not white and not black."

It seemed to me he was leaving out something important. "Very well, then," I said flatly. "If a man's going to fight to keep his race pure, don't let him go down to the flat and leave a half-white, half-black child down there."

Bob jerked the steering wheel so abruptly that we almost ran off the road. "Well, damn it," he groaned. "There's something there that you don't understand."

He looked at me, ran his hand over his face, and glared. "Well, sometimes a man—Well, damn it. Sometimes a man has to—"

He stopped, glared at me, sighed, and settled back in his seat. "I'll tell you the facts of life, even if you never speak to me again. When a man wants—Oh, well, damn it to hell—"

He pounded the steering wheel, lurched forwards and backwards. "Girl, listen. Don't you ever talk this way to anybody but me. No other man's going to understand it. I don't understand it myself." He paused and shook his head. "It's a funny thing that I can't make you understand that men are men."

When he couldn't get any more words out, I said, very quietly. "I still say that a half-white, half-black kid is as good as the white man who sired him."

Bob moaned and muttered something in a language I couldn't understand.

We rode in silence for a while. I wasn't ready to let the subject drop.

"You say that blood makes a difference in the way a man acts and feels," I said. "If your Aryan or Celtic race, or whatever you're so proud of, was not satisfied with their lives as they found them; and if that blood led those men to crawl up from the abyss millions of years ago, then the half-white, half-black men who are not satisfied with their lives will reach for glory some day."

Bob's anger had cooled off. He looked at me, and there was a sudden twinkle in his eyes. "Now, girl," he said with a touch of his old whimsy, "you listen to me and see if you can learn something. Men—white or black—ain't worth a damn. And you're right about one thing. There's something wild and inhuman in all men. It goes back to prehistoric times when men walked the jungles with a piece of rock to fight off wild beasts, and when they cowered, frightened, at the strange things happening as the world became habitable where nothingness had been before. But there's something you forget. Today, we're living in a decadent civilization, a decadent age, but if we did the things you're talking about, we'd face a cataclysm greater than any the world has ever known."

"You're always talking about that wild thing—that prehistoric blood in men's veins, and I guess you're right," I said, remembering something from my childhood that lay deep in my mind. "I think there is a wildness in all men—white or black. I know something about that, too."

"I don't doubt it," Bob said laconically.

"I knew a fear once that I've never forgotten." I said. "Since you've been talking, I realize that it was fear of that wild thing in men's nature that my father, mother, and I experienced."

Bob was interested and curious. "What happened?" he asked.

It was a thing I rarely talked about, for I still woke up nights with a vague, unreasoning fear. I told Bob how my mother, father, and I lived in the country below Santa Anna, where we went to buy groceries and to sell our milk, butter, and eggs. One day while Mother and I were in a store, an old man stopped my father on the street and said, "What's an Indian doing here on the streets of this town?" Hastily, my father said, "I ain't no Indian."

"When my Mother and I came out of the store," I said, "an angry crowd of men were around my father, and he was telling them that he wasn't an Indian in spite of his dark skin, hair and eyes, but the old man insisted that as a former Texas Ranger he'd fought enough Indians to know one when he saw one. After my Mother and I walked up, a man, who lived on a farm near us, told the old man that my father wasn't an Indian, so the crowd let him go; and Mother, Dad, and I got in the wagon and started home."

Bob and I knew that men were nice to a good woman and that was the reason that more hadn't happened.

"Was that the end of it?" Bob asked.

"While we were in the wagon going home, there was no laughter and talk as usual that day," I explained. "Mother held me in her lap so tight I could hardly breathe. When we were about half way home, we looked back and way, way down the road a man, riding a horse, was coming our way, riding hard. My dad said, 'Hold on,' and he whipped the horses to make them run. He and Mother kept looking back, because they were afraid of that wild thing— whatever it is—in man's nature. It's a strange and awful fear. It's not tangible— something open that can be seen; it's dark, hidden, and it doesn't reason."

"Was it someone after you?"

I shook my head. "I don't know. I don't suppose we were ever sure. Dad stopped the wagon by the back door of our house. About that time, the rider stopped by our gate. He just sat there, looking at us. Dad took me into the house. Mother followed with a box of stuff in her arms, trying to act perfectly natural, but dad buckled on his gun—"

"He had a gun?"

"Yes." I pointed to the glove compartment. "Like that one of yours only he had a gun belt and holster. He strapped on his gun, told Mother to get the shotgun, and went back outside. But when he got outside, the rider was gone."

"Was that the last time you ever saw him?"

Homer Hall Price and Etna Reed Price

Parents of Novalyne Price. This photograph was taken shortly before Mr. Price was mistaken for an Indian in Santa Ana, Texas. This incident, related to Howard by Miss Price, became an issue with Howard's mother who did not like Indians.

I waited a minute. "I'm sure it was. I do remember that after that night, we ate supper almost in the dark; and my father always wore his gun while he took care of the farm, the horses, and milked the cows. When we'd hear a horse's hooves coming down the road, my father and mother would stop talking, or singing, or whatever they were doing and my father would put his hand on his gun. He and Mother would be perfectly still, listening, until the horse's hooves passed by the house, or a neighbor came in to pass the time of day."

Bob laughed softly and reached over to put his arm around me. "Honey," he said lightly, "a minute ago, I was mad enough at you to wring your neck, but now— Hell, I reckon maybe it's no wonder you get crazy ideas in your head."

I didn't answer. The wind was blowing harder than it had all day, and I sat for a minute watching the bare branches of trees move with the wind. I thought of things Bob had said about that hidden something men had known eons ago. Was that black fear still a part of man? Even if my father were an Indian, what did that old Texas Ranger and those other men have to fear in one lone Indian?

"I can imagine a Negro coming through Coleman, or Santa Anna and having his car break down," I said, after a moment. "He'd be scared to death, not because of something bad he'd done, nor of the white men themselves, but of that wild thing that's inside men."

"God, girl!" Bob said. "When I say things like that, it makes normal, good sense, but when you say it, damned if it makes any sense at all?" He didn't say anything else for a minute. Then he said, tenderly, "I'm just shooting my mouth off, girl. There ain't nothing for you to be afraid of. Nothing at all."

It was dark and the wind's edge slashed at us when Bob walked up to the steps with me. "Girl," he said, touching my hair, "I want to tell you again: Don't you ever say to anybody else the things you said to me today. If you say things like that about Negroes or tell what happened to your father, the Board of Trustees will fire you and Nat Williams can't keep them from it."

"Oh, I don't think—" I began.

"Yes, they would. Now, trust me. I know this town better than you do or ever will." He laughed. "Why if my mother knew you had any Indian blood in you, she'd be afraid you'd scalp me."

He meant for me to laugh. I tried to, but I was serious. "I've always said exactly what I thought. People may not like it, but they don't say much."

"Why, girl," Bob said. "what you said about Negroes today no man in this town would understand, and they might even run you out of town, or tar and feather you. And I don't want that to happen to you. I've got kinda used to having you around, and the crazy things you say don't bother me . . . much. I'm a big guy. I can take care of myself, and I won't let anything happen to you either. I want you around, so that I can straighten you out on a few things. Besides, I'd a hell of a lot rather kiss you than that old cow of mine."

I couldn't answer because he kissed me then and left. I didn't go into the house immediately. I stood on the steps, just thinking. There were times when I thought Bob was such a human nut that surely I must be in love with him; at other times, I knew I didn't love him. Our love of books, our need to find someone to talk to had brought us together. Could these same things drive us so far apart we'd never find each other?

I had very little Indian blood. Would that small bit really make a difference to his mother? To the people in this town? To Mr. Williams?

The moon was rising. I went inside and closed the door.

After play practice . . .

I forgot to tell Bob that I was working full time on my play now and that I went back to school every night to rehearse. He came by after school looking for me. Mrs. Hemphill said that she told him I was still at school, but I guess he didn't believe her because he came by again tonight. I tried to call him when I came home for supper, but Mrs. Howard said he wasn't in.

Every day, he either telephones or comes by while I'm still at school, or after I've gone back after supper. When I try to call him, his mother says he's not home.

This has been going on for almost a week. This morning at 5:30, I was awakened by a loud knock on the outside door. I was wide awake in an instant, and I knew . . . I knew without being told that it was Bob. I hopped out of bed and grabbed my pink and blue housecoat. It was wrong-side-out, of course, and I had to struggle getting it on, trying to brush my hair at the same time, so that I would look half-way decent when I got to the door. Mrs. Hemphill, bundled up in her housecoat, knocked on my door.

"Miss Price," she said very primly and precisely. "Miss Price, you have a visitor . . . a visitor at this unearthly hour."

"Coming," I called cheerfully. I grabbed a powder puff, raced it over my nose and sped to the door. Sure enough, there was Bob standing on the steps, with a twinkle in his eye. I guess he hadn't heard Mrs. Hemphill, or if he had, he was determined to be good humored in spite of it.

"Look, girl," he said when I stepped out the door. "Where have you been all week? I've been trying my best to get in touch with you. Finally, I decided the only way I'd get to see you was to come over at 5:30 in the morning. So here I am. Where have you been?"

I was laughing so much it was hard to talk. "I've been rehearsing a play," I managed to gasp out.

"All night?" he said unbelievingly.

"Nearly," I laughed. "I got home at twelve last night."

"My God," he said, "you mean you were up at that school until midnight!"

"How else are you going to get a play in shape when you have got a bunch of the sweetest kids in the world who've never been in a play before and who don't know the first thing about crossing the stage or saying a word?"

"They let you stay up there that late?" Bob was serious.

I was still good humored and laughing. "There's no way to keep me from it. I've got the play to put on, and I'm going to put it on the way I think it should be done. If it takes keeping the kids out all night, I'm going to keep them out all night."

He assumed an exaggerated hurt pose. "Where do I fit in? What am I going to do?"

"After play rehearsals—"

His eyes were twinkling again. "Girl, you mean I come after the play?"

"That's right," I said. "You fit in after play rehearsals are over for the week."

"All right. All right, what about tonight?"

"This is Friday, but I've got rehearsals tonight."

"I've never heard of anything like that before," he said. "Friday night! Will the kids be there?"

"They'd better," I said ominously, "or I'll kill them."

"Say it like that and I know they'll be there," he grumbled. "Okay. How about tomorrow afternoon? You want to go to Brownwood? We'll go see your mother and grandmother, and maybe to Dublin's to see if they've got any books worth a damn, see a show, then come back home."

"I'd love it," I said. "I'd love every minute of it."

"I'll be here," he promised.

My heart was beating fast, and I felt silly and giggly. I knew Mrs. Hemphill didn't approve, but I went on in the house and sang all through my bath and while I was getting ready to go to breakfast. I sang all day, not out loud . . . just in my heart.

It's great to have a friend you can depend on.

"The first fluttering of its silken wings . . . "

I don't think I've ever been so glad to see anyone as I was to see Bob today. Play practice every day after school and at night had gotten a little too much for me. I wanted to be with someone my own age, not high school kids, cute as they are.

Another reason I was glad to see Bob was that I'd just gotten a story back with a silly compliment and no real reason for their not taking it. It's a sort of "It's good, but we don't want it" bit that infuriates me. I hoped Bob could tell me what is wrong with it.

He was all dressed up and looked great. He was in a good humor, too, and that counts for something. He put his arms around me to kiss me when I let him in the house. Then he stopped, pushed me away from him, grinning. "Girl, have you been eating onions?"

I was so embarrassed I wanted to crawl under a chair. "Oh, goodness, Bob," I said contritely. "You mean you can smell them?"

"Well," he drawled, "not until I stopped the car out front."

I put my hand over my mouth. "I washed my teeth and used a mouthwash, I thought surely I'd gotten rid of it."

He shook his head, still grinning. "Well, by God, this is the first time in my life I ever heard of a girl eating onions before her boyfriend came."

I backed away from him. "Bob, I tried not to eat any. I honestly did. But today, Mrs. Hemphill had red beans, cornbread and little green onions. I simply couldn't help myself."

He laughed heartily, and I relaxed. "Well, girl, you're sure right about that. When you have red beans and cornbread, you gotta have onions. I can see that. It just struck me as odd, though, that a girl ready to go on a date with her best beau would eat onions."

"I'll get some mouthwash," I promised. Although he was making a big to-do about it, I couldn't tell whether he really minded or not. I promised myself that I'd resist the next onion temptation . . . if I could. However, I didn't expect him to walk in the house and try to kiss me.

"It's too late now," he said. "I've already got the full benefit of them. No use hiding behind a bottle now. If we want to get to Brownwood before dark, we'd better get going."

"I'll hurry," I dashed off and grabbed the mouthwash, got my hat and gloves, and came back into the living room. He was standing by the chair, looking at a book of Mrs. Hemphill's. He put it down and we went out to the car.

It was a beautiful day. The wind was brisk but it was not so cold you couldn't enjoy the warmth of the sunshine. I sat on my side of the car as far away from Bob as I could, so that I wouldn't asphyxiate him.

"It's a beautiful day," I said to get things started.

"Fall," he said, in that light, whimsical way he has of talking. "It's a hell of a time of year. Cold. Dry. But when you're in your 'sere and yellow leaf' the way I am, cold doesn't suit you."

That quotation again! I laughed at him. "You're not so old."

"Not old?" He grinned. "Girl, when you've lived as long as I have and seen as much as I have, you hate the fall that reminds you that your life is slipping away from you, and all you've got left is hanging by a slender stem that the wind will tear from its socket. It's a hell of a shame that life is taken from the old when that's all they've got left."

I tried to make a joke. "You're just two years older than I am. You haven't lived so long."

"It's experience that makes a man old," he shrugged his shoulders. "I've lived before. I remember it. My ancestors came from a cold, bleak island, and I feel their blood beating in my veins. I feel the frustrations—though I hate the damn word—they felt. I turn my face to the warm and sunny south the way they did, and—"

I couldn't take any more of that.

"I don't feel old," I said emphatically. "I don't even feel twenty-six, though apparently people think that's old. Before you get twenty-five, people say to you. 'When are you going to get married?' but after you get twenty-five, they look at you and shake their heads, sigh, and say, 'And so you never married.' "

Bob laughed. "I guess it is harder for a girl. With men it's different. Oh, there's a lady who visits my mother who always says to me, 'My goodness, Robert, how have you managed to keep from marching down to the altar?' I tell her my innocent face will always protect me. But where, I think to myself, could a man in his 'sere and yellow leaf ' find a school teacher who'd have him?"

I ignored the school teacher remark and concentrated on the quotation. It bothers me to hear a quotation that is familiar, yet, for the life of me, I cannot place it.

Bob began to talk again, and, at first, I was amused and glad he was not on a Jenghiz Khan track today. He did talk about a prehistoric time in which he lived on a cold, bleak island. While he was forced to stay on the island in the ice and snow, he longed for the warmth of the south.

He talked of the trees with their great limbs aching underneath the ice and snow as the wind screeched through bare, lifeless branches. Once as he waved his arms at the dead trees and grass beside the road, he said, "Look at that, girl, those leafless branches, sere, bending in the shrieking wind. It's a cruel and ruthless time of year."

Being with Bob, I was always aware of the life around me. Trees, the elements, nature affect my life. But, today, I refused to be taken in by his melancholy, for, in the distance, I saw among the dead mesquites and oaks a tiny green blob, probably a small cedar, still green. We passed a field where fat cattle grazed on a green winter feed crop.

"It's not all 'sere and yellow,' " I said. I pointed out the green field and the green of the cedars and insisted that the bare trees and brown grass were but nude corpses of summer's voluptuousness.

He was excited. "By God, girl," he said enthusiastically, "I like that 'nude corpses of voluptuousness.' Now, by God, you've been around me so much you're getting to be a poet."

Then, chagrined, I confessed that the "nude corpses" were two words from a short poem I'd read in which a discarded Christmas tree had been called a "nude corpse of happiness."

Bob said one had to watch phrases like that which he picked up in his reading. "Find your own words," he said emphatically.

Down the road in front of us, we saw a man riding a horse. He was hunched over the saddle to try to hide from the sharp wind. Bob waved his hand as we passed him, and began to talk of cowboys, early Texas, and the way the Indians swept across these same hills and tried to find a good life in a harsh land.

"Girl," he said once, "didn't you say that story you've just got back is about fox hunting here in this part of Texas?"

I said it was.

"Some damn editor don't know that those eastern lace-on-their-draw— uh—underpants-fox-hunters would be scared to death out here in this wild country. This country is rich in stories. Write about it. There are enough stories here for you and me and a hundred other writers, and we'd never get it all said. This is the place to be. Most people don't stop to think about it, but west Texas is older than east Texas."

Then he began another in his long series of stories about Texas, the old Texas, from the 1500s to the beginning to the 1900s. I listened, interested, fascinated. It was exciting to hear about the Mexican vaqueros and how they became known as cowboys in Texas.

As he talked, pouring out a stream of words about cowboys that should have been written down, I felt frustrated. I could not remember all the things he said.

Suddenly, I began to see him in a new light.

Here was such a man as he talked about, an adventurer, a man born to live in another century and to fight, to brawl, and, as Kipling said it, "to take his fun where he finds it." A man of adventure. But a man in chains. A man shackled by his own gentleness of nature. He was held firmly to a small town, to a chair at a typewriter, bound by the chains of love and duty to an old, sick woman while he dreamed of another life, another time, another exciting world.

I looked at him with love and pity. I wanted to urge him to set himself free. I wanted to shout and make him see that there are still worlds to conquer, deeds of valor to do.

I sat on my side of the car, never speaking what was in my heart. I listened to wild tales of daring adventure.

I watched a man chained.

Monday . . . Midnight

This afternoon, cold as it was, I rushed down to the post office as soon as I could leave school. The only letter in my box was from Bob. I didn't have time to read it, but I glanced at it and burst out laughing right there in the post office. He didn't write "Dear Novalyne" as he usually did. Instead he began: "My Cherished Little Bunch of Onion Tops."

The letter was nearly two pages, typed, single spaced, and I knew it was going to be mostly about the story I'd gotten back which he had taken home to read. I stuffed it back in the envelope, hurried home, ate supper, and went back to school for play practice.

It was so cold that I didn't keep the kids later than ten o'clock tonight. I came home and, being afraid I'd wake Ethel if I stayed in the room, I came into the bathroom to be alone. I looked over my lessons for tomorrow, then settled down to read Bob's letter and make notes on the things he had to say about the story. I laughed again at that "My Cherished Little Bunch of Onion Tops."

First, he explained that men made a terrible mistake when they called their best girls their rose or violet or names like that, because a man ought to call his girl something that was near his heart. What, he asked, was nearer a man's heart than his stomach? Therefore he considered it to be an indication of his deep felt love and esteem to call me his cherished little bunch of onion tops, and, judging from past experience, both of us had the highest regard for onions.

The rest of the letter was about my story—"Vixens Climb Trees." He said that he'd gotten the best laugh he'd had in a long time, for he understood perfectly the girl's discomfiture riding a rough, ornery cayuse like the one I had described in the story.

Something he really liked, he said, was the background for the story. It was just there. The fox hunt, he went on, was absolutely true to the way men in this part of the country hunted foxes, but, being of low mentality and with lace on their you-know-whats, editors couldn't appreciate that. He suggested that he write to Kline for me and see what Kline thought. At times, Kline seemed like a good, intelligent man who agreed with him on almost everything. Personally, he knew that Kline agreed with him that editors were all bastards, but you had to deal with them.

I reread the line where he said he'd gotten a good laugh. That surprised me just as it had surprised me when the editor, or whoever it was, wrote: "Good use of humor" on the note with the returned manuscript. There wasn't anything funny to me in that story. Riding horses was a pain in the abdomen and hunting foxes was impossible. I empathized with the foxes.

I also went over and over the line "The background is just there." He said a lot of people thought they had to explain where a person was, how the moon looked, the flowers, the grass, the trees, but the best background was just there.

I thought about his story "The Devil in Iron." Hadn't he described in detail how the castle looked to the fisherman? I was not trying to argue; I was trying to understand.

He talked on for nearly a page about stories in general—something, he said, I might think about. One thing he wanted to stress was that stories had to be real and important; the characters—real people with real problems, important problems. He was sure, he said (and he was right), that I wondered how Conan could be a real person, but I needed to remember that deep inside every man there was something of the barbarian, something that civilization could not destroy. A man reading his story about Conan, then, would feel again in the depth of his being those barbaric impulses; consequently, Conan acted as they felt they would act in similar circumstances.

While reading my story, he did wonder why Phil was such a dumb bastard he couldn't appreciate a girl like Carol. There were mighty few women in this day and age who went to college but who still thought it was important to love a man enough to want to cook and keep house for him. Did I know any girls like that? He'd sure as hell like to meet one, and you could bet your last goddam dollar that he wouldn't get carried away with a battle-ax like Matilda who had no more womanly feeling than the hounds she followed.

That amused me because I'd fashioned my heroine's looks after Dolores Dalton's.

Another thing he said was that I had a talent for writing, and I should devote more time and attention to it. We'd send this one to Kline, and I could get started on another yarn. Writing was like eating onions; the more you did, the better you liked it. Some day, soon, he was sure I'd find an appreciative editor. But the secret, he said, was to write, write, write.

That was discouraging. How could I write and write? I am behind with my paper grading and Enid is on my back constantly. But working with individual students after school, then going back at night to rehearse plays, how could I write more and more? These diaries and journals, of which he is so skeptical, take about all the time I have to give. Here it is after twelve o'clock, and I'm tired. All I want to do is go to bed and forget everything.

These diaries and journals are good practice. They are filled with my thoughts, my fears, my hopes, things I love, and things I hate, how the weather affects me. There's conflict here too . . . conflict among flesh and blood human beings of this century. Maybe when I go home this summer, I'll have time to write.

Maybe I'll never write. The way people feel about writers—Bob—or any writer getting started—is very discouraging. The way I like teaching, I don't care . . . much.

Robert E. Howard

In the fall of 1934, Howard had two photographs of himself made in his new brown suit and tan hat. This profile photograph was hand tinted and framed as a gift for his girlfriend, Novalyne Price.

Problems . . . Love . . . Problems . . .
Two more weeks and my play will be over . . .

It's been, as Bob put it in one of his letters, a "hell of a week." He was referring to the weather which has been cold, wet and miserable. When I use the term, I refer to the weather and also to some miserable problems at school. Play rehearsals get to the place where they're not much fun. They also get to the place where they interfere with other teachers and that involves the superintendent. If Nat Williams weren't the best superintendent in the State of Texas, I don't know what I'd do.

Right now, Bob just may be the strength I need to keep going in spite of all my problems. In some ways, he's been great. The only bright spot in the whole week has been the cute little notes or letters I've gotten from him every day. All of them begin with "My very dear little Bunch of Radishes," or "My very dear Beans, Cornbread and Onions," or "My dear Sausage and Big, Brown, Fluffy Bisquits." He's still on the kick that a man ought to call his girl names that are close to his heart—his stomach.

In one letter, Bob talked about how much it was raining and that neither man nor animal could keep his feet dry. But all this proved, he said, that he'd walk through floods for me. Then, in the postscript, he said he'd be over Saturday afternoon if it didn't rain. That was the letter in which he called me sliced red beets with butter over them. All-in-all, I've gotten some good laughs and when things were really rough at school, I said a few "Thanks Gods" for a friend like Bob whose business is writing and not teaching school.

Then I found out that I wouldn't be able to have play practice on Friday night . . . tonight. I wrote Bob, and he wrote me another goofy note to tell me he'd be over tonight, and we'd ride around and he'd shoot his mouth off. I had told him in the letter that I loved to walk in the rain, and he said maybe I'd just as soon ride as walk. Apparently, he has received a lot of fan mail he wants to tell me about.

He didn't seal the letter, and so the first thing I said tonight when he came in was, "Bob, you forgot to seal the letter I got today."

He was emphatic. "I did not forget to seal that letter. I never forget to seal a letter. That's the damndest thing I ever heard of. Those bastards in the post office opened that letter and read it."

My nerves were on edge, but I managed not to sound too irritable. "Oh, Bob, you know better than that. It's against the law to open a letter and read it."

"What makes you think people in the Cross Plains post office know what the law says?" he raged.

I laughed without mirth. "Just be sure you seal the next letter you write me."

We were almost ready to walk out the door, but he stopped and looked at me. His eyes were deep and shadowy, almost as if he were afraid of something. He wanted to know if I were ashamed of his letters. Did I wish he wouldn't write?

"Oh, no, no, no. Absolutely not," I said positively. "You know I love those letters you write me. I wouldn't take anything for them. I just want to make sure you seal the next one."

He was somewhat mollified. Still, he stood and made no move to open the door. "I seal every damn letter I write, and I'll tell you one thing. I'll fix those bastards in the post office if I have to wring their necks."

I pulled my coat around me and reached for the doorknob. We didn't say anything else until we got in the car. Then I told him that I was not exactly happy about things happening at school. He said he could see that I wasn't in my usual happy frame of mind, and that if I needed a shoulder to cry on, he could offer me one of the world's best.

I was glad of the chance to talk about it, to get the whole thing out of my system. "The play has kinda bogged down in the middle," I said. "The kids still can't get their words right, and they still can't walk across the stage right. You'd think Mr. Williams would understand how important it is for me to practice every day and night, but I don't think he does."

Bob grunted. "I don't see why you think that Nat-Brain would understand."

That shook me a little. I know Mr. Williams isn't quite perfect, and I may even criticize him a little when I think he isn't, but it sounded different when Bob did it.

I explained that Nat was a brilliant man, but there were some things even he didn't understand. At the first of the week, I'd explained to him that I'd have to have the auditorium every day the last hour, after school, and at night.

"Day before yesterday," I said dramatically, "as soon as I got to the top of the stairs with my kids, there came Louise with her chorus students to rehearse."

Bob could see where that would create problems.

"We got in an argument," I said. "I told her that Mr. Williams said I could have the auditorium. She said he'd told her she could have it, and besides, she said I'd had it every day for a month and that it hadn't been built just for me. I told her she thought the whole school had been built for her. Just as I started downstairs to see Mr. Williams, he came up."

"I hope he let you use the damn auditorium the way you wanted to," Bob's voice was hard and his jaw was set.

"Oh, yes. I got to use it. Mr. Williams just looked at me and went over to Louise and said something. She took her kids and left."

Bob visibly relaxed. "Then what are you so upset about?"

"I got the auditorium, but I didn't win the battle," I groaned. "Later, when

I went to the office, Mr. Williams looked at me and said, 'Let me remind you that any teacher who can't get along with the other teachers on this faculty will be looking for a job next year.' "

"The dirty son-of-a bi—gun," Bob exploded. "I'll go up and beat hell out of him. I never liked him anyway, and by God, this gives me a chance to beat him up."

That was irony! I pushed my hair off my forehead and sighed. When I was a kid and needed that kind of help, I prayed for my cousin Neil, Enid's older brother, to come to my aid and beat up other kids for me. Now, when I finally got somebody to fight for me, this was a grown-up problem that I didn't think could be solved with fists.

"Then I'd be sure to lose my job," I sighed. "I want to be re-elected next year. I want it bad."

"Why is it so damned important to you?" Bob was still belligerent.

I moaned a little. "Because," I said, and I felt tired again, "this is the first job I've ever had that I really like. I'm teaching speech this year and that's what I want to teach . . . Speech . . . Nothing else."

Bob didn't answer at once. He seemed absorbed in driving, for which I was grateful. It was a cold, windy night. It occurred to me that people out on a night like this were crazy.

"What about getting married? Ever think about that?" Bob asked.

I thought about making a wise-crack such as, "Yes, do you want to marry me?" But I didn't. "I don't see why I can't get married and still keep on teaching school," I said honestly.

Bob lunged around, banging the steering wheel. "No," he said shortly, "I suppose there's no reason you couldn't."

I had the feeling that he thoroughly disapproved of the idea and of me. Then he shrugged his shoulders and laughed. "The Cro-Magnon man had it all over us modern men. He saw a woman he wanted, grabbed her by the hair of the head and dragged her back to his cave."

Usually, when Bob talks about the romantic involvements of the Cro-Magnon man, I enjoy the account. This time, I only made a feeble attempt at a laugh. My neck felt stiff, sore, aching. I put my hands underneath my hair and tried to massage the back of my head.

The road seemed unusually lonesome because there were so few cars out tonight, but I could understand that. In the distance, flashes of lightning lit up the sky, showing dark, threatening clouds. Overhead, the clouds were heavy and oppressive.

"What about your writing?" Bob asked. "You've got talent, Novalyne, and a hell of a lot of vitality. It seems to me you've had some encouragement . . . letters instead of printed rejection slips. The way I see it, what you need to do is sit down at the typewriter and just pound out yarn after yarn. It wouldn't be long before you'd be a selling writer. I feel pretty confident of that."

I moved around, trying to stretch my neck. "I still get rejection slips with nothing on them."

"So do I, and so do some of my friends, guys a lot better than I am. Do you not like to write? Had you rather teach?"

"I'm not sure," I said slowly. "But right now, I don't have any choice in the matter. The farm is not doing more than just eking out a living. The other day, Mother sold a bale of cotton for about thirty dollars. That means she'll have trouble paying for next year's seeds and planting."

"The good thing about being a hack writer is that you don't have bosses to put up with," Bob said.

"True," I acknowledged. "I've thought of staying home and writing, but it would be impossible now."

"Why?"

I took a deep breath. "I can just imagine what my family would say if I lost this job and went home to be a writer! Even Enid." I sighed. "Enid's an English teacher; you'd think she'd be a hundred per cent back of me."

He glanced at me quickly. "She wouldn't be?"

"Heavens, no," I said. "She's like everybody else. She knows me and all my faults. To her, I'm a flesh and blood human being who gets behind with her paper grading. She doesn't think it would be possible for me to write something somebody else would want to read."

"Have you ever shown her any of the letters you get?" he asked.

"Yeah. The last one." I sighed, remembering. "She looked at it and said, 'You'd better grade those English papers and quit messing around with that stuff.'"

Bob laughed and ran his fingers through his hair. "I know. I know."

"The neighbors, too," I went on with my doleful story. "If some lady drops in for a visit, and I tell her I'm going to be a writer, she'll say I'd be better off trying to get a job at Woolworth's."

"I know. People understand you have to learn bookkeeping, but not that you have to learn how to write. But what about your mother and grandmother? It seems to me they're the only ones who matter."

"Oh, they'd let me do whatever I wanted to do, and Aunt Georgie would think I'm smart whatever I do."

"Then if you really want to write, why don't you tell the others to go to hell?"

"I've tried writing at home," I mourned. "It's not easy. Mother and Mammy want to help, but a farm needs a lot of work. Last summer, I thought I'd never get that story written. Just when I'd get started, Mother would come in and say she hated to interrupt me, but she needed help with a cow that was having a calf, or Mammy would come in and say she needed me to follow that old turkey hen with the bell on. Some of the best stories I've ever written were composed while I followed that derned old turkey hen with a bell on. I just never seemed to have time to write them up."

Bob was enjoying my story. "The more you talk, the more I can see how lucky I am. My family understands. If the phone rings or somebody comes to the house, Mother makes sure I'm not disturbed until I finish."

When he said that about his mother, I figured she had other reasons in mind also, but I didn't say it. The lightning was getting closer, and I began to wish I hadn't told Bob I liked to walk in the rain. It looked as though he had understood me to say I wanted to ride around in a storm.

I tried to massage the back of my neck.

"Have you got a headache?" Bob asked.

I said I did have. He reached over and put his hand on the back of my neck and began very gently to massage it. "My mother has headaches like this, and I try to help her get rid of them."

His hands were gentle, firm, and I could feel myself relaxing in spite of the weather. I did think: "Always your mother!" But I kept quiet and listened to him.

"I know how people in this part of the country feel about writers. Everybody thinks I'm a lazy, no-good rat, sponging off my family, and they wonder why I don't get out and get a man's job."

"Not everybody thinks that about you," I corrected him. "I'm sure some people do—those who think books appear full-blown from the head of Zeus. But many people have the utmost respect for you and some envy you."

"First time I ever heard that," he said. "I don't think you know what you're talking about."

"I certainly do," I said positively. "Jimmie entertained the Junior Study Club the other day. After the program while we were having refreshments and talking, Ava said that she'd heard about you, knew you, and had read some things about you. She—"

"Where was that?" Bob interrupted doubtfully.

"I don't know where," I said quickly. "She just said she'd heard how good you were. She'd also heard some writer had come to see you—"

"Ed Price."

"Okay, Ed Price," I grumbled. I hate to try to tell somebody something when he keeps interrupting, and so I waited a minute.

"Well, what did she say about him?"

"Nothing about him," I said, and a little irritation crept into my voice. "She just said you were pretty important, because she'd heard you had a lot of writer friends and that somebody important had come to see you a few months ago. She—"

"Ed is a damn big writer," Bob said. "He's one of the best and—"

"Are you going to let me tell you this compliment or not?" I was completely undone, and I couldn't help showing it.

"Hell, yes, I'm going to let you tell me. You know how vain I am. I'm a sucker for any damn compliment I can get."

"Okay," I said. "She said that it was great that our little town of Cross Plains had an important writer like you, and that this country might look wild, but it wasn't. Over in Rising Star is Lexie Dean Robertson and a lot of other writers in and around Brownwood. But she thought you were the best. And—"

"She's right," Bob grinned. "She's sure right about that. Do you think she might like to ask me for a date?"

I laughed because he wanted me to, but I wasn't really amused.

"She said she'd like to talk with you, to ask you about your writing, and I believe she said she'd tried to get in touch with you, but you were never home." Even I could hear the accusation in my voice. I really wanted to say, "But your mother wouldn't let her talk to you." I don't think I said it, but he answered as if I did. Maybe I just thought so hard he read my mind.

"People don't understand me or my mother," he said defensively. "Writing is pounding out one damn yarn after another, pounding them out whether you want to or not, and it takes a family who understands that and who tries to help you by keeping you from being disturbed every minute of the day. I know people think I'm a freak and a damn nut, but the only way I can get anything done is to keep pounding away." He moved about running his fingers through his hair. "But what I have makes up for what people here think. I mean the writer friends I have. I think it's pretty damn good that Ed Price came out here to see me. I think—"

"People here would like to be friends with you if you'd give them a chance," I interrupted. "Other people at the study club said nice things about you too. One girl said she'd tried to write some stories and would like to talk with you about them. Fanny said you were one of the politest men she knew. She said you always tipped your hat—"

"That doesn't take much effort," he laughed. "I didn't know it was important to Fanny. Next time I see her, I'll take my hat off and let her walk on it if she wants to. It does surprise me, because I thought everybody hated me."

"You're a nut. They—the girls in the Junior Study Club—said they'd tried to get you for some church programs. Somebody said Mrs. Voyles used to call—"

"Oh, God," Bob groaned. "Just give the church people a chance and they'll put anybody to work. My family used—"

"Look, I'm beginning to feel half-way good, and I don't want to talk about things like that anymore. If you talk about things I don't want to listen to, I'll just sit here and think about something else. I'll only say one thing more. Not everybody thinks you're a freak, and a lot of people would be friends with you if you gave them a chance."

"Just like a woman." Bob patted my shoulder. "You don't want to talk, but you get in the last word before you quit."

Then he told me about the fan mail he'd gotten. He had received letters from somebody in England; one from Australia; letters from several different states like California, Pennsylvania, and far away places like that. He talked about writer friends of his—Price, Lovecraft, Derleth whose name I had seen in a writer's magazine, and other people I'd never heard of. They wrote to him and he wrote to them. It all sounded interesting and was, I guess, a world far removed from Cross Plains. Although it was interesting, it didn't make writing as a profession appeal to me. I want to write, but I also want to be in the thick of life around me.

Bob said that he didn't want to try to tell me how to write the love stories that I like. Nobody could tell someone else what to write, but he thought I might be interested in some great real life love stories. Then he talked about great love affairs that had occurred throughout history—love affairs that made people in other centuries seem real—Shakespeare and the Dark lady of the Sonnets, Napoleon and Josephine, Louis IV and Ninon—I couldn't remember her name.

He stopped the car on the top of a windswept little hill and told me to look at the sky. I was already looking at it, and I still wished fervently I had kept my mouth shut about liking to walk in the rain.

The clouds were closer now and the lightning turned clumps of bushes beside the road into strange mysterious beings.

"That's beauty," Bob said, "the kind of wild beauty my ancestors loved."

I agreed that it was beautiful, especially if you thought you'd like to get blown away. He was talking about great lovers. I watched the sky. It was more important to me at the moment than Dante and Beatrice whose love lasted forever. Bob said the great lovers of history had loved one woman and one woman only. The women, too, he said, loved only that one man. Did I believe that now-a-days, a woman could love a man forever, or had women changed so much, since they got the vote and became college graduates, they could never love again? He was interested, he said, in knowing whether or not a woman could really love like that in this day and age.

The storm was getting nearer, and I had too many problems to think about love. One immediate problem was getting home before the storm broke.

Across the hill, a little to the northwest of the road, lightning dipped down and enveloped a tree; then a ball of fire rolled across the hillside. Thank God it was far enough away to do no more than startle us. Both of us caught our breaths and stared. I shook a little.

"It struck a tree," Bob said triumphantly.

I didn't answer.

He got really eloquent then, talking about how beautiful it was. He leaned against the steering wheel, both hands gripping it as if it were gold. For the thousandth time, he asked me if I knew a modern day woman who could love the way women did of old. I thought about it for a minute, wondering just what a person was supposed to say to a question like that. I looked out the car window, watching the lightning and listening to the thunder and wanting to be home. Finally, I decided to tell the truth.

"Bob," I said slowly, "there's no way to answer a question like that. But I'll tell you something I do know. I've talked about love and about love being forever, and I've been proposed to, but I want you to know this is the first time in my life that I've ever sat on a lonely road, on top of a windy hill and talked about love with a storm coming up."

He laughed. "It doesn't storm this time of year."

"It's giving a darn good imitation of it," I said morosely.

He started the car and we drove back to Cross Plains. He said he was in the mood to write a love story, and he was going home, write me a letter, take it to the post office, mail it, and then go home and write the rest of the night.

I've done some hard thinking since I got home and came to my favorite spot for writing my journals. I don't have any definite answers yet.

Part of the time, I enjoyed being with Bob tonight, but I would have come home before the storm got so bad. It irritated me that he'd take a simple remark like "I like to walk in the rain" so seriously.

What he said tonight about writing made sense, and I knew what he meant when he said that reading about great loves in real life might help me to think more deeply about love for a story. But I couldn't do what he does, sit down, outline a story, write it, throw it away and keep on writing. I couldn't have the privacy at home that he had, and I couldn't face the family criticism, or neighbor's criticism I'd have. Teaching is beginning to be very important to me, and I know I'm doing a good job. Mr. Williams knows it too. I'm not worried too much about not being re-elected.

If Bob wants to write me a letter and go to the post office and mail it, then go home and sit up all night and write, it's his business. I'm not sure what I want.

Saturday afternoon . . .
Last night, he wrote the letter . . .

Today's letter from Bob was the icing on the cake! I went to the post office just to see if I'd have anything from him. Sure enough. Another unsealed letter was in my box!

I thought: For heaven's sake, what's got into Bob? I took the letter out of the envelope. Then I knew!

It began very simply:

> *Dear Novalyne and Members of the Cross Plains Post*
> *Office Staff:*

He went on to say that he'd see me again today at two and we'd drive over to Brownwood or wherever I wanted to drive.

It struck me as so funny, I laughed all the way home to get ready. Both of us were in high spirits today! It's great to have a good friend.

At last, the play is over . . .

The play is over and Bob didn't come! We had such a large crowd that people had to be turned away. But not Bob.

I asked him to come . . . even begged him . . . and I felt a little hurt when he refused. He offered every lame excuse ever thought of by a man determined not to do something. No matter how emphatically I told him he could always find time for something he wanted to do, he insisted he didn't have the time. I couldn't persuade him.

A lot of people have raved about the play, and I'm happy. I have a few weeks to gather myself together and catch up with things I want to do before I start another one. I'll grade those papers Enid's always jawing about!

And you might know that Bob would be here Johnny-on-the-Spot two days AFTER the play is over.

But I was in such a good mood I was literally dancing when he got here. He suggested that we ride around, and he'd shoot his mouth off, but he didn't. He didn't get the chance. I robbed him of that. I did most of the talking!

He asked me how the play had gone. I said things went fine, thank you. I resisted the temptation to say, "A lot you care!" But if I had, he would have known I was hurt by his not being there. He said he'd heard good things about it.

"I hear you had some star performers," he said.

"Some things made me furious," I said flippantly, "and I almost killed one kid. But I guess it's just as well I didn't."

He wanted to know what had happened. I explained that a play really belongs to the director. While each actor is concerned only with his own part, the director has to see every part in relationship to the play as a whole and to the other characters; consequently, scene-steals have no place on any stage.

"What can a kid do to steal a scene?" Bob asked.

"I heard prolonged laughter from the audience," I said. "Laughter that was drowning out important speeches. I peeped out on stage and nearly blew my top! An important character was hulling peanuts, pitching them up, and catching them in his mouth as they came down. The audience was howling, but I was close to shooting him."

"That was a scene-steal?" he said dubiously.

"Anything that takes the audience's attention away from the play and focusses it on one character to the exclusion of everything else is a scene-steal and should give the director the lawful right to shoot the blamed kid," I said vehemently.

Bob seemed genuinely interested. "What did you do?"

"I got close enough to him, so that he could hear me and I hissed, 'Get those goddam peanuts out of your goddam mouth, or I'll break your goddam head.' "

Bob looked absolutely petrified. "You said what?"

I repeated it a little louder.

Awed, Bob shook his head. "God, I couldn't have said it better myself."

He was afraid, however, that if I used language such as that, whether it was to students or not, Nat and the Board would fire me. He was sure of it. I pointed out that I never used that kind of language except under a most severe provocation, such as a scene-steal on stage. I refused to let it worry me.

We talked about other things then, about writers he knew and writers he liked. He was indifferent to most of the writers I liked. Then I very innocently said I thought the play "Candida" by George Bernard Shaw was great. He exploded. Apparently, Bob doesn't think the man has a brain in his head.

Then he made the mistake of his life, or rather of our date. He quoted Kipling. He threw back his head and said oratorically and badly: "There is neither East nor West/Border, nor Breed, nor Birth/When two strong men stand face to face, tho' they come from the ends of the earth."

I know that poem well and have recited it on programs. I settled myself on my side of the car and said the entire "Ballad of the East and West." He looked surprised; but when I finished, he complimented me, and so I recited "Mandalay" for him. When I finished that, I said all of "Gunga Din."

By that time, he thought he'd be smart and he quoted, "A woman is only a woman but a good cigar is a smoke."

Very promptly, I recited the entire poem for him. After I said "The Rival," I told him of one of Kipling's tries at humor when he had one of his girl characters say that kissing a man without a mustache was like eating an egg without salt. I laughed a lot at that anecdote, but he didn't laugh much. He said, simply, that I could recite poetry better than any woman he'd ever heard, except his mother.

That burned me down. I told him I could recite poetry better than any man or woman he'd ever heard. He said he wondered if I made up in sweetness for my colossal self-confidence.

I didn't want to argue, but I knew I didn't have as much self-confidence as he thought I had. Some things I do well; some I don't. It's as simple as that.

Then he began to ask those impossible questions such as did I believe a woman now-a-days could love a man the way women in prehistoric times did—enough to take her sword and stand by her man in battle and fight beside him.

You can't answer a question like that.

Monday night . . . after dramatics club meeting
and a beautiful day at school . . .

On the spur of the moment, I decided to go home for the weekend, and so I went early Saturday morning.

I got back to Cross Plains late Sunday afternoon just before sundown. I called Bob, and this is one for Ripley's "Believe it or Not." He answered the telephone! He said he'd come over and let me enjoy the sunset he'd ordered because it was a beautiful sunset if he did say so himself.

The sun was practically down by the time he got here, but it was still pretty. It had been one of our clear and cold, beautiful winter days that West Texas has to its credit.

Bob wanted to know what I wanted for Christmas besides a diamond ring. I thought carefully. The ring? I needed time to think about that. In the meantime, there was something very important. Saturday, while I was in Brownwood, I went by Dublin's and saw a history I wanted. I didn't buy it because I couldn't afford it right now. I told Bob that I really wanted a good history book and gave him the title of it.

He said he'd never heard of a girl wanting a history book for Christmas and wanted to know why it was important. I said that I needed all the help I could get teaching history. I feel very confident in speech and English classes, but in history, I have to work just to stay ahead of J. H. Childs, who, it seemed to me, was always reading ahead. Although he seemed to enjoy history, I didn't. I also have J. H. in English class, and, in that class, compared with Billy Ruth, Jane Rae, and Wailena, he's nothing to write home about. But, poor me! I have to teach a history buff!

For some reason, Bob got smart and almost ruined the day for both of us. He asked about Mark, for he was sure there was no better student in anything than Mark. It was all I could do to control my anger. I said, sarcastically, I didn't teach Mark history or English because he is a senior.

"Why are you always making snide remarks about Mark?" I asked. "You said you didn't even know the kid."

Bob said he just mentioned him because I was always raving about him. He said he thought I was in love with the damn bastard.

I laughed with as much derision as I could, and I can get a lot of derision in my laugh when I want to. I said, "I'm old enough to be the kid's mother."

Bob said that, in his experience, very few women became mothers at age ten, which, he felt was the probable difference in our ages.

"Besides," he went on, "he's in the prime of his life, because men reach their prime when they're green adolescents and haven't got the sense to take advantage of it. As for women," he looked at me and nearly ran into a ditch beside the road, "women don't reach their prime until they get about twenty-six and on into their thirties. You're just right for each other."

That really upset me. I gave vent to such a torrent of words, he was glad to get off his high horse and apologize.

When I calmed down, I reminded myself that Bob is even more important to me than any high school kid. I like the man. I've never before dated a man who can talk on so many different subjects nor one who uses words so beautifully. Let him describe a scene from history, or a cowboy riding these Texas hills in search of adventure, and I hear English spoken at its best. I think, then, I could fall in love with him. But every time I think I could love him, he pulls some stupid thing such as talking about Mark or not coming to my play. If he'd try to get rid of his shyness and orneryness and mix with people . . . if he wouldn't make obnoxious remarks such as those about Mark and me, I could really fall in love with him. The goon!

When both of us were calm and friends again, he wanted to know what we were studying in history. I said we were to begin a chapter on Alexander the Great. He spent the next hour talking about Alexander. He gave me an insight into Alexander I had not had before. I saw Alexander the Great as a brilliant, scintillating military genius, seeking worlds to conquer, but, unfortunately, not trying to conquer the world within himself. Though he could be boisterous with the best of the roisterers, he was withal a lonely, dejected man. I enjoyed it, but I wondered how a man such as Alexander, or one that I knew, could be such a complex person.

I was in early last night, and nothing could destroy the good humor I had over the success of the play. Today, when I went to school, I was still glowing. It was a beautiful day.

After all is said and done, I remind myself that when you've got a good job, a good friend like Bob, a good boss like Nat, a new dress, and you think you're half-way pretty, the whole world is okay. One hundred per cent okay.

Thursday night . . . early . . . eleven o'clock . . .

In my life, things happen by twos and threes. There is no such thing as peace and harmony with one thing to enjoy. No. I must have two contradicting things to bother me. Two choices to make between two diametrically opposed things.

Bob and I had talked of getting together during the Christmas holidays. We'd made plans, and they were plans I looked forward to. He wanted to take me to San Saba for a day, for he said he knew I'd enjoy it as much as he would; besides, he'd have a chance to tell me about a lost gold mine in San Saba. He's always wanting to tell me something about Texas history, as if I had moved here from somewhere else. He says I don't talk like a true Texas native.

My problem is that now I'm going to have to manage someway to keep Bob from coming to Brownwood at all during the holidays, and I must do it without making him mad! An old boy friend of mine is coming to spend the Christmas holidays at our house! Oh, God!

Today, after school, I went to the post office. In my box, I had a letter from Mother. She enclosed a letter from an old friend of mine which she had opened because she thought it might be important. She said that my friend wanted to come to Brownwood during the holidays and stay a few days at our house . . . if we'd let him. Then she told me to write him at once that we'd be glad to have him! I won't write him, because I know she has already written him to come.

At one time, I thought I loved the man. He's dark, tall—a little over six feet, weighs about 190 pounds and is built like a Greek god. But, as it always happens to me, when I was dating him and asking myself if I loved him, I met a handsome blond man, a little over six feet and built like a Greek god.

Here I am again. Two choices. Two dates at once.

Bob was at his best tonight. He was kind, sweet, sympathetic because my cold has gotten to the stage where even I think I'll die any minute. Bob urged me a dozen times to see his father to get something for it. He was afraid I'd have pneumonia if I didn't do something.

Mostly, to get Bob to shut up about my dying with pneumonia, I promised to see Dr. Howard tomorrow afternoon. He brought me home early, saying I had worked myself to death and that I ought to try to get some rest.

I didn't object to coming home early. Anybody faced with the problems I face might as well rest. Ethel is going home Saturday morning, so I'll have the room to myself Saturday and Sunday. How beautiful! It has nothing to do with Ethel. I like her. I just want to be by myself.

When I came in tonight coughing, Ethel and Mrs. Hemphill wanted me to put some gookey stuff on my chest, but I didn't. If I'm going to die, I don't want to die smelling like that.

One thing stands out in my mind. Bob was the sweetest man in the world tonight. I would have enjoyed hearing the story of San Saba's lost mine. I wonder what Dr. Howard will say to me tomorrow!

Friday night . . . I think I'll live even
though no one else seems to . . .

Some days are so miserable they shouldn't happen.

I taught school today with everybody from the superintendent to the students telling me I ought to go home. It began early this morning. Mrs. Hemphill and Ethel thought I ought to stay home because I was so hoarse I could hardly talk; so stopped up I could hardly breathe, and I coughed on the average of once every three seconds. I didn't have the patience to argue with them; I just got ready and went to school.

Enid was the first person I saw when I got inside the building. She started to tell me something about some books she'd put in the library for freshmen to read. I suppose she was so astounded that I didn't bother to argue with her about the Cabell book that she stopped right in the middle of one of her long paragraphs and said, "You're crazy. You have no business being in school with a cold like that!"

Later, in the office, I saw Mr. Williams and Lewis Norman. Mr. Williams told me that I could have the day off if I wanted to go home. When I said I didn't want to go home, Lewis asked me if I were trying to die in the saddle with my boots on.

After school, I went to see Dr. Howard. He is the gruffest doctor I've ever seen in my life, but, as Mrs. Smith says, his bark is worse than his bite. I sat down in his office and wheezed out that his son, Bob, had told me to come to see him. He grunted, stuck a thermometer in my mouth, and checked my pulse.

When he read the thermometer, he mumbled something that may have been a swear word. He jerked his chair and lunged against his desk. The way Bob does. "Nearly 103°," he barked. Probably an exaggeration, but I didn't give a continental. "Now, you listen to me, young lady. I'm going to give you some medicine, and I want you to go home, take it, and go to bed. And don't you get up until you're over this cold. I'll come by in the morning to see if you've done what I told you to do."

When he gave me the medicine, I coughed out that I would do as he said. But I asked him to tell Bob for me that I was going to bed and stay there. Bob was supposed to come over tonight.

Dr. Howard gulped and slammed his chair around. I didn't wait for him to say anything. I came on home.

Ethel had a chance to go home today . . . Thank goodness . . . and she was hurrying around trying to get ready. "Oh, my, my. You look just terrible," she said.

I thanked her and began getting ready for bed. Before I remembered I needed a spoon to take the medicine Dr. Howard had given me, I was all ready for bed. "Oh, my, my, I'll go get one for you," Ethel said. "You go on to bed."

She ran out of the room, and I sat down on the bed to wait until she came back. She and Mrs. Hemphill came together.

"Oh, my, my," Ethel gasped. "Why aren't you in bed? Oh, my, my, you should have gone to bed."

Mrs. Hemphill said something, but I didn't answer because I swallowed the medicine. That medicine! I'd never tasted anything like it before! It was the most godawful stuff ever concocted by an inhuman doctor. I coughed. I gasped. I sputtered, snorted, tried to breathe. Ethel and Mrs. Hemphill just stood there, petrified, staring at me.

"My God," I groaned when I could speak, "I believe that old man is trying to kill me."

"Oh, my, my," Ethel said.

Thursday . . . almost midnight . . .

Bob is the soul of kindness and consideration when he thinks your life may be cut short, but he can be absolutely impossible when you're hale and hearty.

I've been talking to my good friend Merle Mitchell. She and Mitch are planning a party just before the Christmas holidays, and we teachers are going to be the main guests. While Merle and I were talking, I told her that I did wish Bob would come with me to the party. I told her how clever and interesting he is to talk to. I said that I wished other people could know him as I do, because I was sure they'd like him.

Merle was enthusiastic and thought it would be a great idea if he came too. She said she'd call him and invite him, or if I'd rather, she'd leave the inviting up to me. I said I'd deliver the invitation, for I knew his mother wouldn't call him to the phone for the President of the United States.

I felt a little guilty when I thought about Enid. She thinks Bob is such a lunatic that I was afraid she'd want to stay home if she knew he'd be there. I decided not to tell her about it. I'd just surprise her.

In a way, I had my doubts all along that Bob would go, but I hadn't expected the explosion I got! He said he'd be damned if he'd go to any tea-drinking, cookie-pushing, stupid party. It was a crazy idea as far as he was concerned. It upset me so I was on the verge of crying. I pointed out that I would be happy to have him go, so that people could see how nice he really was.

Flattery didn't budge him. He said that as far as he was concerned he thought of himself as the same kind of Bull-in-a-China-Shop that they thought he was. He was pretty damn sorry that I wanted him to go to some damn party where he'd make a fool of himself. He said that he wanted me to know that he'd done a hell of a lot for me. Didn't he wear a goddam tie and a fool hat because I wanted him to get himself up in such a way that he figured people thought he wore lace on his—you know damn well what.

Finally, I got mad and said that I didn't see how he could stay over there in that house, chained to a typewriter, and never get out and mix with people. He said that if he listened to me, his writing would go to hell. He wouldn't be able to pound out a yarn in a blue moon; certainly he wouldn't be able to write steadily enough to earn a living. He'd be wasting all his goddam time keeping diaries and writing down conversations with every Tom, Dick, and Jackass he met. Though, in all fairness, he would admit that he himself had written a conversation once in a while. For example, he sometimes wrote down conversations that he, Clyde, and Truett had because they were erudite, learned, something for posterity, not drivel the way most flea-brains talked.

I tried to fight back. I said that I didn't see how he and Clyde could talk such magnificent talk because I hadn't heard either one of them say anything very learned. I didn't know Truett too well, but if he were like them—intellectual snobs—he probably couldn't say anything important either.

We were hitting at each other, and I wanted to stop. He must have felt the same way, for he changed his tune and began to talk of how mistreated he was—the kind of talk I'd heard before.

That infuriated me. I reminded him that not everybody hated him. "Besides," I said, "you don't need to feel exclusive. People don't like me either. I'm just a fourth at bridge."

He ran his fingers through his hair. "What does that mean?"

"If you have three really good bridge players, almost anybody can sit at the table, hold the cards, and play," I explained. "If you're the fourth at bridge, you're not important for yourself; you're just a 'fill-in' until they get someone better."

"That's not a hell of a compliment," Bob said.

I began to feel a little frustrated. It's hard to explain a deep emotional feeling to Bob. "I'm just trying to say that people like me in a vague, indifferent way. I'm not the first person they think about when they're ready to play bridge. I'm—"

"That ought to make you hate people," he cut in swiftly. "I'd see the bastards in hell before I'd make their damn fourth at bridge. Why would you want to live, if things are like that?"

I tried to think of the right word to defend myself. "I enjoy life," I said, and it sounded so trite I was embarrassed. "Even though I don't have many close friends, I do have friends. Merle Mitchell likes me for myself. I think Mrs. Jackson does, although she may like me mostly because of her two kids— Jennie Laurie and S. R., Jr."

"What about your students?" Bob asked. "They like you, don't they?"

I considered that, laughing to myself. "I'm not too sure," I admitted. "Did you see Frederick March in that movie 'Death Takes a Holiday?' "

Bob nodded.

"Well," I went on, grinning, "the kids call me 'Death' and wish I'd take a holiday."

"The dirty little bastards—" Bob snorted.

"Oh, no," I interrupted. "I think that's funny. You see they call me that because I'm strict. I think when they come to class that they ought to behave themselves and try to learn something. When I have them in studyhall, I think they should study. If they don't have anything to do, I insist they be quiet and let other people study. I'm strict."

He glared at me but didn't say anything.

I felt I had to justify my not being upset about it. "Nat—Mr. Williams says that kids actually like the strict teachers, even though they complain about them. I'm one of the strictest teachers he has on the faculty."

Bob was still unconvinced that it wasn't a bad situation. I tried to think of something to explain it better, but couldn't. I settled myself in the seat, drawing my foot up under me, looking at him. He was staring straight ahead at a coming car. The car passed, and he still sat, his eyes intent on the road.

"I don't give a damn what people think about me," he said suddenly.

Even though I didn't want to talk about it any more, I couldn't let that pass. "If you never give people a chance to know the 'real' Bob Howard, how can you expect them to appreciate you?"

I didn't get my point across.

My own feelings were all mixed up as they frequently are when I'm with Bob. I was hurt that he wouldn't go to the party with me and upset by some of the things he'd said, but I could still go to the party and enjoy myself.

I moved closer to him, reached up and touched his cheek and said in my softest voice, "Okay, Bob. I won't ask you to go to another party with me anytime soon. I promise. You're a nut, I suppose, but I like you better than any other nut I know."

He laughed and put his arm around me and apologized for all the things he'd said. He realized that parties meant a lot to me as they did to other women, and, if I really wanted him to, he'd take me over to Merle's and wait in the car until I was ready to leave. He was sorry, but he just couldn't come in and listen to the drivel he'd have to listen to and sip coffee which was a worthless concoction developed by some fool to try to keep its imbibers from facing life as it really was.

One thought was in my mind: how different Bob and Nat Williams are! If you count as success the amount of money one makes, then Bob was almost as successful as Nat, for he made practically as much money with his writing as Nat made as superintendent of schools. But Nat would go to the party, laugh and talk, and be the most popular person there. Bob could sit at home, pounding out a story that told of a lonely, morose barbarian in an age that never was.

As he started out on a long rigmarole about people not understanding anyone in his family, I moved away from him, so that we wouldn't run into the ditch. I listened to him talk about his mother. He said she was a wonderful lady, having come from an old and honored family of redblooded Irishmen.

"In fact," he said in an awed voice, "we've traced the Ervins back to the 1300s to royalty."

He raved on about how his mother wasn't appreciated, although she tried for a long time to mix with people in Cross Plains, going to church, entertaining the various church groups. She had stopped after her health became so bad that she could scarcely venture outside her own house.

If there was a virtuous woman whose life story I was not interested in, it was Mrs. Howard's. I asked Bob point blank about his father. "Your father seems like a nice person too," I said crisply. "I went to see him on Friday afternoon, and he came by the house for a few minutes on Saturday and Sunday mornings to see if I was taking that awful medicine he gave me."

Bob nodded, pleased. I didn't tell him that the medicine cured me because I didn't take it all. After Dr. Howard came by Sunday morning, I got up, dressed, and poured the rest of it down the lavatory. In spite of his gruffness, I like Dr. Howard much more than I ever could like his wife.

Bob seemed enthusiastic about his dad, although he said that it had long been a matter of regret for his mother and him that his father insisted on staying in Cross Plains when all of them would have been happier in a larger town.

I listened as I always do, with mixed and turbulent emotions. He began again on how wonderful his mother was. How she encouraged him to write. Gave him all the freedom in the world.

But, suddenly, truant thoughts flashed through my mind. Does he love or hate his mother? Quickly, I slashed the thought out of my mind. I mustn't think such things!

I looked out the car at the lonely little farm houses with cheerful lights burning in the windows. Those houses held love. Families together. Families stay together because they love one another. Mrs. Howard, Bob, and his dad love one another.

The night had been a deeper emotional experience for me than I wanted it to be. I must get myself under control and listen to Bob talk about his writing.

I know enough about writing to know that to make a living at it, one must spend hours alone every day at a typewriter. I can even understand that, at times, a person will work eighteen hours a day, or even all night, as Bob does. But I still can't get it through my head that a successful writer can't take some part in the life around him. How does a man know how people think and feel if he has only his own feelings to guide him? To learn to portray emotion, an actor must search his own heart, but he must also understand how those emotions affect other people; a director must study people; and a playwright, if he would portray "real" people and "real" emotions, must study mankind.

When Bob finishes a story, he doesn't always start another one immediately. Couldn't he be with people some between stories? Couldn't he go to church?

I closed my eyes to shut out the clear, cold beauty of the night. Why are there so many questions? How can Bob's mother satisfy his every need and longing? How can a young woman, to whom Bob is important, compete with his mother? Is it possible for Bob to be drawn into the life around him? If he were to get married, would he expect his wife to be a stay-at-home like his mother?

Funny. Just as I opened my eyes, someone blew out a light in a house we were passing.

Fan mail always brings happiness to Bob . . .

Several times, Bob has shown me letters he's gotten from fans of his. He had one from Providence and one from New York just the other day. They have all been nice letters, and I can understand his pride.

But he has never been prouder than he was to receive a sonnet dedicated to him by a man named Petaja. He showed me the sonnet a couple of months ago.

I'll never forget the night he brought it to show me. He stood silently while I read it. Then he asked me if I wanted to read it aloud. I said I would, and so I read it aloud. When I finished, I told him I'd like to have a copy of it. That pleased him. He said he'd make me a copy and either send it to me or bring it the next time he came.

"What about some of your poetry?" I asked. "I'd like to have something you've written too."

He seemed very pleased; however, he tried not to show it too much. Like some of the rest of us, he's terribly afraid to show emotion around someone else. He looked shy and boyish and very proud that I wanted a copy of the sonnet to him and also some of his poems. That was two months ago. I've seen him dozens of times since then.

Today, I received a short note from him with two of his poems and the Petaja sonnet.

The letter was short.

Dear Novalyne,

Like my meal-ticket, Conan the Cimmerian, I am a man who eventually fulfills his obligations. So here are the poems I promised to copy for you several months ago—Petaja's sonnet, and my own junk. Mashallah.

Bob

ECHO FROM THE EBON ISLES

A sonnet—

Dedicated to the Modern Master of Fantasy—

Robert E. Howard

From ancient, fabled Cimmeria he came
With sword uplifted, on that bloody day,
To join the beaten forces in the fray,
And triumphant refuse eternal fame.
Men trembled at the mention of his name,
And humbly stepped aside to make his way.
"You are our King," they said; he answered "Nay."
And left them wondering what could be his aim.

I saw him then, and I still see him now,
Cryptically silent—on yon hill's brow;
Watching with brooding eyes the scene below
Where flame the earth and sky in scarlet glow,
He grasps his curious staff in mighty hands—
And strides into the dusk . . . toward other lands.

—Emil Petaja

Bob included two of his own poems which were published last year, and both of them leave me rather speechless. I'm not speechless because I like them so much or think they're great; I am speechless because they tie in with some of the things he keeps talking about. They also tie in with another thing I feel deep inside him, a thing he tries to hide from himself.

Bob talks a lot about reincarnation. He says that in former lives he has lived, his best girl was always stolen from him by his best friend. His talking about that has gotten a little old to me; consequently, the other night, I told him that if he had been as hesitant about making a commitment of himself in his former lives as he is now, his best friend didn't steal his woman, he gave her to him.

I've read this poem "To a Woman" a dozen times, and I wonder if this is a subtle way to remind me of his reincarnation unhappiness.

TO A WOMAN

Robert E. Howard
(Modern American Poetry - 1933.)

Though fathoms deep you sink me in the mould,
Locked in with thick-lapped lead and bolted wood,
Yet rest not easy in your lover's arms;
Let him beware to stand where I have stood.

I shall not fail to burst my ebon case,
And thrust aside the clods with fingers red:
Your blood shall turn to ice to see my face
Look from the shadows on your midnight bed.

To face the dead, he, too, shall wake in vain,
My fingers at his throat, your scream his knell;
He will not see me tear you from your bed,
And drag you by your golden hair to Hell.

His second poem "One Who Comes at Eventide" rouses in me a fear I have often felt in him but cannot explain. He says there are two kinds of women: Eve and Lilith. Eve marries a man and chains him to a way of life that frustrates him, takes away his freedom to be himself, his freedom to roam the world seeking adventure; for, since the beginning of time, he says, man has been an adventurer. Lilith seduces a man and sends his soul to hell. I laughed at him once and said he didn't give men much of a choice.

Still, sometimes it seems to me that chains and the resulting hate they burn in a man is another of his principal fears. He seems almost to prefer Lilith to Eve. The thing that bothers me with that is that he is not married to an Eve, but he is chained, even more firmly, to his mother. Way down deep in my heart, I begin to fear violence in him. It's true he seems such a devoted son. Devoted? Yes, and I hate myself for thinking, every now and then, that he is too good to be true.

ONE WHO COMES AT EVENTIDE

Robert E. Howard
(Modern American Poetry - 1933.)

I think when I am old a furtive shape
Will sit beside me at my fireless hearth,
Dabbled with blood from stumps of severed wrists,
And flecked with blackened bits of mouldy earth.

My blood ran fire when the deed was done;
Now it runs colder than the moon that shone
On shattered fields where dead men lay in heaps
Who could not hear a ravished daughter's moan.

(Dim through the bloody dawn on bitter winds
The throbbing of the distant guns was brought
When I reeled like a drunkard from the hut
That hid the horror my red hands had wrought.)

So now I fire my veins with stinging wine,
And hoard my youth as misers hug their gold,
Because I know that shape will come and sit
Beside my crumbling hearth—when I am old.

After I think bad thoughts and give myself over to one of his black fears, I chide myself severely. I'm not crazy. I know that there is such a thing as a deep love and devotion to one's parents or to a lover or sweetheart. Why do I know such fear? What is there in me that allows me to fear?

It is not even necessary to remind myself that Bob is a good man, a kind and thoughtful man, a little troubled perhaps. What he needs, and I need, and I suppose most of us need, is a clear vision.

Sunday . . . There is a presence here . . .

Sometimes, Bob and I forget that a town like Cross Plains wears many faces. It is strict and unbending where teachers are concerned; it does not understand the worth of its writer; but it has another side—a good, kind, compassionate side.

Death hangs over the town. Two men hang precariously under the shadow.

A short time ago, one man was standing on the sidelines at one of our football games, cheering the team. A player was shoved out of bounds and the man was injured. Now, death is near.

Another man has been gravely ill for a couple of months. He is an old pioneer, who has lived here for more than thirty years. A man who raised a family and was a part of the town. An old man whose death will not be a shock.

Bob and I have talked about these things, and it is the old man about whom Bob has worried. Bob rails against death that takes life from the old because, he says, that slender thread of life is all the old person has left. To Bob, the death of a man in the full vigor of his manhood is not sad. Such a man has more than just his life.

I am depressed. These two men were a part of the town, sharing its loves, its hates, and the robustness of its life and hope. Is it the loneliness of the writing profession that keeps Bob from being a part of his town? At one time, they tell me, he participated in the town's activities. Now, he doesn't seem to be a real part of it. I wonder why.

Today, when he comes, I'll talk about the good part of his town.

Mrs. Hemphill tells us not to expect too much in the way of meals for a while, for she'll be spending a lot of time cooking for the families.

"At a time like this," she said, shaking her head, "families certainly can't cook with all they have to do; the sick need someone every minute. We neighbors have to help out."

Tonight, Mr. Hemphill and some of the other men will sit up all night. They'll take turns every night. Whenever a family has illness or whenever something is wrong, the rest of the "town family" tries to help out.

Bob is coming at two o'clock. He will come from another world.

Friday, December 21, 1934 . . .

Christmas is in the air! It's everywhere. We had parties at school, gave and received gifts. One of my classes gave me a pretty little jewel box. Some students gave me perfume, stationery, boxes of handkerchiefs, a flower, and a couple of boxes of candy. I love everything and all the kids.

I have a date with Bob tonight. He'll give me my present then.

This afternoon, I'm going to Brownwood with Enid and Jimmie, and Bob is coming over tonight. He's taking his mother somewhere today instead of taking me home. It's just as well. Enid and Jimmie have their car, and I'll enjoy going with them. We're out of school early, so I'll get home early.

Bob says he is disappointed that we're not going to get to go to San Saba during the holidays, and I am too. Oh, well, the only thing about it is that I'm afraid that Bob thinks I just don't want to go to San Saba. I definitely have not told him about my friend coming to visit. I hate women who talk about other beaux to the man they are out with.

Bob may be a little suspicious. He wanted to know if we were having relatives visit during the holidays. I said that we were and also an old friend of the family. That's true. During the holidays, all of the family and our visitor will get together for a big Christmas dinner at our house. Our guest is a friend of the family. Mother likes him. I just forgot to tell Bob that he is young and handsome.

I'm looking forward to Bob's gift! I know it will be the history I want. I've certainly hinted enough about it. He keeps saying how surprised he is that I don't want a diamond ring. He says the idea that I want a good history indicates that I'm a very rare and intelligent woman. Naturally, I agree . . . almost.

I do wonder, however, what Bob would have done if I had said that I wanted a diamond! As long as he knew I definitely did not want one, he could pretend to be impressed with my intelligence.

But I won't worry about a thing. I have so much to look forward to—a chance to talk with Bob tonight, the holidays, plus a beautiful new history book!

Saturday, December 22, 1934 . . .

Bob came last night and brought the book. I opened it expectantly with Mother, Mammy, and Bob watching, sharing my excitement. When I opened it, I may have looked surprised. *The Complete Works of Pierre Louÿs.* It definitely was not like any other history I'd ever seen. I looked at Bob who sat, looking smug and complacent.

"A history?" I asked bewildered.

He shifted his weight in his chair and grinned. "Well, . . . Yeah. It's a *kind* of history."

I kept turning pages, trying to see a familiar history pattern. Mother and Mammy, all interest, watched me. Then Bob said the book described very vividly our "rotting civilization."

I looked from Mother and Mammy back to Bob. I wanted a regular history. I wasn't interested in a description of a "rotting civilization." But the Lord was with me at that moment, I think. Carefully, I put the wrapper back on the book, folded my hands on it and watched Bob, ignoring Mother's interest. Later, I thanked God I hadn't handed it to her to look at even for a minute.

We sat in the dining room, where we always sit when family or close friends come to see us. Mammy had baked a chocolate cake with thick, fudgy icing. Bob took a big piece and a glass of milk. I ate a small piece and drank part of a glass of milk.

Bob was at his best, complimenting Mammy on the best chocolate cake he'd ever tasted and managed someway to get her started talking about the Civil War. He does that so easily! It amuses me and always makes me want to hug him. He makes Mammy feel just his age and all the time she's talking about something that happened more than seventy years ago.

One thing surprised me though. Mammy was talking about the hardships her people encountered during the War. She told about her father's friend who, when the soldiers came, refused to tell where his money was hidden. They tied him to a chair, hit him, beat him. They heated a poker red hot. Over and over, in spite of everything, he refused to tell them where his money was buried. They burned his eyes out. Bob reacted to the story as if he himself had had his eyes burned out, or had seen the tragedy unfold. He dropped his fork, clenched his fists, and wanted to kill them all. I thought, "Is this the man who writes so vividly of murder and torture, yet who seems so afraid of real life descriptions of such things?"

After a while, Mother and Mammy excused themselves and went to bed, and Bob and I sat and talked for nearly two hours longer. He said several times he was sorry we were having company and I wouldn't be able to go to San Saba. I was sorry too, and said so for the umpteenth time. But I said I could accept this as just another one of the eternal complications I face in life.

After Bob left, I sat down, unwrapped the book, and began to look at it very carefully. I read the inscription again, trying to make sense out of it:

The French have one gift—the ability to guild decay and change the maggots of corruption to the humming birds of poetry—as demonstrated by this volume.

Bob
December 21,1934

It was early, only a little after eleven-thirty. I moved the lamp closer and began to scan through the book. I glanced at a page or two without interest. I turned the pages rapidly and came upon the story of Leda and the swan. I frowned. I'd heard of that, I was sure, but I couldn't remember exactly what I'd heard. I began to read, noticing, in the first paragraph, the easy flowing style of the author. I thought: "Well, he certainly can bring emotion into his story." Then I thought? "Emotion! My God!"

Never! Never in my whole life had I read anything like that before!

Emotion! I'm no prude, for heaven's sake! When I was in high school, I'd read a book I wasn't supposed to read—*The Sheik*. I'd been thrilled and embarrassed because the girl waked up the next morning and saw the dent in the pillow his head had made! But this story! My God! *The Shiek* was a Sunday School picnic—a Baptist Sunday School picnic—compared to this!

The house was quiet. Still. In here, you couldn't even hear the brisk north wind blowing outside. The lamp, flickering, made no sound. Suddenly, the quietness was broken. Mother coughed. I jumped. Gasped. In one fluid motion I had that book under me and was sitting on it. Dear God! Mother would peel my head and shoot Bob if she got hold of that book! My heart pounded. One thing I knew about Mother. She read everything she could get her hands on. I'd have to eat this damn book!

Finally, I settled back and sighed. Mother wasn't coming in; she'd just coughed. I got off the book and began to turn the pages, telling myself I'd better know what it was all about before I burned it!

It was incredible! That a gentleman had written this book, I could not believe. That a young man—my boy friend—had given it to me—his best girl—I could not believe. The further I read, the more I froze! I could hardly breathe. I wanted to get up and kick the door down. I wanted to go to Cross Plains, find Bob, drag him out of his house by the hair of his head, and kick him clean up to the North Pole.

Humming birds of poetry! Pornography! That's what this stupid book was all about. Pornography! Read it at random—a page here. A page there! A paragraph here! A paragraph there! Pornography! My mind was made up. I'd kill Bob the next time I saw him. History of a rotting civilization? He doesn't know a rotting civilization from a .38 revolver!

A little after one, I decided to go to bed. That book! What would I do with it? Mother and Mammy must never read even one page of it! After all, Mammy was only seventy-seven years old, much too young to read things like this! I groaned. In the morning, the first thing Mother would do would be to ask about it. I had to hide it!

What would I tell them? It was just a school book? A history? That it wasn't much good? I'd belittle it and try to get them to think about something else! How? A vision of my old boy friend flashed across my mind. My God, suppose he saw it! I did not want any man, woman or child to know Bob Howard had given me that book. The two-headed monster! Killing was too good for him!

Where would I hide the damn thing? I took it into my room and put it in my dresser drawer. Dear God, no! That wouldn't do at all. It made an underwear mountain that would shout for attention. My closet shelf? No. No. No. In the closet was a dress Mother and Mammy were working on. Under my hat! Absolutely not! My hat didn't cover half that obnoxious book.

I bolted for the front door. Under the house beside the chimney! After reading a little in that book, I could walk outside in the cold north wind and never feel a thing. That is, I would only feel a sincere and honest desire to slug Bob. My hand was on the doorknob. No. No. The only way to crawl under the house was in the back by Mammy's bedroom. If I made any noise, she'd wake up, shoot me, and ask questions afterwards! Or worse than that, Mother would look out the back door and say, "What in the world are you doing out in the cold without a coat on?"

I went back into my room, holding the cursed book in my arms and sat down on the side of my bed and stared at the wall. I pictured myself with my trusted scimitar cutting Bob's ears off.

At last, I looked at the one suitcase I hadn't even begun to empty. It's a strong, oversize suitcase, gray, that I use to carry books in. It was full of papers to grade, a couple of history books, my English book, and the *Story of Philosophy* by Durant. I put "the thing" in the bottom of the suitcase and arranged the books and papers to hide it.

I crawled into bed and thought about the time I got a letter from an old boy friend, and I said, "Mother, do you want me to read you this letter?" She had said, "Well, it all depends on whether you want to read it to me or whether you want me to steal it out later and read it."

We laughed about it, and she was joking, of course, but there was a ring of truth in it. If she got the idea I was trying to hide that book—which I most assuredly was—she'd read it in spite of hell and high water. Tomorrow, under the house it would go.

What little sleep I got was marred by dreams of Mother coming in and opening that suitcase.

Breakfast was worse, because they asked about it. I said, off hand, that I had wanted a history for reference work and that Bob had given me one. I also said that now I wished that he had given me a box of candy. That was probably the best way to get their minds on something else.

It was decided I'd go to town this morning and get a few things for Christmas dinner and also several sacks of cow feed. Everybody seemed interested in that for the time being. After breakfast, I got ready to go to town. When they weren't looking, I slipped the book out and hid it under the front seat of the car. That way, I'd be sure to keep it out of sight, and, I hoped, out of mind. All the way to town, I kept telling myself that I never wanted to see Robert E. Howard again as long as I lived!

Whom did I see when I got to town? Bob and his mother! I hated both of them on general principles.

I went to Woolworth's for some pens, paper clips, glue and notebooks to put English outlines and notes in. I was standing behind the counter, waiting for my change, and for some unknown reason, I looked up and across another counter. Mrs. Howard was standing there, looking at me. Bob and Mrs. Howard! The way he hovered around her! His left arm was around her waist, and he was holding her close to him. His head was down and his right hand was picking up objects and putting them down as if he were looking for something. Mrs. Howard was standing straight and tall. We looked at each other and neither of us gave any sign of recognition, but she knew me and I knew her! She said something to Bob; he looked up, smiled, and spoke. I spoke, got my change, the things I'd bought and beat it out of there. I'd never had any woman stare at me with such malevolence before.

I didn't want to be in the same store with either one of them. I dashed down the street and into a drug store, sat down at a table and ordered a cup of coffee. Naturally, they didn't have fresh coffee, so I ordered a coke.

I drank it slowly, and tried to straighten out my chaotic thoughts. Would I ever see Bob again? Did I care? By some strange power of precognition, I knew that Mrs. Howard had looked at me, weighed me, and decided to look elsewhere for a daughter-in-law.

I wanted to run back to Woolworth's. If they were still there, I wanted to run up to her and say, "I wouldn't have your dern son if he were rich as gold and on a silver platter." I wanted to shout: "I don't care if I never see him again!"

I was angry! I was angry about everything. I was angry about that book! It was, in no sense of the word, a history. Could I tell my class about Leda and the swan? If I were crazy enough to do it, Nat Williams would fire me and never blink an eye.

Still. Something else was bothering me. I closed my eyes and admitted it to myself. I don't hate him. I really don't hate him. I enjoy talking with him more than with any man I've ever seen. He and Clyde are the only selling writers I know. If I ever want to write, I'd better try to put this Pierre Louÿs book out of my mind. After I give Bob a piece of my mind, I will go on and try to accept him as someone who is brilliant but stupid.

I shook the ice in my glass gently, reasoning that Cross Plains didn't have too many men of any description. The truth was that Bob was a find as far as being pleasant to be with. When I am out with him, he is nice to the point of being ridiculous. He might read books like that, but I certainly didn't have to fight him to keep him on his side of the car. In fact, I'll bet he'd get in his car and drive it and me off a cliff, if he thought I had any of the ideas that Bilitis and Leda had. Especially Bilitis.

Another thing. Mrs. Howard did not look at me with any hint of friendliness. She'd find some way to get rid of me. I shouldn't worry about getting rid of Bob; she'd do it for me.

I finished my coke and walked out into the brisk wind. I'd get the things I'd come to town for and go home.

Home is a quiet place. I managed to keep the book out of sight until Mother went to the barn and Mammy to the chicken house. Then I slipped out, crawled under the house, and put it beside one of the pillars.

Once I worried for fear they'd find it, but I reasoned that neither one of them was in the habit of crawling around under the house. Even so, I knew I would not have an easy moment until I got that book back to Cross Plains where I planned to hit Bob in the face with it.

Thinking of Bob, in my mind's eye, I saw him hovering over his mother and her hostile stare at me. His mother, it seemed to me, was rather strait-laced and puritanical. She had brought Bob up to be very courteous to women in general, and to someone he liked especially. Why, then, had he given me *The Complete Works of Pierre Louÿs*? It didn't make sense!

Back in Cross Plains . . .
The holidays and vacation are over . . .

I wonder what you call a nitwit who makes up her mind never to speak to a particular man as long as she lives and then calls him the minute her mother walks out of the house and heads back home? Soft in the head? That's me.

Mrs. Howard answered the telephone. I told her who I was and said that I'd like to speak to Bob. She said, very friendly like, "Yes. Yes, he's here. I'll call him."

I nearly fainted. I heard her say to Bob, "It's for you, honey."

Bob blustered up to the phone with a cheery, "Well, well, you're back in town!"

I agreed that I was, and he said he'd be over right after supper, and I heard myself say that would be fine. In my mind, I argued that I'd have to see him in order to ask him why he'd given me that obnoxious book.

Coming back after the holidays is like beginning again except that there are no surprises. Ethel and I greeted each other like long lost relatives and asked each other about the holidays, then lied to each other about how happy we'd been. She was curious to know if Bob had given me the history I wanted. I assured her he had, crossing my fingers, piously, in the face of such a big lie. The book was buried under the papers and books in my suitcase. The suitcase was locked!

Evidently, the Howards eat an early supper. I barely had time to powder my nose before Bob was knocking on the door and trying to greet me like a long lost sweetheart. I was as responsive as a cold fish, and he looked surprised. Then his eyes took on that helpless, questioning look that hurts me. I should be prepared for it, but I never am.

He asked me if I wanted to ride around, and I said that would be fine. We drove toward Rising Star which is, for some reason, the direction that inspires me to want to write and to talk about writing. Maybe it's so many little houses beside the road with lights burning in the windows.

Bob was busy telling me about a yarn he'd just completed. Not a Conan yarn. One for *Spicy Adventure* magazine. That gave me my opening.

I took a deep breath. "Bob, why did you give me that book by Pierre Louÿs?"

He whirled and looked at me. "Didn't you like it?"

"It was a little strong for my blood," I said, defensively. "I didn't read too much of it."

"Read it." He drove all over the road, watching me. I held tightly to my side of the car. "You lead a sheltered life. You don't know what's going on in the world."

That irritated me. "I don't care to know things like that," I said hotly. "It seems to me knowing about them doesn't make the world a better place; it only makes you a silent partner."

"You're a silent partner, whether you like it or not." He was getting warmed up now. "You see, girl, when a civilization begins to decay and die, the only thing men or women think about is the gratification of their body's desires. They become preoccupied with sex. It colors their thinking, their laws, their religion—every aspect of their lives. Did you read 'The Songs of Bilitis?' "

"No," I said. "I read a page here and there of several stories, but I couldn't take them all."

"Why not?" he barked the words out. "It's a masterpiece—Louÿs's—"

"They were not really stories—yarns as you call them. They were nothing but accounts of naked men and women desiring . . . desiring only the pleasures of the flesh."

He looked at me. "That's what I'm trying to tell you, girl. Men quit reading fiction, because they want only true stories of men's sexual exploits. They want—"

"Bob," I said irritably, "you're always talking about our 'rotting civilization.' I don't think the world is so bad. Sure, there're a lot of bad people in it. There've always been bad people, but it seems to me that as the world advances, we have more good people—people who don't read and think about pornography."

Bob was impatient, bouncing around in his seat, running his hand through his hair, and waving his arms frantically. "Everybody wants to read pornography, even those half-baked preachers who tell you not to read it while they go off and revel in it. Who—"

"That's stupid," I said emphatically.

"No," Bob said loudly. "You're just naive. Things go on you don't know about. And it's going to get a lot worse. A few years ago, I had a hard time selling yarns about . . . about sex. Now, I'm going to have to work to catch up with the market. I can tell you the demand is growing for more and more sex. In a few years, there won't be anything held back. It'll all be sex, and since language plays a part in sex, the language will become the language of dirty men talking about sex."

He waved his arms and almost ran into the ditch beside the road. "Girl, you don't realize what we're in for, and nobody can tell you. You can't realize how this civilization is eaten up by the maggots of corruption. But you will learn it, girl. You will. In ten years, every play you direct will be filled with sex and dirty talk. And when it happens, I want you to remember old Bob told you it would. Damn it to hell, girl, sex will be in everything you see and hear. It's the way it was when Rome fell. A depraved world where rape and murder took place on their stages, and the damn people loved it. Back in Rome—"

"I don't believe a word you're saying," I interrupted him. I was bouncing around on my side of the car as vigorously as he was. "You've just got some crazy idea that civilization is dying and you're trying to convince yourself that it's true. Depraved people? Sure, there are some. I admit it, but just you remember this: There are always enough good people around to keep the depraved ones from taking over."

He faced me, letting the car find its way the best it could. "Enough good people! Girl, you don't know. There aren't enough good Christians to keep the sinners in check. Good people around here don't know what's going on anymore than you do. They try to hide what they know. They think they're upholding Christian principles when they're riding around trying to catch some poor little school teacher out dancing. You ought to know that. You religious people stick your heads in the sand, and you get upset when somebody tries to tell you what's going on. Damn it. You stick your heads in the sand!"

"My head is not in the sand, and my mind is not in the gutter," I said tartly. "And I think that book is terrible. I read a few pages of a story about the Princess Aline and Mirabelle. It—"

"That was from the 'Adventures of King Pausole,' " Bob interrupted. "What did you think about that?"

"It was ghastly!" I barked. "Ghastly. I was glad when the Page came along and rescued the Princess Aline. I can't imagine any fool writing a bunch of junk like that."

"A fool writing!" Bob raised his voice even higher. "Girl, I'm working on a yarn like that now—a Conan yarn. Listen to me. When you have a dying civilization, the normal, accepted life style ain't strong enough to satisfy the damned insatiable appetites of the courtesans and, finally, of all the people. They turn to Lesbianism and things like that to satisfy their desires."

I raised my voice as high as he raised his. "I'm not going to talk anymore about that, and you can just shut up. If you write something like that, I hope they send it back so fast it makes your head swim. You—"

He ran his fingers through his hair frantically. "I'm going to call it 'The Red Flame of Passion.' It's—"

I wouldn't let him finish his sentence. "There may be a few people like that, but I don't believe it. The Bible says, 'Male and female, He created them.' And that's the way He intended it, and that's the way it always will be. Male and female. I've said it once, and I'll say it again: There'll always be enough good people to hold the contaminated ones in abeyance."

He shook his head vigorously. "Girl, you've got a lot to learn."

We drove in silence for a while. He seemed to be deep in thought; I was trying to decide whether or not to tell him to take me home and never darken my door again. I was nearly crying. I was so close to my side of the car I was about to fall out.

After a minute, he spoke again, quietly and calmly, "Did you ever read what Edmund Burke said: 'The only thing necessary for the triumph of evil is for good men to do nothing.' You'll live to see what ol' Bob is telling you. Pornography will be the order of the day, and the good men—if there's a damn one left—will feebly attempt to do something about it for a while; but they'll give up, and the depraved, as you call them, will take over. Enough good men will keep silent."

I didn't agree with that either. I think Edmund Burke was a great man, but I didn't think that good men would sit idly by and let pornographers take over.

"There's some good writing in that book," Bob said after a few minutes. He was not argumentative. "It takes a Frenchman to describe the rotting civilization and give it the essence of poetry. You should have read the 'Songs of Bilitis.' "

"Bob, the writing may be good," I said, "but the subject destroys it. You say that you can sell that kind of story better now than you could a few years ago?"

Bob settled back in his seat, looking out the car window toward the lighted lamps in the windows of the houses we were passing. Our fight for the evening was over. Neither of us had won.

"The plainer a yarn is now, the better chance it has of catching on," he said.

I lifted the hair off my neck and gently massaged it. It bothered me that I had not convinced him.

Bob broke the silence. "I'll tell you this. I'm going to write some yarns like that. That's what people want, and that's what I'm going to give them. None of this Sunday School junk for them or for me."

I laughed. "No, you won't. You're too good and decent a man to write junk like that. I know you. You're a swell guy. A nice guy." I wanted to pinch myself to see if this was really me talking. To think I'd begun this date wanting to bawl him out! I had come full cycle now and I was ready to think nice things about him.

He, too, melted. "But if you're trying to make money—"

I put my hand on his arm. "Making money is not everything," I said softly. "Doing the right thing is important, too."

He laughed. "Girl, you make it hard for a man to earn a living."

It wasn't much, but I knew things were back to normal again. I moved away from the door on my side of the car. He held my hand in his.

We rode for a long time without talking, and that, I thought, meant that the relationship between us was a strong and steady one. If you can be silent with someone important in your life, there is a depth to the relationship that makes words unnecessary. In the silence, I could think of many things and try to understand them. I thought of Bob and me.

His mother had him so completely in her power that he hovered over her, even in a store. She was, of course, the only woman in his life, but that he had given me such a book must mean something. That he read such things and wrote them must mean something, too. Evidently, she could control his actions but not his mind. Where would that lead him?

"Why all these struggles for the triumph of an hour?"

Since the Christmas holidays, I have noticed a subtle difference in Bob's attitude. It is not a definite thing that I can put my finger on. I could, with a little effort, convince myself that everything is as usual. That there has been no change. He is between "yarns" now and maybe a little nervous and uncertain. He says every writer fears a dry spell, which seems to be an exceptionally big worry to him. I could easily tell myself that is what is the matter, and I do. Still, I have a sharp, clear mental picture of Bob and his mother in Woolworth's during the holidays. I knew as plainly as if Mrs. Howard had said so that she rejected me . . . completely and *finally.*

But that, too, is probably my imagination. After all, when I looked up, I didn't speak. I waited for her to make the first move. Maybe she waited for me. It is quite possible that I had an antagonistic look on my face because of what I thought I read in hers. Another thing that irked me was the way Bob hovered over her.

But I'm not afraid of her, really. When you come right down to it, what can she do? Bob is a grown man, a man of brains and intelligence. Being with him right now is very important to me.

Now, I'm learning what a writer does to get ready for the next story or book. This spell between "yarns" has lasted for some three or four weeks now and, it seems to me, it is driving Bob up the wall. He's written some, he says, but before he gets half-way through a story, he destroys it. When that happens, he goes back to doing research, planning, thinking, dreaming. He calls it—filling the reservoir.

When I am with him, he talks a blue streak. I watch him closely, knowing he's trying to work out something in his mind. Other than learning about writing, I don't know what I see in him or why I still, in spite of everything, like the big lummox. Women certainly are the weaker sex; if they weren't, they wouldn't like the dern fools so much.

Some people might think that Bob is just loafing around and not working at anything at all. But that's not true. His mind is hard at work. Although he doesn't get too far from home, he drives around over the country, thinking of stories, talking them out loud to himself. He'll stop the car on some little hill, get out and walk around, listening to the wind blowing across the prairies. He says that on the wind he hears the tuneless little whistles the cowboys made as they rode, stretching themselves now and then, throwing a leg over the saddle horn to ride sideways to relieve the strain, being almost unseated when the horse shied at a prairie-dog or a rattle snake. These are the things he wants to write about . . . someday.

While he's riding around in the country, he may see an old man sitting on a porch by himself. Bob stops the car, gets out and visits with the old man, just to hear his stories of the country when it was new and fresh and uncluttered with the trappings of civilization.

He reads history, too—the history of this country, about the settling of it. The other night, he told me the story of a Negro slave, who escaped from his masters back in Alabama or Georgia, made his way out here to the wilds of Texas and became a cowboy. According to what Bob has been able to learn from his research, the man made a damn good cowboy.

Then Bob turned to me with a twinkle in his eyes. "You know, girl," he said whimsically. "You may be right. The only trouble with those fellows is that they're just human."

Bob's been to Comanche, Coleman and Santa Anna, hunting stories, old books. Anything he can find. He's been to newspaper offices to go through old files, hunting stories and the things that interested the people. He's filling the reservoir with these things, he says, so that someday soon, he can spend all his time writing about this country.

He's sold some stories about it. He brought me one the other day. I didn't read it all. Just the first paragraph. That paragraph was wonderful for setting the stage. It also hinted at some horror that was about to take place. Horror stories like that upset me. He also brought a recent magazine with a Conan story in it. I read two paragraphs in that one. I wasn't about to read of a lurid light with a human head in it. I'd hate to have a nightmare, wake up, and see a light with a woman's head in it!

I'm glad he's going to write more about this country. I think it's a great country too, and I'll look forward to reading his stories about it so long as they're not filled with horrible events. I like this modern day country with its schools, churches, dressing up on Saturday and going to town to shop and talk with friends. I like a party during the week. All such things that Bob says no self-respecting cowboy or Indian would have any use for.

He says that the hero he likes best is a cowboy who is a little bit larger than life. But, then, all of Bob's heroes are somewhat larger than life. His cowboys are dumb too. He says they are real live, flesh and blood characters whom he knows on a first name basis. I doubt that. Most of the characters he knows on a first name basis are Clyde Smith, Truett Vinson, Dave Lee and Lindsey Tyson. They're not big and dumb.

Though Bob is not one to mix with people, he'll start conversations with strangers when he's trying to find a story.

He also hunts through stores for books. He found one the other day in Brownwood that has him in ecstasy. It was written by a captain of the Texas Rangers, and is about the early exploits of the Rangers. The book is a reprint of one published years ago. Listening to Bob talk about it, I became a trifle upset because it sounds exactly like one that belonged to a friend of my family, and the trouble was that I had lost it! I was upset hearing about a reprint as well as upset because I had lost the book.

Besides reading old newspapers, Bob stands on the street corner or sits on a bench on the courthouse square to talk with some old men.

But Bob is not the only one in his family who is changing. So is Dr. Howard. I was standing in the drug store the other afternoon. Dr. Howard came up to the counter where I was standing instead of bolting out the door with a hasty hat tip and a gruff "good afternoon" thrown in my general direction. He was very friendly.

He didn't growl at me, glare at me, make me want to run. Instead, he seemed to be willing to talk with me, as though I were human. He even talked to me about how wonderful Bob was, as if he were giving me a sales pitch for Bob's benefit. I listened to the story of Bob and his dog, Patch. It is a wonderful story of a relationship of a boy and a dog *if* you wanted to write a story about it.

Dr. Howard told me how much Bob and his dog loved each other; how they ran over the countryside, walked together. When Bob rode a horse, Patch trotted happily behind him. Wherever Bob went, Patch went. Patch even shared Bob's food at the table and was a real companion. Boy and dog. I kept thinking about it and felt I *should* make a story out of it.

But there was something about Dr. Howard's story that bothered me.

As soon as the dog got sick and they knew it was going to die, Bob went to

Brownwood, so that he wouldn't see his dog in his last few days on earth before he went to whatever dog heaven there might be. When the dog died, Dr. Howard buried it somewhere on the back of the lot. Grass and flowers grew there, and the dog slept, undisturbed, near Bob.

Dr. Howard was proud of that, and, believe me, I didn't say a contrary word. But I listened silently, smiling, shaking my head and "uuuuhing," and "ooooohing" at what I hoped was the proper time. Dr. Howard is like Bob. I think a lot of things I don't say, a lot of slightly sarcastic remarks I don't make, or even remarks with a double meaning, and so I said good-bye to Dr. Howard, waved to Mrs. Smith, left the drugstore, and went on my way, wondering about Bob, wondering how he could write such blood-thirsty stories about Conan and some dope-head brawler. How could he write about horrible deaths and dying, yet be so afraid of a dog's death he could not even stay near? It didn't make sense somehow. But if Bob made sense, I probably wouldn't like the big ox.

Mrs. Howard, too, has changed, with a cloying sweetness that seems unnatural to her.

I called over to the Howard's the other day to tell Bob that I had missed his letter, but I wanted to let him know it was all right to come over. Mrs. Howard said, "Well, yes, I think he's here. Let me see." And in a few minutes, Bob blustered up to the telephone with a cheery, "Hello, there!" And I said, trying to pick my dumfounded self up, "It's too late to write you a letter, and so I thought I'd tell you it would be nice for you to come over."

Why is Mrs. Howard so nice these days? But perhaps last night I got part of the answer. Bob and I were riding around, and he was talking about cowboys and about some cowboy stories he'd written, or wanted to write.

"Cowboys rarely got married," he said, warming up to his subject. "These western heroes were men strong enough to resist a woman's wiles."

I just looked at him. At the moment, I wasn't particularly interested in cowboys' love life. But, to my surprise, it seemed, suddenly, to be quite an issue with Bob.

The cowboys were free. Free. Cowboys had to be free! They couldn't be tied down to a woman; a woman cramps a man's style. A man's got to be free—free to roam the world. Free to go where his imagination takes him. Free. Free to wander.

Free to come and go? If ever I had ridden with a man who was *not* free, it was Bob.

"A wife would handicap a man," Bob explained for the thousandth time.

I was not amused. To me, it was not a joke; it was an effort to convince himself. I knew that no wife could ever keep his feet so firmly planted in the plot of ground he resided on as his mother kept his. I wondered, as he raved and ranted about a woman's handicapping a man, killing his freedom, if he felt his mother's chains.

"Marriage with a man who dreamed of freedom wouldn't last, you know," he said, as if to impress it upon me. "A woman ties a man down, and a man's got to be free. He's got to get out and do a man's work. He's got to go. He'd have to leave her behind. So it's better for a man to stay free, never hinder himself with a wife. A man can't stand the ropes, the chains of marriage."

Finally, I got tired of listening to that baloney. "Well, don't worry about it, Bob," I said sweetly. "I wasn't planning to ask you to marry me any time soon. I like to be free too."

Then he said that was because I was a college-educated career girl and wanted to work instead of staying home and keeping house for some man. I pointed out that washing clothes, ironing, sweeping floors, cooking, and washing dishes wasn't exactly what I'd call taking life easy. He ignored that and went on worrying about the chains women put on men.

"A woman puts chains on a man, and in time he'll hate her for it." He raved on. "Whatever you tie down turns on you with hate."

I wondered if that held true so far as his mother was concerned.

Another Sunday, hectic and unpredictable, has come . . .
tarried awhile . . . and flown away . . .

I honestly feel that I am facing some kind of crisis in my life and I hope being with Bob will help me solve the problem. My question is: shall I keep on trying to write stories as I am now, or shall I put writing completely out of my mind and concentrate on teaching?

All my life, I have thought writing was what I wanted to do. Bob says I've had more encouragement than he had in the beginning, but the thing I would call encouragement would be selling something.

I like teaching. But teaching has its problems. As a speech teacher, I find that classroom work is not even half the job. I have very little free time, because I have to work coaching students, presenting plays and programs. Teaching English means grading papers . . . grading papers . . . grading papers. Teaching history . . . working like mad to stay ahead of some kid like J. H. Childs, who reads ahead all the time.

Before taking this job, I thought that I would be able to teach during the day and write at night and on weekends. It hasn't worked out that way. I don't even have time to write in my journals before one or two o'clock in the morning.

By failing to write in my journals, I'm missing a lot of things that contain the essence of story material. The other day, some of the teachers, including

Enid, had problems. Nat handled the situation beautifully. I should have written down everything that happened, but that night I was so tired I went to bed early.

Another thing that's bothering me now is that I want companionship and love. I know it's dumb, but I do. I'm afraid it would be possible to be more interested in Bob than I should be, what with his being so tied to his mother.

He has whipped the "between yarns" problem and is working away. We were supposed to go to a show in Cisco this afternoon, but he was in a jovial, expansive mood. I got so interested in talking about writing that I didn't want to see a show. We drank a coke; then headed out toward Eastland, Ranger, and on nearly as far as Mineral Wells.

We didn't keep to the highways, but we explored old country lanes and roads. We drove pretty far and had a lot of time for talking, even though the country looked desolate and uninspiring. Dry grass. Leafless trees. But it was not all grim and foreboding. The sun shone brightly at times. Here and there, a green cedar stood out gallantly from among its lifeless surroundings, the harbinger of hope for better things to come.

A sharp restless wind bent the nude trees and spindly grass. It felt good to be inside a car with the windows up to shut out the cold. The loneliness of the rocky hills we rode among, the infrequent cars on the road, all made human companionship inside the car more dear. Human nearness and understanding! That, I told myself, was the good thing.

Bob seemed as full of life and energy as if he hadn't been up all night reading and "banging out" a yarn. But if it hadn't been for Bob and his exuberance, I might have been listless and droopy. For several weeks now—with the exception of one or two nights—I hadn't been to bed before two or three o'clock in the morning. I'd been sitting up hunting material for my speech students, reading history, and, for pleasure, reading some of Henry James's novels. I was tired.

With all Bob's enthusiasm, joviality, he was still a little distant, and I couldn't keep from wondering what Mrs. Howard had done to cause it. I didn't have to wait too long to find out.

"Ever read *Coronado's Children?*" he asked.

"No," I said, "but I've heard of it. J. Frank Dobie's?"

"Yeah," he said. "It's a damn good book. You ought to read it."

He began talking about the settlement of Texas by the French and Spanish. The big point he made about some of the men from La Salle's company, who joined Indian tribes, painted their bodies like Indians, and lived among the Indians, puzzled me. He made another big point about Spanish adventurers who did the same thing.

He turned and looked at me, grinning. "By God, I went to Santa Anna again the other day. I went up on those little hills that the townspeople call the

Santa Anna Mountains. I walked around and looked out over the country. I could imagine an Indian brave coming there, bronzed body, sitting on his horse, watching the settlers move in. I can imagine more than that, too. I can imagine an Indian coming into town, posing as a white man, being caught, and strung up by his heels."

Then I thought he changed the subject. He wanted to know if I were interested in writing about some of the Indians who used to roam this part of the country. I told him that I wasn't the least bit interested in writing about Indians. He said he thought writers carried the lives of their former ancestors in their memories, memories of which they were not consciously aware, but which made wonderful stories.

"These memories probably go back a thousand years." He looked at me half laughing, half serious. "Have you ever read something in ancient history and suddenly felt that you knew that place? That you'd seen that event happen? Did you ever have a vivid picture of some incident in history that involved Indians, and you felt you had seen it, knew all about it?"

Since I didn't know what he was getting at, in my innocent ignorance, thinking how marvelous my imagination was, I said, "Oh, yes, I can always see a forest and an Indian girl, stepping out from among the trees into an open space and looking across the prairie."

"Now, there!" He banged the steering wheel excitedly. "By God, that's one of your ancestral memories. That's what you ought to write about. That's your story. You listen to that. Dream about it. Let it come through, and you've got the right story. The story of an Indian girl! Maybe she's in love with a brave, and he's gone off to war."

I was amazed at how enthusiastic he was about my ancestral memory. "I just don't understand," I said, interrupting a long tirade about ancestors who passed on their experiences to those of us who were still living. "Why should you think I have an ancestral memory—if there is any such thing—about an Indian?"

"Didn't you tell me your father was mistaken for an Indian?"

"Well, yes," I said, "but that was probably because he was tall, black headed, dark complexioned, and sunburned. The old man who stopped him was searching for an Indian, whether or not one was there. He was an old man. His exciting days with the Texas Rangers were over, and he was trying to relive them."

Bob shifted his weight to get more comfortable and pushed his hat to the back of his head. "Well, he had to look a whole lot like an Indian to be stopped on the street and accused of being one."

"Oh, I don't know," I said quickly. Then I suppose I just went right on cutting my own throat. "When I was a kid and got sunburned, my cousin, Neil, was always teasing me and calling me an Indian. He used to say that Mother could take me to Oklahoma, and they'd give me Indian land. But—"

"That's just what I thought," Bob interrupted. "That's it exactly. You remember during the Christmas holidays my mother and I saw you in Woolworth's?"

"Yes," I said, beginning to be suspicious.

Bob nodded. "Well, my mother asked me if you didn't have a lot of Indian blood, maybe as much as half-Indian."

All I could do was just sit there, staring at him. Something was about to make sense.

"My mother used to live in Oklahoma," he went on. "You can't fool her about Indians. But she didn't know any of these strong, silent, noble savages. Those she knew were dirty, thieving rascals who came around at night, stealing, burning, murdering. She saw terrible things when she was a girl. She saw white people tortured and murdered. She knew of young girls being kidnapped by Indians. She can tell an Indian when she sees one, and she thought you looked more Indian than white."

I simply could not believe it. If I had had enough breath, and if I had known how, I would have given the loudest war whoop ever heard in this part of Texas. The very idea! I thought: well, that woman! She doesn't like Indians. She doesn't like me. She has painted me as an Indian!

Suddenly, it was so funny to me I laughed. I just threw back my head and laughed. Bob frowned and began to look belligerent.

"Bob," I said, when I could get my breath. "I don't know why your mother would think I look like an Indian except that I have dark eyes, dark skin, and dark hair."

"It's the shape of your face," he said complacently. "Do you know how much Indian blood you do have?"

"No, of course not," I said. "Not enough to count. My father's grand-mother had some Indian blood, but not enough to make any difference. Besides, she was only one of eight of my great-grandparents. The other seven would far outweigh her contribution to my life."

"Not necessarily," Bob said positively. "Sometimes we get what we call a 'throw-back.' It's the thing that happens when Negroes marry white persons. One day, you'll get a Negro child, no matter how white the parents are."

I didn't know exactly what he thought that made me, but there was one thing I was sure of. That day in Woolworth's I had wondered what his mother would do to get rid of me. Now I knew. She had convinced Bob of two things: first, that a wife handicaps a man; and, second, and more important, that I was an Indian woman!

Sure, she could be nice to me and let me talk to Bob over the telephone now. She'd already done away with me. I was part of a mongrel race, not a pure "Irish-Gaelic" race! For a moment, I seriously considered telling Bob what I thought of him and his mother and their mongrel race, but I didn't. We were a long way from Cross Plains, and I had on high heels. Besides, I wasn't Indian enough not to be afraid in this deserted country.

"We are part of our earliest ancestors," he chortled enthusiastically. "Our blood, our genes, our brains are still part of the flesh and blood and brains of our remotest ancestors. We never use all our brain capacity, not even geniuses like Einstein. And stored deep in our brain cells are memories that go back to our earliest human experiences. We are human beings because our ancestors were human beings. Now, by God, girl, that's one thing that persuades me the Bible is right. I can think of a lot of things, but that man was once a monkey I cannot believe."

I could buy the idea that we had human beings in our ancestry. That was simply reasonable, but that the experiences they had were still in our brains, I didn't believe. Bob was carried away with the presence of our early ancestors, and so I let him talk. I didn't listen closely. I just kept quiet and wondered if any woman could ever break his mother's grip on him? Would it be worth the effort?

Then I realized that he was talking about something else.

"By God, girl." His voice boomed out cheerfully. "In this writing game, you have to read as much or more than you write. You've got to read the magazines you want to write for and the ones you *do* write for." He stopped and looked at me, smiling. "Do you read the confessions?"

I shrugged my shoulders. "I don't read them from cover to cover and practically memorize them the way you do the magazines you want to write for. I don't like the confessions much."

"Well, for God's sake," he laughed. "How in the hell do you think you can write for them? You have to read 'em to write 'em. At least, I do."

"Oh, I buy a confession now and then," I admitted. "When I find something in it that looks halfway interesting, I skim through it. I get the jist of what the story's about."

"That doesn't seem to me to be the way to do," Bob said with a touch of amusement in his voice. "I mean it wouldn't work for me. I don't pretend to be able to tell you what to do. What works for one won't work for another. It just seems to me that you've got to study the magazines you want to write for. I mean study them. Tear each yarn apart. Put it together again. Try to figure out why that one sold and yours didn't."

He stopped talking for a minute, reached over and playfully pulled my hat down over one of my eyes. Before I could hit him, he went on talking.

"Now, a friend of mine wrote a yarn a few years ago. It was one of the greatest yarns I ever read. I think about it a lot. Sometimes when I finish a yarn and am getting another one ready, I think about that yarn of his, and why I think it was good. Sometimes I sit at my typewriter and think about it. I think about it on my way to and from the post office. Why, girl, I even think about that yarn when I go out to milk the cow. As I think about it, I begin to have my own thoughts and ideas. Maybe there was something I believe about life that he didn't say."

I caught at the phrase "believe about life." Bob went on talking about how great that yarn was, but I was deep in my own thoughts. Maybe Bob had put his finger on what was wrong with my stories. Most of them were pretty thin. I could see that now. I wrote: Girl sees boy; girl wants boy; girl gets boy. What was I saying about life? Was I saying that a woman in love always gets her man? That wasn't true and I knew it. I listened to Bob a minute. He was telling me about the yarn his friend had written, and I was sure he was repeating it word for word!

"Bob," I interrupted him. "Do you mean that writer friend of yours—that Lovecourt—"

"Craft," he said emphatically. "Lovecraft."

I controlled an impulse to laugh. "I can never think of his name," I said.

"Lovecraft," he repeated, still emphatic. "One of the greatest writers of our time. Now, girl, I'll bring some of the things he's written for you to read if—"

"Oh, no," I said hurriedly. "That's perfectly all right. I don't want—I don't really have time to read very much right now, with teaching and trying to get kids ready for interscholastic speech contests."

He looked at me without speaking as if he were trying to make up his mind if I meant what I said.

"All I wanted to know was what kind of comment about life does he make?" I asked. "And I want to know what kind of comment you make about life in your Conan stories."

Bob began to talk about good and evil in life. He said that life was always a struggle between good and evil, and people like to read about that struggle. He said that even though the Conan sagas were set in a prehistoric time, Conan often faced the same kind of evil and decadence we faced today.

He said that he wasn't about to write those psychological yarns that sophisticated, half-educated people went for. No. He wrote for readers who wanted evil to be something big, horrible, but still something a barbarian like Conan could overcome. Evil could be found in another person who was about to kill you, or it could be found in a different race of people, a witch, a ghost, or some manifestation of the supernatural.

"These damn pseudo-scientific writers of today who try to explore a man's inner mind ain't worth a damn. Evil, they say, lurks inside a man. I hate the damn bastards who write stuff like that, because every decent impulse a man has is given a dirty meaning by these damn sons-of-bi- guns. A man loves his poor old sick mother, and those damn bastards call it the 'Oedipus complex.' A doctor goes to see an attractive sick woman, and it's portrayed as lust."

"I think a person might write a story that was psychological and not have those things in it," I said, trying to find an answer to some of my questions. "I read 'Daisy Miller' by Henry James. It's bothered me the way you say that Lovecourt-craft's story bothered you. There was evil in that story, I suppose, and maybe what you'd call a decadent society, but I did not see ghosts after I read it. I believe Daisy Miller was just too dumb or too selfish to care a hang about what other people thought."

"That doesn't seem dumb to me," Bob said seriously. "It makes damn good sense not to let other people's opinions affect you, or the way you want to live. My mother's always told me that a man has to stand alone, if he wants to accomplish something."

For once, what his mother thought and said didn't matter to me. I wanted to figure out what "comment about life" in stories made them good.

"I'm not talking about people who are just independent and able to live their lives in their own way without worrying about it," I said, "but with Daisy Miller, it was different."

Bob glanced at me but didn't say anything. I went on, slowly, "Daisy was an American girl traveling in Europe with her mother and little brother. Because of their money, they came in contact with a class of people who had money too. These people were a shallow lot with rules and regulations that were pretty silly. But it doesn't really matter whether the rules were silly or not. To be a part of that certain social group, Daisy had to live up to those rules and regulations."

I stopped for a moment because Bob was reacting almost angrily to what I was saying, not to me personally, but to the ideas which, I gathered, he did not like. I waited a moment, but he didn't say anything. He just ran off the road and had to give his attention to getting back on again.

"If Daisy had lived up to the rules and regulations of the social group," I said, "she would have had love, respect, and the social position her money would have given her."

"Maybe she thought the price for society's acceptance was too high to pay. That seems to indicate a pretty strong person to me."

I shrugged my shoulders. "To me, she seemed too dumb to know good from bad."

Bob exploded. "My God, I'm surprised at you, Novalyne." He always called me Novalyne when he was mad. "You're saying that a person should give up being an individual if his ideas or ways conflict with what society calls good or bad! Is that what you're trying to say in what you write? Well, hell. It's no wonder your yarns don't sell."

I laughed ruefully. "I guess I don't know what I'm saying."

He relaxed and started to say something, but we rounded a corner just then. Down the road in front of us, a car was pulled over to the side of the road. A couple of men seemed to be working on a tire, pumping it up. Another man behind the car was hunched over, intent on something in his hands. There was barely time for me to take it all in. Bob speeded past the car throwing gravel and dirt high. I grabbed for the seat and the side of the car to steady myself. As we flew past, I had a glimpse of shocked faces. The man at the back was holding an innertube. We were well past them before Bob slowed the car down.

"Wow!" was all I could say.

Bob was unperturbed. "You have to be careful out in this country," he said, taking his hat off and scratching his head. "You never know when you see a car like that whether it's someone needing help or someone ready to hold you up and take your life and your money."

It was my time to keep quiet. "This country out here was settled by a lot of people wanting to get away from a crime they'd committed back in the old states," he said. "A lot of bad men came out here to get away from the law, liked the country, and settled down. You have to be careful. People might not be what they seem."

He talked on about the bad men who had come to Texas. I didn't listen. I was still bothered by an idea that was mixed up with Bob and Henry James, though two more unlike writers had never before inhabited the earth. But it seemed to me they had a philosophy in common.

It did not occur to Daisy Miller to accept the ordinary rules and regulations which would have given her the life she wanted. What about Bob? When he refused to come to my programs, refused to mix with people, to come to a funeral of a fellow citizen, was he selfish like Daisy? What perversity in him kept him from real life? Did he have no sense of the moral obligation to a neighbor? Was this what James was saying? What happens to a man when he will not or cannot accept what he finds in life?

Then I realized that Bob had asked me a question and I hadn't heard him. I jumped, turned and looked at him. He was staring at me with a quizzical expression on his face.

I decided to admit I wasn't listening. "I'm sorry. I didn't hear what you said."

He grinned. "I asked if you were trying to write anything now?" His voice was as soft and pleasant as usual. "Are you still keeping diaries?"

I didn't want to tell him that teaching was almost all I was doing. An idea flashed into my head, full blown. "I'm thinking about writing a novel about teachers in a small Texas town."

He frowned. "You have to be careful with something like that."

"Why?"

"You can know too much about a subject," he said. "It can be too close to you. You're right that you need to know what you are writing about, but you also have to be objective about it. Can you be objective about teaching? If you can, you'll be all right, but the chances are you can't be. The truth is that you're not objective about anything."

He grinned one of his very nice grins that makes me melt and think he's great. His eyes were twinkling as he went on, "Maybe ten years from now . . . twenty . . . you might write about teaching in a small Texas town in the year of our Lord, 1935. At that time, you'll be in a big school somewhere else, far enough away from all this to be objective."

I took a deep breath. I didn't want to be in a big school somewhere. I wanted to be right there in Cross Plains ten years from now, with everything exactly as it is now.

I looked at Bob; he was still looking at me, half smiling, half fearful.

"I think I can be objective," I said slowly. "School teaching in a small town is real life. We teachers have all kinds of troubles: those we bring to school, because we are who we are; troubles with the kids, with each other, the town, the Board of Trustees, the boss. If we don't know real life before we come to a small Texas town to teach, it doesn't take us long to learn. I'd like to keep things here the same, but I know they won't stay that way. Enid may leave at the end of this year, and I feel miserable about that."

"Why is she leaving?" Bob asked sympathetically.

"She has the funny idea that she ought to be paid as much as a football coach."

Bob laughed dryly. "My God, how can she be so naive? Doesn't she know that in this rotting civilization of ours that nobody cares a damn about whether or not kids learn ideas? Doesn't she know nobody has time for literature, grammar and history? My God, girl, she's more naive than you are."

A car was coming toward us, and he gave his attention to that for a moment. He always makes a production out of meeting or passing a car. I watched the proceedings indifferently.

"The more I think of it," he said, "the more I think you ought to write a novel about teachers in a small Texas town. You could write about a pretty young teacher going into a small town and falling in love with one of her pupils, the way you did with Mark!"

That made me furious. "I wish you would try to understand how I feel about Mark," I said angrily. "I'm not in love with him. Not the least bit."

"You talk about him all the time," Bob said laconically.

"I do not!" I almost shouted. I was so upset I couldn't sit still. I moved around, holding myself to keep from hitting him. I turned so that I could stare at Bob, hoping to make him nervous. At that moment, I thought if I could say something to hurt him and upset him, I'd do it.

"I guess I am attracted to Mark," I said defensively. "But not in the way you imply with your dirty mind. In our school, we've got some of the nicest, most talented kids in the United States, and I want you to know that I have a heart like a hotel, room for all of them. But I do have to admit, even among those talented, intelligent, good kids, there's one that stands out. One who seems a little different from the others. I can't describe it. I can't even tell you what it is, but it's a kind of—Well, a kind of—of what James Barrie would call a 'sort of bloom' on him. Such a kid is at peace with himself and with other people too. Maybe I envy a kid like that. I don't know. But it is that special quality about a kid that makes me want to give him something he'll take with him the rest of his life. Something that will make him a better person because I gave him encouragement, help, or interest."

"You're a dreamer, girl," Bob said, and suddenly there was anger in his voice. "I've said it before. You're an impossible dreamer. Don't you know that Mark will forget everything you've tried to teach him? Don't you know a year from now, he won't even remember the name of that little brown-eyed, dark-skinned teacher who gave him her heart?"

I felt as if I'd had a bucket of water poured over me. I turned around and sat down in the seat, leaned against my door and stared out the window. The talk about writing had taken a strange turn. I thought about Mark and the other kids in my classes who were talented and smart. I wanted them and Mark, too, to be better people because I'd helped them in some way.

I thought of Henry James's short novel: "The Turn of the Screw." Was I like the governess in that story? Was I an ineffectual, bungling, do-gooder who couldn't even save myself, and, therefore, unable to save someone else? I couldn't speak. Maybe my dreams were the kind of nightmares Bob and his friend wrote about. I felt the cold wind as if the door were not shut against it. I was like the burned out world around me. The brown, sparse grass. The gaunt, bare trees.

Bob busied himself turning the car around to head back toward Cross Plains. The car lurched with the sharpness of his turn. He bumped against the steering wheel. He was still angry and so involved with his own private world, he was not thinking of me. Certainly he was not aware that he had hurt my feelings. He began to push his point relentlessly.

"You don't think, really, down in your heart, that what you say or do is going to make any difference to Mark five years from now?"

"I suppose not," I said miserably. I wanted to tell Bob that every teacher wanted to feel that she could have some influence on her pupils, but I couldn't.

"I suppose you're going to write a love story—a woman in love with a—" He stopped. His eyes were stormy, angry, and uncertain.

Did he resent my writing a love story? I wondered. What else would account for the troubled look in his eyes?

"In a way, I suppose I want to make it a love story," I said, thinking and planning as I talked. "But I want the woman to have a man-sized man to love. I was thinking that someone—a young woman—from another state who had had an illegitimate child—"

"Why are you always thinking about illegitimate children?" he asked. "How many illegitimate children have you had?"

"A dozen," I snapped. "One every thirty days."

He grinned and relaxed a little. "I suppose if any woman could do it, you could."

I was too hurt and mad to care what he said. "A girl who lived on a farm near us had an illegitimate child, and her life was horrible," I said. "I even argued with Mammy about this. I think the price she had to pay for her mistake was too high for any human being to pay. When I was sixteen, a girl I knew had a child. I think of those things to write about because there was drama in their lives. Drama. Pain. Heartache. And always the question: What happens next? I can imagine a school teacher, coming into a strange little Texas town and finding among the pupils, a talented, smart child with a great personality, and she could wonder if it were hers. All the problems a teacher faces would be compounded and more poignant in that situation."

"Well, now, by God, you may have something there," Bob said becoming enthusiastic. "You go right ahead and write your novel. Who in the hell am I to say whether it would go or not? I'm always shooting my damn mouth off. It's a goddam habit of mine."

I didn't smile, and I didn't answer. We rode in silence for a while. He stopped the car on a small hill. "Now, girl," he said, with an effort at humor, "now there . . . that's a beautiful sunset if I do say so myself."

I smiled at that. I'd heard it so many times before. Both of us were in our own separate worlds. My problem was still with me: To teach or to write?

I looked at the sloping hill, the clump of leafless trees, the dead weeds and brush. I could see no reason why I should not write stories that sold instead of spending my days and nights teaching pupils who would not even remember me. I had qualifications for writing—qualifications that Bob did not have, yet he had learned. He was brilliant. I could give him that without rancor. But I had not found it difficult to learn when I wanted to. I had another qualification that differed from Bob's. I knew what it was to love someone so much that I woke up nights and could see the way he smiled, the way he looked when he said, "I'll be over tomorrow at seven." I could still hear him laugh. I could hear my own laughter.

This was different from Bob. He was a child where love was concerned. In the Conan stories I'd glanced through, Conan treated women with great deference. But there was no boldness about him, no consciousness of his power to attract and hold the interest and love of a woman.

I turned and looked at Bob. He was lost in dreams. But I could not let all that had happened today be forgotten. Although he'd hurt me, I no longer had any desire to hurt him.

"Bob," I said, choosing my words carefully. "This afternoon you've hurt my feelings twice. You—"

He looked so startled, I stopped, confused. "Why, Novalyne, what did I say? I—God, I didn't mean to hurt your feelings. I've been shooting my damn mouth off, but I didn't mean to say anything to hurt you. My God, I—"

I couldn't stand it. I interrupted him and went doggedly on, trying to make a point. "I'm not in love with Mark. Certainly not the way you think. I—Well, I think he's talented. I wanted so terribly much to help him. I—"

"I'm sorry," Bob said contritely. "I guess, I've just never seen another teacher like you. All the teachers I had didn't give a damn in hell whether the kids in their classes lived or died or whether they learned or not. You care so damn much, I couldn't understand it."

I was pleased and displeased . . . still uncertain what to do, but I had to go on. "Another thing, Bob, I'm not an Indian. I'm much more English, Irish, and Welsh. When you talk about good ancestors, Mammy had a few too. There were lords and royal lines in the Landrum and Reed families, but I think it's crazy to talk about it. Mammy says if you're what you ought to be, you don't have to tell people. If you're not, all the talk in the world won't convince them."

He looked agitated, throwing his hat into the back seat and running his fingers through his hair. "Well, goddam, there's nothing wrong with being an Indian. I—Hell, there were some damn good Indians. Trouble is they got mixed up with the Spanish and French who came over here. Hell, I'm sorry. I sure won't call you that again if it hurts you. Hell, I feel like a louse now. I sure as hell didn't want to hurt your feelings."

He sounded so upset I stopped trying to tell him how I felt.

"Okay," I said. "But please don't call me an Indian again or accuse me of being in love with some young kid."

His eyes were large, and they held the shadows I'd begun to dread. His smile lighted his face, but didn't touch his eyes. He pushed the hair back off his face.

"I'm sorry," His voice was almost a whisper. "I'm a clumsy ox who doesn't deserve to have a school teacher put up with his ravings."

I laughed, then, to let him know that everything was all right again. I had learned something about writing this afternoon, but I'd learned more about Bob and about myself than I had about writing. I didn't want him to put his arms around me or touch me, and so I turned and looked back at the sunset. The red, gold and orange were fading to a soft gray, like love on a cold winter day.

When the hounds of spring are on winter's traces,
The mother of months in meadow or plain
Fills the shadows and windy places
With lisp of leaves and ripple of rain . . .
                                        . . . Swinburne . . .

When I left school this afternoon, I was so far down in the dumps that I thought Bob was right—the world was doomed.

Things hadn't gone right at school. I was mad at my boss. At that moment, I didn't like Louise, and I wanted to sock Enid in the jaw. I wish she'd shut up about those damn papers. As if that weren't enough, I was working like mad, trying to get my students ready for Interscholastic League meet, even though Mr. Williams hadn't seemed to notice!

I walked slowly, glancing up now and then at the slate-gray, dark, threatening clouds. It had rained hard today, but I hoped it wouldn't rain tonight while Bob and I were riding around. Yet because of the rain, I felt a new warmth in the air. Spring was coming. Beside the walk, little clumps of green spindly grass pushed up through the mud.

As I picked my way slowly over a section of broken, uneven sidewalk, suddenly, from one of the plain, nondescript houses, a hollow, throaty, gasping voice of a woman broke the stillness.

"Help. He-e-elp. Help, somebody."

On this dark, dismal day, that gasping voice congealed my blood. It was a perfect scene for one of Bob's horror stories. I stopped, turned, and looked back at the house.

A few feet inside the front door, a dim and eerie daylight silhouetted a large, slow moving woman. One hand was pressed against her heart, the other was beckoning to me.

"Come help me," she said in a quavering voice, as if she didn't have the breath to make a strong sound. "Help! I can't do anything with him. Help me. I think he's dying. Come help me."

The mood I was in . . . the day . . . that strange, misshapen silhouette inside the door frightened me. I didn't know what to do.

The woman called again but with less urgency. "Help. Come in. Help."

I took a few steps toward her and stopped when she turned her head, looking back into the room behind her. What could I do? What was I supposed to do? My mouth felt dry, and my heart pounded. I tried again to go toward her. I stopped. I couldn't help. I just couldn't! Someone else—

I whirled and bolted down the street as fast as I could, without stopping until I got to Smith's drug store.

Mrs. Smith hurried to me. "What in the world is wrong? You look like you've seen a ghost. What's wrong?"

A nauseous sickness swept over me. I'd run from a strange, helpless woman! I blurted out I was scared—too scared to help a woman who needed help. My words hurt me. "Down the street, a woman came to the door of a house and called for help."

Mrs. Smith grabbed my arm and shook me. "Which house? Which house?"

I described it, the woman, the call for help. "I didn't go in," I moaned. "I didn't help her."

"Good thing!" Mrs. Smith snapped. She dropped her hand off my arm and hurried back to Dr. Howard's office. Seconds later, he bolted out the door with his little black bag. Too preoccupied to tip his hat.

I wanted to talk with Mrs. Smith, to ask her about the woman and the house. But customers had come into the store, and Mrs. Smith was busy talking to them, getting things off the shelves, putting them back for other things. My breathing returned to normal. I left the store and came home.

When Bob came tonight, I asked him if he knew what had happened. But, evidently, his dad had said nothing about the incident, for when I mentioned it, Bob wanted to know from me what had happened. I described the scene to him. He seemed upset. "Which house was that? Which house?"

I told him as carefully as I could.

"Well, don't you ever stop and go in that house," he said brusquely. "I don't care how many times that woman calls for help; you go right on and do as you did today. Run. Find my dad as soon as you can, but whatever you do, don't you go in there and try to help."

"I feel terrible because I didn't go in and try to help someone calling for help."

"I know," he said simply. "A person, especially a woman, calls for help, and you feel you've got to do something. But if you were a man, I'd still tell you to be careful. I'd tell you to call my dad. That's the kind of help she needed. A doctor. Listen. I sure don't want you going into that house, trying to help."

"Why?"

"I just don't want you going in there trying to help those people, that's all. You remember that. If you ever pass there again and the woman calls for help, just keep going. Get my dad."

The rain was beginning to fall, and the water was trickling down the window on my door. Yet I saw more than rain. I could still see that dim, bulky figure of a woman, a hand on her breast, the other beckoning to me to come in. I could still hear that throaty, breathy cry for help. Now, a new fear was insinuating itself into me. Suppose someone dear to me needed my help. Could I help them? Would I run to someone else?

In my mind, I went over the incident, remembering things to try to erase my guilt. The first thing Mrs. Smith had said was "Good thing!" Now, Bob was telling me I'd done the right thing by running to town and telling Mrs. Smith. Were they just trying to help me? Was Bob trying to make me feel less guilty?

Their justification that I had gotten help didn't answer my own personal questions. Why had I run? I felt pity and compassion for the woman. Why couldn't I help?

Bob's voice brought me back to the moment. "Mrs. Smith knew you shouldn't go in."

"But nobody has told me why not."

He put his arm about my shoulders. "I don't think that's all that's wrong with you tonight, is it?" he asked. "What's wrong? Tell ol' Bob."

I made a feeble attempt to joke. "Old Bob? How did you get so old so soon?"

He laughed. "I'm in my 'sere and yellow leaf,' girl. I've been around this world a millenium or two. Who knows? The Egyptians used to believe you kept on being born over and over until you got all your work and dreams taken care of. I've been here before. I know that, but I still haven't got things all straightened out and in the proper order yet. In some future time, some remote, undreamed of millenium, I'll be back again. I'll work my damn fingers to the bone, for I've got to keep looking, until I find what I have to find. Then it will be peace and quiet for all eternity."

I shivered, and his arm tightened about my shoulders. "That's a crazy thing to think," I said.

"Who knows?" He took his arm from my shoulders. "Can you prove we haven't lived before?"

I didn't want to try.

The lights from an approaching car sparkled in the tiny rivulets on the windshield. The car passed and the cloudy, murky night settled about us. I sat still on my side of the car and listened to Bob. He, too, was in a strange and different mood tonight. Whether he was trying to talk about things to get my mind away from the harrowing experience of the afternoon or whether he was just in a mood to talk glibly of the various lives he'd lived before, I didn't know.

He told me about the cold, bleak North he'd lived in where the "Little People" had once bound him and held him prisoner, until by super strength and cunning he managed to escape. He talked about Atlantis, how he'd walked the narrow, rocky streets. In the stories again tonight, there was the girl whom he had loved and been willing to die for, but whom, in every different age and place, he'd lost to his best friend. He still hoped, he said, that in some future, kinder millenium, he'd find his girl again.

But I couldn't listen tonight as I usually did. School problems and a strange, bulky woman calling for help were on my mind.

Finally, I said, "Things aren't going well at school."

As if waiting for a chance to talk of other things, he turned to me, all interest and concern. "What's wrong? Has Nat-Brain been giving you trouble?"

"Yes, and no," I answered morosely.

He grinned. "Answers like that are so damned explicit."

"I wish I had a pretty figure like Jimmie or Louise," I said.

"Well, hell. Ain't nothing so damn wrong with you," he said quickly. "Man don't have to look at you twice to see you're a girl."

Even a silly compliment like that will make a girl feel better. But my troubles were big.

"When Nat hired me, he made it a point I was to teach speech and dramatics. I was supposed to have charge of school programs and plays."

"You're always at it. Seems to me you've been doing a pretty damn good job. How many programs have you put on?"

"A play, a stunt night, and some assembly programs."

I explained that since my programs had been so successful, other teachers wanted to direct plays too, but I thought people who weren't trained in dramatics would do more harm than good. Nat didn't agree. He said no matter how good your speech teacher was, you couldn't let her have charge of everything. Other teachers had to be allowed to do things they felt they had to do. He didn't think schools were just to teach kids to act because they'd never be actors.

"Sounds like him," Bob said harshly.

His sympathy inspired me to tell him more of my troubles. "I tried to tell Mr. Williams the best speakers were at ease in front of an audience, and there was no better way to train speakers than to give them an opportunity to act with restraint and skill."

"What did Lame-Brain say to that?"

I sighed. I hadn't meant for Bob to be so down on Mr. Williams. I still appreciate him as a great school man.

I looked at the little streams of water running down the windshield and went on miserably. "I've been working on declamations, oratory, poetry, and extemp speaking contests after school every day until barely time to get home for supper. Then I go back at night for dramatics club. I've been trying to find a good one-act play for the one-act play contests."

Bob was sympathetic. "Have you found one?"

"I think so," I said with a surge of hope. "It has four characters, and I have four great kids to do it: Dixie Little, Jennie Laura Jackson, Melvin Plaucke, and Jimmie Settle. The play is 'Judge Lynch' and it says something I think should be said. The Dallas Little Theatre under Dr. Oliver Hinsdell won the national Little Theatre competition with it."

"You're pretty interested in the Dallas Little Theatre, ain't you?"

"Sure. Dr. Hinsdell was great; he set standards in theatre for all of us to try to live up to."

"Nat doesn't appreciate that?" Bob sounded as horrified as, at that moment, I wanted him to be. However, in my heart, I had the feeling that Mr. Williams heckled me because it made me work harder, but tonight, I was down in the dumps.

"I'm not sure Nat really knows how hard I'm working for County Meet," I went on. "He said yesterday other teachers were working, and with the chorus teacher—that's Louise—working on chorus and quartettes, we'd win those events, but he guessed he'd hope for the best in the speech events."

Bob clenched his jaw. "Do you want me to beat him up? You mean he doesn't know how hard you're working?"

I wasn't certain, and so I shook my head. "No, and I didn't tell him either."

Bob muttered something under his breath which I figured I'd be just as well off if I didn't hear. We rode in silence a while. Both of us were watching the rain, the road, the way the car lights cut the darkness.

It came as a little shock to me that we were already in Baird and were turning around. "Right now, before County Meet, everybody in Cross Plains hates everybody in Baird."

Bob laughed. "They must be pretty good."

"Yeah. They win a lot. Nat wants to beat them so bad he can taste it."

The few lights of Baird disappeared behind us as we drove back toward Cross Plains. I felt better, but I still hadn't gotten over my jealousy of Louise. "If I were as pretty as Louise," I said enviously, "Nat wouldn't be so hard on me."

"Pretty," Bob gasped. "What are you talking about, girl? You're pretty as hell. Why, girl, you're the *meanest* pretty there is."

I stared at him. "What do you mean?"

"Why, you're a *mean* pretty," he said. "Like tonight when you came to the door, I thought to myself, 'God, she's pretty.' Last Sunday, when you had on that sassy hat and was all fixed up, I thought, 'My God, she ain't pretty; she's beautiful.' Saturday a week ago, I saw you at the post office and thought, 'Now, how in the hell did I ever think that girl was pretty?' I just ask you, who would want a woman to be the same pretty every time he saw her? Hell. Not me. A man wants variety. He wants a woman who is beautiful once in a while, pretty once in a while, and downright ugly twice a year. My God, variety is the spice of life. A woman who is *mean* pretty is always different. That's what every woman ought to be."

I could feel a great weight lifting off my shoulders. A mean pretty? A woman who's different! I'd never have thought of a thing like that. I looked at Bob, intent on the road, and I liked him a lot! He was good looking in a big, substantial way. But more than that, he was understanding. A good writer. He always knows the right thing to say to make a girl feel good. Important.

And—Yes. Beautiful.

On a day that started off all bad, a compliment like that could last a long, long time.

Saturday night . . .
"All alone by the telephone . . ."

Late this afternoon, Bob called and broke a date with me for tonight. His mother, he said, was ill and he felt that he'd better stay home and take care of her to be sure that she got her medicine and to be with her, in case she needed anything. I wondered where Dr. Howard was.

Bob apologized for breaking our date, saying that he had been looking forward to being with me again tonight. He wanted to know how I was feeling, and if I were still worried about school. He said if I'd just say the word, he'd bash Nat's head in.

I thanked him for his interest but expressed doubt that the question could be solved with bashing a superintendent's head in. I said that I was fine and I'd been looking forward to being with him tonight because he had said such wonderful things last night. He didn't say anything for a moment, and I began to wonder if he'd left the phone. I said, "Bob. Bob."

He said he was trying to think of some way he could take care of his obligations and still come over to see me, but he guessed he'd better stay home; however, if his mother was all right, and if I'd let him come tomorrow, he'd be over about one-thirty or two.

To me, Sunday afternoons are a lot longer than Saturday nights, and so I said I'd look forward to seeing him and I did hope his mother got along all right. The truth is I doubt she's really sick.

The funny thing is I'm not too disappointed that Bob didn't come tonight. Maybe I should be angry enough to tell him to go jump in the lake, but I actually felt relieved along with my irritation that his dad couldn't take care of his son's mother.

I wrote some on my novel—a couple of chapters. Then I got out my college English book "Canby and Others," as Mrs. Wright used to call it, and did some exercises in it, describing the days, people, events and their effect on me.

Now, it's nearly two a.m., and I've had a nice pleasant evening at home.

When Ethel went to bed at ten, she said, "Oh, my, my. Don't worry about me. I'll go right off to sleep."

But I didn't want to take a chance on keeping her awake. I put up my typewriter, gathered up notebooks, pencils and my English book and came into the bathroom.

I still keep thinking about Bob. I wonder why Mrs. Howard would let him stay home tonight and break a date with me. I wonder why Dr. Howard can't take care of his sick wife. Does he think, as I do, that she's not sick? Isn't a twenty-nine year old man like Bob supposed to be free to be with a young woman if he wants to?

Once we walked in the rain together . . .

Spring is in the air. The days have been warmer and the little clumps of green grass are beginning to grow together to make a soft green carpet. The trees are alive with budding leaves. People predict that we'll have spring-like weather until the trees are fully budded; then it'll come a freeze and the trees and fruit will be killed. It's happened like that before in this country.

I am enjoying the warm weather, and I don't mind the rains we've've had the last few days. I'm working extra hours at school, but it's a time for feeling good, being cheerful and feeling as if a new world has come along. I'll worry about the freeze killing things when it comes, and I'll try not to worry about school.

Bob came today. Since I wanted to go to Brownwood, we drove over. We talked about going to a show, but decided against it. His mother is pretty sick, and he's worried about leaving her too long. My mother is making me a new dress. Really, we didn't have time for a show. On our way to Brownwood, we ran into a couple of light showers. Not much rain. It left a few drops of water hanging on to the windshield.

Bob was interested in talking about Mencken. Several years ago, Mencken wrote something in which he was most uncomplimentary toward Southerners. Bob read the article, and it made him so furious he never got completely over it, no matter what else Mencken wrote. In a way, I can understand how Bob feels. Things like that aggravate me. Where you live and the people you know are important to you. When you hear bad things said about them, it's as if someone had berated your own family. But where Bob gets really upset, I pass it off facetiously by saying, as I said to Bob, "You'll have to forgive Mencken for thinking such things as that about Southerners. After all, he hasn't met me yet."

Bob was amused. "Yeah. He doesn't know what he's missing." Then he said he guessed you could expect something like that from a damn yankee.

"Good heavens," I said. "It could be true that we Southerners are still fighting the Civil War, too, and we say bad things about them. After all, I was twenty-five before I knew that damn yankee was two words."

Bob agreed and acknowledged it was all in the point of view because, though he hated to do it, he had to admit that he'd read some of Mencken's things he liked. He himself couldn't make a remark about Northerners like the one Mencken made about Southerners, for there were many erudite and brilliant people up north who appreciated the yarns he banged out.

"We enjoy a satirist as long as he isn't ridiculing something we love," I said.

Bob laughed appreciatively. He said that he had enjoyed Mencken's book: *A Treatise on the Gods*. He was a little taken aback when I said that book made me as mad as what Mencken said about Southerners. Bob insisted that *A Treatise on the Gods* was the best thing he'd read of Mencken's. He thought perhaps we ought not to be so quick to condemn the man. He said he himself was very broadminded about things like that, and that I should try to be.

When we got home, Mother had my dress ready to try on while Bob talked with Mammy about life during the Civil War. I think he'd really rather talk with her than with me anyway. After I tried on the dress, Mother said she had a little adjusting to do here and there, and she had to put the hem in. I told her we'd wait, so I could take it back to Cross Plains.

While we waited, I thought it was a great opportunity to take Bob to see the remains of an old log house down in our pasture. I asked him if he wanted to go cactus hunting.

He thought I meant those little red apples that grow on prickly pears and wanted to know how I ever got the stickers out of them. I explained, with amusement and patience, that the cactus I was talking about were tart, red, delicious, with no stickers—the ones that grew in small pin-cushion-like cactus.

"For a country boy," I said, "you don't know much about what grows here in Texas!"

He agreed that it was a shame he didn't know more about the plants around this section of the state. We had to walk carefully to keep out of the mud, and it was a little early for cactus. We found a few. Bob ate them and said that it just goes to show you that sometimes a girl learns something in college.

Our pasture is small, and it doesn't take long to walk over it. We came to the last few logs outlining the old house which had been built here long before our parents were born. Bob fell in love with it, as I knew he would. We walked around it, and I showed him where an old loom had been when more of the cabin was standing. When I was a kid, part of one of the chimneys was still standing. We looked into the old cistern near the house. Like all people do, for some unknown reason, we put our heads down to the opening of the cistern and called down into it. Then we laughed about the echo it made.

We sat down on a big rock near the front door. Bob picked up a stick about two feet long, rested his elbows on his knees, began to tap the ground aimlessly with the stick. As I also knew he would do, he began to weave stories about how he'd lived in this old house a hundred years ago.

I looked at the trees and watched a mocking bird fly up out of a big oak close to the fence, beside the field. Mocking birds put so much action into their songs I like to watch them.

When Bob realized I was watching the mocking bird, he told me how the mocking bird song came to America. He explained that the mocking bird had no song of his own but had borrowed, or stolen, the Nightingale's song. That made him philosophize about people who took other people's songs and tried to sing them. He said there were writers who tried to steal other men's ideas, characters, and most of all, because it was easy to steal, they stole plots. But, he reasoned, that was what you could expect in this decadent civilization we live in.

Suddenly, without warning, I began to feel sick at the stomach. I tried to fight the nausea off with a facetious thought, "My God, is it possible this brilliant man makes me sick at my stomach?"

I tried to keep the irritation out of my voice. "Bob," I said, "it seems to me you're building up a lot of trouble for yourself."

He turned quickly and looked at me. "How in the hell do you figure that?"

It was hard to explain just what I did mean. "You're always condemning this civilization, and it only makes you unhappy with things around you. Besides, I don't think it's right to praise every age but your own and every place but the one you live in. How can you live in a world that you don't like?"

He looked at me strangely, then he took a deep breath and smiled slowly. "I guess maybe I don't have much choice about the age I live in." He tapped the ground with the stick, giving that his attention. "But, of course, a man can always get out of it, if he doesn't want to put up with the hell he has to go through. Can't he?"

Inside myself, I fought against the nausea and impatience that swept over me. "You don't have any more hell than the rest of us," I snapped.

He grinned as if determined to be cheerful. "Yes, I do." He looked across the few remaining logs of the old house toward some of our cows that had come up near the place we were sitting. "You don't know, girl. You just don't know the troubles I have."

He smiled and continued to tap the stick against the ground. "I wouldn't have any troubles, if editors paid me what they owe me. I wouldn't have any troubles, if I could sell all of the stuff I bang out. Damn sorry editors keep a yarn till they wear it out, then they send it back to you and tell you they don't want it. Sorry bastards. They don't have to worry about where their next meal is coming from."

The clouds were hanging low, and it looked as if it would rain any minute. Still we sat. So, he was troubled by hard work and disappointment? So, he was starving? I knew darn well he made a good living—twice as much as I did. I thought of all the work Mother and Mammy had to do to get what little the farm made. Sure. Those cows looked fat and good, especially for this time of year. The farm looked prosperous. But Mother milked twelve of those cows by hand twice a day to buy groceries! If he and his mother worked like that, they'd have a right to complain! Complaining was something Mother and Mammy did *not* do.

"You don't look as if you need to worry about your next meal," I said drily. "You're not exactly what I'd call skin and bones."

He grinned boyishly. "Looks are deceiving. It's all blubber. Not healthy fat. Too much blubber and no substance."

He looked at me, and his eyes were beginning to grow dark with the anxiety and questions I dreaded in them. His eyes made me feel guilty, even when I had done nothing to feel guilty for. I looked back at the mocking bird, away from Bob.

He still had complaints to express. "I could put up with my living hell, if my mother wasn't sick and needing things I can't give her. If the damn editors paid me what they owe me, I could see that she got better treatment. I can't give her the things she needs. She's got to have an operation and, even with the professional discount my father gets, I'll have a hard time making it."

This was the time for me to be sympathetic and understanding. I could not! "What about your father? He takes care of her too, doesn't he?"

Bob grunted and didn't answer for a minute. "It takes all his time to take care of patients who don't pay him, or pay him with meat and vegetables."

We sat quietly for a minute. I tried to think of some way to change the subject. He looked so dejected sitting there, humped over, tapping the ground with the stick. I felt terribly sorry for him and impatient with myself for my lack of understanding and kindness. I wanted to take his mind off his troubles; but I didn't know how, for I still couldn't see that his troubles were worse than anybody else's.

When I went to see his father, Dr. Howard charged me a dollar for the visit, and I paid him. I knew several other teachers who went to him and paid him! Did his father make more money than Bob said he did? I had the feeling he did. Yet Bob always talked as if he himself were the sole support of his mother and dad. Impatience welled up in me again.

"It's hell to be old and sick," Bob said. "I don't see how a just God can punish people like that. My mother has never harmed anybody in her whole life, and look at all the things she has to suffer. It's not right! Not a damn bit right. Her life is hanging by a thread, and it seems a damn shame to me that life should be taken from her. Life is all old people have. When it's miserable and painful, it makes me so damn mad I want to tear up the whole damn universe."

I still could not sympathize with him. "Mammy is seventy-seven years old," I said. "She'll be seventy-eight in July. She loves every minute of her life. She says that every year she's lived is the best one. It doesn't seem so bad to get old, when you have had a long life and a lot of good things to look back on."

He hit the ground so hard with the stick, it broke. "You don't know what you're talking about," he rasped out. "Your grandmother is a remarkable woman. I admit that. She's not sick either. She's healthy and able to work harder than some men I know. My mother is almost an invalid. Has been for several years. I don't know when she's been really healthy, probably not since I was born. She needs every damn bit of help and care I can give her. And the hell of it is that I can't give her as much as I'd like to. I don't expect you to understand that. You've never had the trouble she's had. Your grandmother has never had the kind of trouble—"

"Trouble?" I interrupted. "Mammy's had as much trouble as anybody in this world, but she never gives up. She's a fighter, Mammy is, and I admire her with all my heart. She and my grandfather had seven children. When the oldest was a little past nineteen and the youngest a year and a half, they decided to move to Texas from Arkansas. In August, just before they were to move, her husband died. Because they had planned to come to Texas, she determined to bring her children and come on. The next January—five months later—her oldest boy died. Still, she didn't give up. She came on to Texas the next spring, and to add to her burden, the next August—a year after her husband died—her little ten-year old girl died. Oh, she's had her share of troubles of all kinds, but I'll tell you something: She never bends. She stands straight and tall. She never quits. She—"

"I told you your grandmother was a remarkable woman." Bob glared at me with miserable, turbulent eyes. "I'm not arguing about that. My mother is a fine woman, too. She never complains, even though her little body is wracked with pain. She's had a hell of a life. And I think it's a damn shame that she's been such a wonderful person and now she has to suffer all the pain and heartache she has to. By God, don't tell me about bravery, for she's the bravest. Don't tell me that this goddam world with its pain and sorrow and trouble is worth living in. It—"

I interrupted him. For some silly reason, I wanted to laugh, not at his mother's troubles, but because of what we were arguing about. We were sitting there like two kids arguing about which of the two women was braver—his mother or my grandmother!

"Bob," I said, "let's not argue. You love your mother and think she's the greatest, and I love my grandmother and think she's the greatest. Let's leave it at that, huh? I want to be happy. I've got a pretty new dress and spring is coming! Listen to that silly mocking bird. He's been flying up out of that tree and singing for the past hour. He thinks we don't appreciate him."

Bob relaxed and almost smiled. "That's right," he said. "We're acting like kids." He stopped, and I watched him slowly straighten up. "I remember when

I was a kid, I fought another kid once because he said his dad was bigger than my dad."

The good mood we'd had today was restored. We talked about other things then . . . about the old house, and we wondered about the people who'd lived there. Did a man and woman ever sit on this big rock and talk about their farm, the cattle drives, and the fence cuttings that'd been in this country in the late 1800's. What about Indian fights? Had the people who built this house ever worried about Indians stealing up on them in the night? As we talked about the Indians, I remembered something I thought was interesting.

I picked up a stick and pointed to the northeast corner of the pasture. "The last Indian killed in Brown County was killed right over there on our farm."

"Where?" Bob asked quickly.

"Over there close to the railroad," I answered. "Mr. Cheatham, an old Texas Ranger, lived on the farm adjoining ours. He told us all about the last Indian fight and how the Indian was killed. Mother wrote it down because she thought it was the kind of history we might want to refer to someday."

"Yeah," Bob grunted. "That's a good idea. What happened.?"

"Mr. Cheatham was in the fight. The Indians came down from Oklahoma and raided several places around Santa Anna. There was a big fight there. The Indians stole their horses; the Rangers got them back; the Indians got them again. A man by the name of Foster was either the captain or just in charge of the Rangers. He divided his men up into small groups. That's the reason only a few of the Rangers were in on the last fight. A small group of Indians got away and came down about a mile below here on the Clear Creek. Finally, only two Indians were left. Mr. Cheatham and another Ranger, Andy Mathis, were chasing them and killed one. But before they could get the last one, he almost got away. The two Rangers ran together down on the Sears place. Mathis got off his horse. Mr. Cheatham said, 'Are you shot, Mathis?' Mathis said, 'No. His gun's empty. Go after him.' So Mr. Cheatham got on his horse and took off, nearly overtook the Indian, shot his horse and was getting ready to shoot him when 'Boom' right behind him a gun sounded. Andy Mathis rode up, followed almost immediately by a small group of Rangers. The Indian was dead with five bullet holes in his chest. No one knew exactly who killed him, although Mr. Cheatham thought it was Andy Mathis, and Mr. Cheatham was mad about it."

"I can see why," Bob said. "The more scalps you hang on your belt, the better man you are." He looked at me again and the shadows had gone out of his eyes. "You're sure the last Indian killed in Brown County was killed over there on your grandmother's farm?"

"Of course, I'm sure," I said peevishly. "I know it's true. Mr. Cheatham said so. Do you doubt my word?"

"Now don't get upset again," he grinned. "I reckon, though, I don't think the last Indian was killed there, or else he was the damndest fool who ever lived."

"Who?" I gasped.

"That crazy Indian," Bob said. "That was the damndest fool Indian I ever heard of."

"What are you talking about?" I asked with amazement. "He was part of the raiding party, and the Rangers got him, that's all. I don't see why you should call him more of a fool than the others."

"He didn't have a bit of sense," Bob said, tapping the stick against his shoe. "A few weeks ago, I talked to an old man up in Cross Cut. He told me positively that the last Indian killed in Brown County was killed a couple of miles west of Cross Cut. While I was in Brownwood, I lived close to an old man who'd been one of the first cowboys in this part of the country. He was with the Rangers, too, and he swore to me that the last Indian killed in Brown County was killed around Indian Creek. When ol' Clyde was working on his history of Brown County, he said the last Indian was killed over on the Sears place. Now, you tell me he was killed over there, close to the railroad on your grandmother's place."

I stared at him, speechless.

Bob sat looking off toward the place I'd said the Indian was killed. He spoke softly, lightly, whimsically, all trace of anger gone. "That damn fool Indian didn't do a thing but go around getting himself killed all over the damn county."

I managed some sort of laugh. Neither of us said anything more. We just sat. Thinking. I was thinking about the Indian, a young brave killed for no reason. I wondered why men thought they had to fight and kill each other, just to settle differences. I started to say something like that to Bob when he began to talk, almost as if putting my thoughts into words.

"Wherever that Indian was killed, he was trying to get away, trying to live," he said slowly, thoughtfully. "It's a damn shame that men are always trying to take another man's property or woman away from him. He figures he has to kill to keep them safe. The white men who killed that Indian killed him because they were afraid of him. Afraid of his way of living, his way of fighting, sneaking up in the middle of the night, knifing them, stealing their women and carrying them off to a fate worse than death."

"I know," I said. "The Indian was human too. Maybe he was running away to get back to his camp, in order to take care of his wife and baby. He was a young brave, according to Mr. Cheatham. I guess there were good men on each side."

"Not many white men would agree with you," Bob said. "I know there were good Indians, but not many white people, who came out here when this country was wild and new, thought that. They were afraid. They couldn't guarantee their own safety and their families' safety until they killed the Indians."

"Men are crazy," I said. "They are so quick to shoot; they don't take time to think about the problems and loves of the one they kill."

Bob gave a short laugh. "If they did, they'd never be able to fight a war. The battle would go to the one with the least feeling for other men. I'm not saying your romantic ideas about that Indian having a wife and baby at his wigwam wasn't true. Maybe he did, but in a war, you can't think about that. All you've got time to do is shoot."

"Have you read that essay by Bruce Barton against war?" I asked.

Bob shook his head.

"I like the way it ends," I said. "It ends: 'In the dictionaries of the future, let it be written: War, an armed conflict between men . . . now obsolete . . . Unknown.' "

Bob shook his head. "You're a dreamer, girl. Men are going to fight wars as long as men exist. They are going to fight because they're afraid. That primordial fear they took with them into the first caves they ever crawled into for shelter is still in them. They were afraid of the elements, afraid of the animals that roamed the forests. But mostly they were afraid of men like themselves. You can't get that fear out of men. It only gets worse. Look at the world today: guns, tanks, airplanes, bombs that destroy a hundred men at a time. Damn rotten civilization where war is no longer a contest between men. It's a contest of bombs. Tanks. Big guns. Men are still afraid, but they've made war no longer a man's fight with another man. It's a fight against women and children and helpless men who can't fight."

Suddenly, I felt the whole weight of the world on my shoulders. I was tired. Too tired to argue about something to which there was no answer or solution. I got up.

"We'd better be going. I'm sure Mother has fixed my dress by now."

Bob got up and we started toward the house. He began to talk about war in the time of Alexander the Great and Jenghiz Khan. How war in their time was real war. He could get excited about the careful plans they made for taking over a country. I didn't listen. Not today. Not when spring is coming and birds are singing, cactus is ripening.

Just before we got to the house, it began to rain. "We'll get wet," I said ecstatically. "We'd better run." I started running, looking back at Bob and laughing.

He laughed, too, and began to walk as fast as he could. "Go on," he called exultantly. "Go on. Don't get wet because of me. I can't run with these damn weak ankles of mine."

We were near the house and so I ran and hopped on the porch and stood there, watching him. He was bent nearly double, keeping the rain out of his face; I had held my face to the rain. He walked with long loping strides. He reached the porch, and we stood there laughing at each other. It was crazy. Fun. The rain stopped as abruptly as it had begun, and we laughed, for most of this day had been filled with laughter. Bob shook the water off his hat and I pushed my wet hair back off my face. I was thinking. Maybe someday I'll write a story about this. I'll begin: Once we walked in the rain together.

But I couldn't think of a plot to build it on. A story like that should be about a man and woman who always understood each other, not about a man and woman who ran laughing in the rain together, but who were worlds apart. . . .

A friend . . . Big word . . . Friend . . .

When Bob came tonight, he asked me if I wanted to go to Cisco to a show. He had on his coat and tie, so that if I wanted to go, he'd be ready. However, I was so blue and discouraged I said I would rather just ride around.

Bob said that was fine with him; he asked if I minded if he took off his damn tie. I didn't care, and so he threw it on the back seat. We rode toward Cisco.

Bob seems rather sensitive to my moods. Before we'd even got to the end of the street, he said, "What's wrong? Nat been giving you trouble?"

"No," I said quickly. "Nat is one of the nicest people in the world. He doesn't give you trouble, unless you give him trouble first."

"I know," Bob said. "He's perfect. What about Mark? Trouble with him?"

"No."

"Well, something's wrong. Want to cry on my shoulder? I've got a big shoulder here. Go ahead. Cry on ol' Bob's shoulder."

I didn't intend to cry, but I couldn't laugh. "I don't have any friends."

"Oh, I don't believe that. What about Merle Mitchell? Mrs. Jackson? Your roommate? All the people whose kids you teach?"

"They like me well enough," I said miserably, "but not close."

Then I told him my story. "The coach's wife and the wife of our commerce teacher had a bridge party the other night. Both of them are in my study club. All the other teachers I go around with were invited. I wasn't."

Bob was incredulous. "You mean you were the only one not invited?"

I nodded. "My cousins, Enid and Jimmie were. There are several teachers in the study club: Doris, Louise, and some others. They were invited, but not me."

Bob was as upset as I had been. "Tell 'em to go to hell; you don't give a goddam whether they invite you to their damn tea-drinking, pink-lace bridge parties or not."

"I do care. I care because I'm human."

"Do you know why you weren't invited?"

"No," I said, trying to think. "From the day I met Coach, he didn't like me. I don't know why."

"Did you like him?"

"Not after I was introduced to him. When I first saw him, I thought: too bad he's married. But when he was introduced to me, he barely looked at me and mumbled something like 'Nice to meet 'cha.' He's a former college football player, supposed to be great."

"He sounds like a goddam sonofabitch," Bob said. "If you want me to, I'll beat his damn head in."

I managed a weak laugh. "Oh, no. That wouldn't solve the problem."

"You say you're in the study club with the wives?" Bob asked. I nodded. "Well, what do you do in the study club that could make the ladies not like you?"

I thought a minute. "I am parliamentarian and critic."

"You mean you criticize them when they do something?"

"I sure do. They're bad speakers. Most of the women in the club don't know how to stand on their feet and face an audience. They asked me to be the critic and to help them."

Bob scratched his head. "Maybe when they asked you to criticize them, they really wanted you to tell them they were good," he suggested. "Do you tell them they're bad?"

"I tell them what to do to improve. I try to be tactful about it. I told one woman the other day, 'If you'd stand up straight and look your audience straight in the face, you'd be all right.' "

Bob turned toward me. "That's tactful?"

I began to think about it. He went on talking. "I don't know, but I've been told you have to be mighty careful when you criticize people. Most of 'em can't take it. Maybe they are bad when they get up to give a speech. I know damn well what I'd do." He laughed. "I'd stand there like a damn fool with my mouth open and nothing coming out. I wouldn't need anybody to tell me I was bad. I'd damn well know it. If somebody did tell me, I might knock the heads off the whole damn study club."

I was beginning to feel a little uncomfortable. "The purpose of a study club is to learn," I said positively. "If there's something you can't do, you're supposed to try to do it, anyway. They need to learn how to speak in public."

"I can see that," Bob said. "Now, I don't pretend to know about women's study clubs, but maybe you might be kinda . . . well . . . kinda subtle about it. It seems to me in my own case, instead of telling a man he's a damn fool, I'd say, 'All of us act like damn fools some of the time.' But here. I sure ain't one to tell you how to criticize a woman's study club."

He leaned toward me and put his arm around my shoulders. "Still. I guess I can see your point, and I'm inclined to agree with you. If a man's bad and doesn't know it, you ought to tell him. I guess the same thing holds true of a woman. If a woman can't speak, let her either keep her mouth shut or try to learn how."

"That's my idea exactly. If you don't want to learn, get out of the study club."

"Right," Bob said. "But I do think you have friends around here, girl. You've been to a lot of parties. Why, you even got me invited to one. Of course I couldn't go, but I was invited."

At that moment, I was so down it was hard for anything to lift my spirits. "I don't think my cousins like to be around me too much either," I said.

"Hell, I guess my cousins like me less than they like anybody. They wouldn't invite me to a dog fight, and I wouldn't go if they did. Hell, I've got to the place where it seems to me to be hated by a relative is a damn good thing."

I laughed. However I still wanted to talk out my hurt. "If either of my cousins were to have a bridge party, she'd invite me."

"Well," Bob said. "I sure don't have any friends."

"Yes, you do. Dave and Lindsey. How long have you been friends with them?"

"Oh, hell. I don't know. Ever since I moved here."

"They still like you, and like to be with you, don't they?"

Bob grinned. "Neither one of them has called me a damn fool to my face. If you want to call that liking, I guess you can say they like me."

"And Clyde and Truett are your good friends."

"They don't cross me much. Course I've taught them all they know. They ought to like me."

We drove in silence for a minute or two. "Well, girl, I'll tell you what I think," he said, and his arm tightened about me. "Hell, it ain't my habit to give advice, but I think you place too much emphasis on having a lot of friends. Most of us don't have many friends. I've had things happen to me like the party you didn't get invited to. When I was a kid, some of our neighbors had parties and didn't invite me. Invited Dave and Lindsey, but not me. Well, hell, I didn't want to go to their damn parties anyway. When it comes to friends, I reckon I'm pretty damn lucky. But I can count my friends on one hand. One hand."

"I can count my friends on one hand, too," I said morosely, "and I don't have to use any fingers at all."

Bob laughed. "As for visiting—Well, ol' Clyde and Truett used to come over here pretty often, but that was when we were young. Ol' Lindsey and me don't get together the way we used to. Seems like when he has any time free, he hunts a girl. Well, hell, I ain't gonna hold that against him. Ol' Dave has got hisself all tied up with that little school teacher." He paused, took his arm from around my shoulders, and speeded up to pass a car. "Tell you a man shore has to watch hisself with these school teachers. First thing ol' Dave knew he was hawgtied."

I was beginning to feel much better. Bob settled himself on his side of the car and tried harder to sound like a dumb cowboy—one who was not giving advice.

"What I'm sayin' is that we do have a few good friends. Mighty few. We see 'em now and then, talk, and that's it. We swear we're goin' to git together sometime soon, but, hell, we've got our work to do. Our jobs is right in front of us. Then, first thing you know we're in our sere and yellow leaf an' ain't got the energy to visit much. I ain't sayin' we shouldn't. We should. But, hell, I ain't seen ol' Clyde in several months. I kinda have the feelin' that his wife ain't got no hankerin' to have Clyde's drinkin' friends hangin' around. I imagine she's got her hands full keepin' up with him and keepin' him busy at the job. And I reckon that ol' Clyde hisself has got other things on his mind, too, making a living, working at some damn job, but wanting to live free. I think you've got to accept that."

I have to accept a lot of things. Bob said things to make me feel better and, sure enough, they helped. I wanted to be quiet and look out at the soft moonlight on the rising and falling hills around us. There was a loneliness there on the road, a loneliness you felt inside you. This is not prairie country, not the way it is farther west, but they say that someday it will all be prairie. A vast and silent prairie. You feel that you need someone near you or the prairie will surge over you.

My thoughts went back to my lack of friends. "Bob," I said, "it's true, as you say, sometimes we see people we just don't like or who don't like us. Why is that, do you suppose?"

"Now, girl, you listen to me, and I'll explain it to you," he said cheerfully. "It happened like this. Ol' Lindsey and I went to Brownwood a short time ago. Didn't have any business. Just went over there. We were walking down the street, and I'll swear. We met a man that made me want to stop and knock his damn head off. No reason. But when I saw him, I wanted to do something to him."

Whether it had actually happened or not, it was one of Bob's fantastic yarns.

"Now, I'm not saying that this is the absolute truth, or that I have any proof of what I'm going to tell you, but I'll just give you what I think could be the answer."

He settled himself comfortably in the car. "They say we never use even a tenth of our brain power. Right?"

I nodded. "I've heard that in school."

"Well, what about that nine-tenths we don't use? Is it just a spongy mass, or are our racial memories buried deep in its cells?"

I didn't try to answer.

He went on. "I believe it's all stored right there; and if we could just find the key to unlock it, what historians we'd be! Maybe back a thousand years or more . . . maybe when mankind lived in caves, there was a fellow who encroached on my cave property. Maybe he came to my cave and stole my woman, or worse—maybe he stole the bear I'd killed for food. Could be anything . . . anything that would make men fight. A man will fight for his woman, and he'll fight for his food. In which order, I don't rightly know."

"That's a ridiculous thing to believe," I said, laughing.

"No, not ridiculous. Could be just exactly the way ol' Bob is telling it to you. Maybe, way back a thousand years or so ago, you have a controversy with another man. You keep on being born over and over and the memory is gone, but the fear, and the hate or whatever it is, still lingers there, hidden in your brain, making you half afraid and half ready to fight. Well, while you're being born over and over, that man, too, is being born over and over. Then one day you're walking down the street talking to ol' Lindsey, trying to give him a piece of your valued information and, suddenly, coming toward you is the guy who stole your woman a couple of thousand years ago. You hate him. Instinctively. You don't know why. The hate is there, but it has been lying there, locked up in that brain cell those thousands of years and all you can see is that here's a guy you hate."

"Well, I'm not a man, and I didn't steal Coach's food in some former time, and I'm sure I didn't steal his woman."

"Maybe you're the woman who got stolen," Bob said dryly. "That would make a man hate a woman."

He went on talking about racial memories, but another thought had come to me. I thought how strange it was that people did like one person and not another. A child comes into your class, and you think "This child has something special. This child is great. I'll do everything I can to help him." But another child comes in, and for some unaccountable reason you just don't see that he's special. You don't even like him. He gets on your nerves. Maybe he has as much to offer as the other kid, but you don't recognize it. I thought of one student I didn't like, and I said a silent prayer: "I'm sorry, Lord, I'll try to like him better after this."

We were almost in Cisco. We could see the lights of the town, a few close together, one or two farther out, trying to make their light alone. In town, we stopped to get cokes. We talked of other things.

Again tonight, Bob was interested in Alexander the Great. Recently, he had drawn a map and outlined the journeys Alexander had made. On the table he outlined the battles for me. He talked of Alexander's father, Philip, who had taught the young man the art of warfare. But mostly he talked of Alexander's deeds.

He described how he had used the cavalry in his battles. The infantry attacked the middle of the lines, while the horsemen or cavalry attacked on the sides. Bob talked about the fright the men caught in the middle felt when they saw the men on horses coming toward them. Then he described, still using a straw on the bare table, how Alexander conquered the Persians, how he made use of crude, wooden tanks with a huge battering ram to break down the walls. He laughed as he described how Alexander had some of his men on the tanks, using strong bows, learned from the Egyptians, strong bows that could shoot farther and harder than ordinary bows, as much as a thousand feet maybe.

I saw people watching us curiously, and I was not sorry to leave the drugstore.

Bob kept on talking about Alexander the Great and his men. Once, while he described the battle against the Persians, he described it as vividly as if he himself had fought in it. I could see the advantage of being a history buff, the importance of writing about old things and making them seem real and new. When you did that, you didn't have time to worry about such things as not being invited to parties.

Bob laughed exultantly about the way Alexander had acted in the conquered territories. He told how Alexander had gone into Persia, married a Persian princess, and dressed the way the Persians dressed, acted, for a time, the way the Persians acted, in order to be able to rule them well.

"But he made a great mistake," Bob said, laughing softly. "He went too far. Old friends became enemies and were put to death. He even declared himself a god—"

"That was stupid," I said.

"I don't think so. It was a mistake, all right. He became very lonely, and it was the beginning of the end for him. But remember this, girl. The man who chooses to follow a dream to its bitter and ultimate end, walks alone."

This was a rather short date tonight. We left Cisco and came straight home. It was only a little after ten when we got back to Cross Plains. But I felt good. Wonderful.

I said good-bye and came into the house to think and write for a long time, before going to bed. I said to myself, "Thank God there is a good friend around who, when I'm unhappy, blue and discouraged, knows how I feel. He, too, has been snubbed by acquaintances.

Bob rises above the hurts and the snubs and goes on to find his happiness in creating new worlds from the pages of old books. I must never forget what he said tonight—the words he tossed off so exuberantly.

"The man, who chooses to follow a dream to its bitter and ultimate end, walks alone."

There was the Door to which I found no key;
There was the Veil through which I could not see;
Some little talk awhile of ME and THEE
There was—and then no more of THEE and ME.
              . . . Rubáiyat . . .

Bob came unexpectedly this afternoon. He said he thought I might enjoy riding around for a while before time for supper. Although he said the dark melancholy of his Black Irish ancestry was on him today, at first, I didn't think he seemed too depressed. However, I was surprised he had come, since tomorrow or the next day, he is taking his mother to Temple for what he says is a very serious operation for a woman of her age.

"The reason I came, girl," he said, "is I thought being with you would help me dispel this melancholy hanging over me."

I could help a friend! That pleased me, and I wanted to be sure to say all the right things!

As we drove through town, we saw Dave Lee and another man, standing in front of the post office, talking. Bob waved and Dave waved back.

"I see Dave in town quite often, standing on street corners, talking with friends," I said to begin the conversation.

"Hell. That's his business," Bob said belligerently. "He has a right to stand on the corners and talk. Dave's a hard worker. It's a great thing to stand on the street corner and talk with your friends. It's damned important."

I hadn't thought of it as being important or unimportant. People stand on the street and talk with each other. It was there and you noticed it, or you did not notice it.

Bob began to talk. But he was not berating civilization; instead, he was praising the simple things that civilization had to offer: standing on street corners, talking with friends; walking with the warmth of the sun on your back, a faithful dog by your side; hunting cactus with your best girl.

"I sold Wright a yarn like that a few months ago." He turned and looked at me, his eyes turbulent. "I'm damned surprised he took it. It's different from my other Conan yarns . . . no sex . . . only men fighting against the savagery and bestiality about to engulf them. I want you to read it when it comes out. It's filled with the important little things of civilization, little things that make men think civilization's worth living and dying for."

I wanted to change the conversation. "I suppose I know what you mean about little things being important," I said, quickly. "By-the-way, thank you for writing Kline for me. He sent my story back the other day, and he stressed the use of 'little things' to make a story seem real. He wants me to rewrite it."

"Are you going to?" Bob asked.

"Not soon," I sighed. "I have too much to do right now, trying to get my students ready for County Meet." I thought about telling him how headachy I'd been lately, but I didn't want to burden him with my troubles. I could still hold my head up and fight the nausea. "I'm too worried about my students making a good showing. I can't sleep, and Mrs. Hemphill worries because she says I'm not eating enough. She thinks I'm going to be sick."

In spite of my good resolution, it was out, and I felt angry with myself. No use worrying him. It didn't!

"You've worked like this before," he said indifferently, "night and day. Why is it worse this time?"

"Worry," I said, and pushed my hair off my face.

Bob smiled faintly. "I know."

I suppose I realized, then, that he really was in a "melancholy mood" today, for he began talking again about the importance of little things in life as well as in stories. He stressed how important it was to be one of a group, to have the fellowship of your own kind, these were the good things in life and the good things to write about, he said. I had never heard him talk like this about his loneliness, and his inability to be a part of the community in which he lived.

But then he brought up that old worry that seems to be such an issue with him: People think he's a freak. It irritated me, but since I was trying to be helpful, I tried a different approach. I told him the majority of people in Cross Plains knew he was making a good living with his writing and thought it was something they'd like to do if they could. I said people knew he was the first writer of any importance in this part of the country.

It pleased him, and he smiled.

Then I almost ruined everything! Suddenly, I remembered something I wanted to ask him about. "Bob, I heard that the poet, Lexie Dean Robertson, invited you over to her house for a dinner. She wanted you to meet some of her friends who are writers. She wanted you to be in a writer's group she was trying to organize."

Bob looked at me frowning. "That little woman in Rising Star?"

"Yes. She's a nice little person. I know her. Did she invite you over one time?"

Bob groaned. "One time? Hell, I only went once, but I seem to remember she had a dozen pink-lace parties she tried to invite me to."

"You only went once?"

Bob became exasperated. "Yeah. Once. Damn it, girl, if you make a living writing for the pulps, you don't have time to go to pink teas."

He began to rave and rant, and I had a hard time getting him back on the story he'd sold to Wright—the one which, he said, was not the usual Conan story.

He was excited about it because it was about this country and it sold! He had a honing to write more about this country, not an ordinary cowboy yarn, or a wild west shoot 'em up, though God knew this country was alive with yarns like that waiting to be written. But in his heart, he wanted to say more than that. He wanted to tell the simple story of this country and the hardships the settlers had suffered, pitted against a frightened, semi-barbaric people—the Indians, who were trying to hold on to a way of life and a country they loved. Since he'd met me, he didn't feel so bad about Indians. But a novel depicting the settlers' fear as they tried to carve out a new life, and the Indians' fear as they tried to hold on to a doomed country; why, girl, all that would make the best damn novel ever written about frontier life in the Southwest.

Suddenly, he shook his head. Such a book probably never would be accepted as a great novel or even a good one. He said that two-bit, sophisticated, pseudo-intellectual critics would never consider a novel about this part of the country as a great novel. The damn fools.

"Write it anyway," I said placatingly. "Tell the critics to go to hell."

He shrugged his shoulders. "I wouldn't say this to anybody but you, but, by God, I know what I can do. I love this country, and I know damn well I can write about it. I know damn well I can write a novel that will move, be about people facing real odds." He became exuberant. "I tried that yarn out to see what Wright would do about it. I was afraid he wouldn't take it, but he did! By God, he took it!"

He turned to face me again, still smiling, interested in the things he wanted to do. "I'll be better to the Indians in this novel than I was in that yarn. I'll have a beautiful, fully dressed Indian girl in it. I know how you feel, and I agree with you. The Indians deserve better treatment than they get. I'll have the hero fall in love with that beautiful Indian girl. He'll be a white man: a morose, ungainly, misfit among men, but his neighbors—"

"Why does he have to be an ungainly misfit? Couldn't he be a big, handsome, kind, wonderful man?"

He laughed, the first time today he'd really laughed.

"By God, you're still a dreamer. Romance! He's got to be handsome! Okay, by God, we'll make him the most handsome man in the west with the fastest gun."

We laughed together, then, and I felt better. He turned the car around, and we started back to Cross Plains. But the joy faded. His eyes took on that fear-filled, haunted look. His words, too, took a different turn. No longer enthusiastic about the novel he wanted to write, no longer filled with fear for his mother's life.

He talked now of wanting to live and to come back again. See the spring come again . . . see new life begin over again. I couldn't understand it. This change was too fast for me. I listened confused, uncertain. He was going to take his mother to Temple for a serious operation. I realized that. Did he plan to leave her there and never come back?

He began to thank me for all the time I'd given him. He said there were very few women whom he had known who let a man talk about his dreams and his work the way I did. He wanted me to know he thought I was a very unusual woman, and he appreciated knowing me. I began to feel nervous, for he sounded as if he'd never see me again!

"Be sure to write to me," I said, again hoping to change his mood. "Tell me how your mother gets along; how you're doing too. I'll be looking forward to having you back again."

He sighed, waited a moment, and said very softly that the one bright spot he saw ahead of him was that he'd come back, for he wanted to see me again.

I was glad he began to talk of other things, then: whether Roosevelt's Work Relief Bill would pass; William Green; and whether men were losing their jobs because they joined labor unions.

The beauty of the sunset was behind us, but today we didn't have time to stop. Now, both of us talked glibly of things that did not concern us personally. I looked ahead as the twilight began to turn into darkness and sighed. His black Irish melancholy had settled over him again.

As for me, I wondered if there would ever be a time when I would understand all the things he'd talked about today.

A light before darkness . . . Hope . . .

After school today, I worked with Jay and Mary on their declamations. A little before five, I rushed to town to see if I had any mail before time to go home, listen to Mrs. Hemphill worry because I'm not eating enough, and go back to school to rehearse the one-act play.

I hurried into the drugstore to say "hello" to Mrs. Smith. She was busy, but Dr. Howard was there, leaning against the counter. When I saw him, I recalled that I had not heard from Bob. Was he all right?

Dr. Howard smiled and seemed glad to see me.

"How is Mrs. Howard," I asked.

He shook his head sadly. "She is holding her own," he said slowly, and I could hear weariness in his voice. "We believe she is going to get better."

He paused and looked at me. For a moment, it was almost like looking into Bob's eyes. Dr. Howard had the same questioning, fear-filled eyes that Bob had. I looked at him and thought how much like Bob he really was. Deep. A dreamer. Dr. Howard straightened his shoulders, and his voice was stronger. "Robert will be all right now, I think."

That surprised me. "Has he been sick, too?"

Dr. Howard looked closely at me for a moment before he answered. He shook his head. "No. Not sick. He is very close to his mother."

So that is unique? I thought, irritated slightly. I thought of my own mother and grandmother, and wondered how I could ever get along without them. "All of us are close to our mothers," I said. "Somehow we manage to make it without them, I suppose."

Dr. Howard sighed and looked toward the street at the passing cars. He didn't see me. "Yes," he said. "We manage."

I tried to think of something else to say but couldn't. I told him I hoped his wife continued to get along all right. I waved to Mrs. Smith and went on to the post office. No mail. Bob had promised to write. Too busy, I suppose. Too worried about his mother.

I started to run, checked myself, walked faster. I felt a vague, unreasoning bitterness and worry about Bob. I was foolish, of course. Bob was all right. He was twenty-nine years old. A brilliant man. He could certainly take care of himself. He didn't need me to help him, or encourage him.

The last rays of sunlight burnt the sky. I walked faster, almost running. Hope was there. A light before darkness. As I thought of Bob, I hoped he would be outside somewhere, so that he could see the sunset. He would know that everything was all right. He, too, would hope.

Bob is still in Temple . . .
Sunday afternoon . . . Alone . . .

The last two weeks have been the most hectic of my entire life! All I can say is that I lived through County Meet.

We are still facing the district and regional meets, but since I only have individual events and a one-act play to worry about, I'll live through it. For the last few weeks, though, I've wondered if I could make it. Mrs. Hemphill still thinks I'll die of starvation, and Ethel keeps saying, "Oh, my, my! Can't you get any sleep at all?"

Bob is coming home. I had a card from him, saying that his mother was getting better, and he was bringing her home. I wanted to write him a letter, telling him how my students did, but he probably will be home before the letter could get to him.

Did my speech students ever pull in the first place wins! Nat said we won so much it was embarrassing, but he liked that kind of embarrassment!

Just before County Meet, Abilene Christian College had an invitational contest for speech events. All the way to Abilene, Nat's attitude was hopeful. He used to teach in Abilene High, and he wanted to do well there. Did we please him? Of course, nobody gave a little school like Cross Plains High with its hundred and seventy-five high school students a chance against schools like Abilene, Brownwood, Breckenridge, and similar schools with their big enrollments, and fine equipment. We showed them!

Cross Plains had more people in finals than any other school, except Abilene High. There were twenty-one schools there with one hundred and twenty-one contestants. Even my little freshman Billie Ruth Loving got to finals in girls' extemp. We learned she got a fourth place, but they don't give honors to any but the first three. W. N. Long got second in boys' extemp! That was good. Jay Mayes took third in senior boys' declamation, and Mary Billingsly got third in senior girls' declamation!

That's a good record, and Nat was proud; but he would have killed me if he had known that I bawled out one of Mary's judges because she caused Mary to get third. The dumb woman! I told her Mary should have had first place because she was by far the best in the senior girls finals! The woman opened her mouth and said, "Well, I guess you can blame me for that. The other two judges wanted to give her first place, and I talked them out of it."

I controlled an impulse to slap her, for she was bigger than I was. With icicles hanging on every syllable, I asked her why she'd done it.

"Your girl was too perfect, and that's what I objected to," she said haughtily, moving her big black purse on her fat stomach. "I want to know that they're just high school students saying a memorized oration that somebody else wrote. Your girl sounded as if the words were her very own! I want them to make mistakes and be just exactly what they are—high school students. I think, young lady, you trained your girl too well. You wouldn't let her make mistakes—"

"What do we send kids to school for?" I interrupted, trying to be rude in a sophisticated manner. "Do we pay high school English teachers to let the kids be themselves and say: 'between you and I,' and 'give those apples to Tom and I?' Do we want arithmetic teachers to let the students say that nine and five are twelve? In history, do we want them to know the war ended November 18, 1918, or shall we let them pick out any date they can remember!"

Her face was as red as a beet, and I knew I had hit a soft spot. She tried to interrupt me with, "Now, wait. I said—"

I went right on talking. "If all of us had the same damn kind of theory you do, we ought to close the damn schools and send the damn kids to the cotton patch. We should—"

I saw Nat down the hall looking at me; I smiled at the woman, so that he wouldn't know I was close to strangling her. I left her and hurried toward him. He was standing, talking to some old friends of his.

At County Meet, competing against schools in our own category, we beat the socks off them. Jay got first in boys' declamation; Mary, first in girl's declamation; Emma Jean Settle, first in junior girls' poetry reading with a

Nat Williams

Superintendent of Schools in Cross Plains from 1929 to 1937. In 1931, under his supervision, the Cross Plains schools had received full accreditation. Later, he became Superintendent of Schools in Lubbock, Texas. He retired from public schools in 1970 and headed the teacher training program at Texas Tech University until 1973.

poem more than half of which I'd written. W. N. Long got first in boys' extemp, and Billie Ruth got second in girls'. My two students in junior declamation didn't place in the top three.

I honestly think Nat was relieved that some of them didn't win, so that the other superintendents wouldn't think he paid the judges!

We go to Breckenridge next week. I have rehearsed the one-act play until the kids think they wrote it, or lived it. If the Dallas Little Theatre won their contest with this play, I'll sure try to win in Breckenridge!

Nat wants us to give it for the school next Wednesday morning. I just hope I live through it as well as the performance in Breckenridge. I must get to feeling better!

I'll be so glad to see Bob when he comes home. I've missed him. When I work with the kids on extemp speaking, I think it would be wonderful if Bob were here because he talks a lot about things that happen in the United States and in the world. Even when I disagree with him, discussing things with him gives me a better perspective on them.

On second thought, maybe it's just as well he's not here to discuss subjects with me. Suppose I were to forget and tell the kids to say, "Our goddam munitions manufacturers are leading us into war." Or, "Look at that damn Germany! Added five hundred thousand men to their army! Those damn bastards ain't got but one crazy idea. They want a war!"

The thing I'm looking forward to is just being with Bob, riding around over the country, talking about everything but school. Maybe I like him better than I think. I hope so.

After more than a week in the hospital . . .

I think my illness really began about a month ago. Dr. Daughtery says it began much earlier. I don't know. I do know that it had nothing to do with Bob. It was caused by worry about my school work. Dr. Daughtery is skeptical.

We were to take the one-act play to Breckenridge. I felt weak and my head ached. I got up at four-thirty to get ready. A feeling of weakness spread over me, and I leaned against the bathroom wall. I was glad I was leaving, so that I wouldn't wake Ethel. Now, she could sleep and get some rest. Mrs. Hemphill got up, fixed me a cup of coffee and a piece of toast, shook her head, and said she just knew I'd be sick!

The early morning trip was beautiful. Nat was taking the four kids and me in his car. The kids weren't the least bit scared, and Nat, bless his heart, talked and laughed with them and kept their minds on things other than the play. We stopped for a cup of coffee, and that time I drank a coke. I appreciated Nat and the kids, and I was glad they didn't notice how little I talked.

I was disappointed that our play wouldn't go on until four in the afternoon. Eight plays had to be given today. I told the cast to see some of the other plays, eat a leisurely lunch, rest a while, and be ready for make-up when their call came.

At eleven o'clock, Nat took me to a hospital. I became deathly sick, vomiting constantly, passing out. It was hard to hang on to any kind of reality. Nat left me at the hospital and went back to be with the kids, and I hardly knew he left.

The nurse insisted I stand on some dinky little scales and get weighed. Then she wanted to know what my usual weight was. I told her that I usually weighed about ninety-nine pounds. She just shook her head. The young, abrupt doctor told me I'd gone down to less than eighty-five pounds. He said it was ridiculous when he found out that, the day before, all I had eaten was a piece of toast, a cup of coffee and half an apple. The cure was worse than the disease. A bunch of shots to make me sleep and a small amount of tasteless food every hour.

Nat came by sometime after six to tell me he was taking the kids back to Cross Plains, and that he and Enid would come back for me on Sunday, provided the doctor would release me.

He hated to tell me the bad news! Our play got second place—second place! Eight plays and we got second place! Melvin got second place as an actor and Dixie was third. Why did we lose? Nat hated to tell me that, too. The judges said the play was too natural! The kids didn't seem to be acting! Yes, they really had put the meaning across and that was strange, because they didn't seem to make any noticeable gestures or cry or scream. The judges thought they might have screamed a little! Why, looking at it you forgot it was a play! Nat told me about it; he said he thought it was great, and that other coaches from other schools told him the same thing. He wanted me to know he was as disappointed as I was.

When he left, I cried until the hospital called the heartless doctor back, and he had the nerve to tell me I should be proud of second place! When I kept on crying, he had them give me another shot of something and left. That's all doctors think of—eating and shots.

The next day, Nat and Enid came after me. I rode in the back seat on some pillows and slept almost all the way back to Cross Plains.   ·

The doctor in Breckenridge told them to be sure to call my doctor when I got back to Cross Plains. Apparently, they had already taken care of that. When I got back, Mother was there, and Dr. Howard came a few minutes later.

I tried to congratulate Dr. Howard on being selected Cross Plains Man of the Year, but I never knew whether or not he understood what I was talking about. I asked him about Bob, and he told me Bob had brought his mother home and something else I couldn't concentrate on. I tried to tell him Bob had said he was coming to see me as soon as he got home and to go tell him I was home. Dr. Howard said something to the effect that Bob didn't have any business over there.

The next thing I knew, Dr. Howard told Mother he didn't have the facilities to take care of me as I was going to need to be fed intravenously; he wanted me to go to Brownwood to Dr. Daughtery's hospital. He knew Dr. Daughtery quite well, he said, and he'd call him and have him at the hospital to meet me. That was a coincidence because Dr. Daughtery was our family doctor.

I tried to ask Dr. Howard to get Bob to take me over, but I either didn't say it, or he ignored it, the way he had ignored everything else I'd said. I heard Mrs. Hemphill telling about my not having eaten anything for so long, and Dr. Howard grunted and said it was terrible! Everybody seems to concentrate on eating.

At the hospital, they slapped a bunch of needles in my arms and legs, and, as if that pain weren't enough, they stuck me with more needles. Once the door opened, and I saw Bob outside; but when I asked what he was doing there, the nurse said she didn't see anyone. I knew she was lying, but I went back to sleep. It really didn't bother me one way or the other, but I guess they didn't know that.

Wednesday night about ten o'clock, I woke up, no more vomiting and pain. Mother and the nurse called Dr. Daughtery. He patted me on the head and kept saying how glad he was I was all right at last. He said that now he could go home and get some sleep. He said the needles would be taken out in the morning.

It was good to be quiet and listen to the night sounds around me. Mother talking and then going to sleep on a couch in my room. Familiar beautiful night sounds all around. Footsteps outside in the hall; cars passing along the street; someone laughing on the street below. But the strangest, saddest thing of all happened, too. The hospital was across the street from the jail, and one could look into my room from an upstairs jail cell. Suddenly, I heard a voice—a young man's nice, clear voice saying, "Are you all right, little girl? You feel better now, little girl?"

At first, I thought it was Bob. I asked the nurse what it was all about. She laughed. "They have a young man about twenty years old over there, I don't think he's slept since you've been in here. He's been talking to you and singing to you, ever since you came in."

Lonesome like Bob, I thought. I asked if she knew anything about the young man. She'd heard he was in jail for stealing some guns.

It seemed so lonesome to me—a young man at the very beginning of his life in jail for stealing guns! A young man with nothing to do but sing to a strange young woman in a hospital bed.

I went to sleep while my unknown prisoner was singing an old love song—"Goodnight, Sweetheart"—in a strong, though uncertain tenor. He talked and sang all the next day. I felt bad about not trying to answer him. About six o'clock Friday morning, I heard him saying, "Good-bye, little girl. They're taking me away from you. Good-bye, little girl!" There was the sound of a car starting and driving away. His long "Go-o-o-od-bye" was lost in the midst of other car sounds on the street. A town was waking up, bustling around, voices, laughter. People facing a new day, interested in their own troubles. A lonesome boy who'd have a terrible fight to come back to make a good life for himself was not their concern, and he'd never know that I cried for him that morning.

I was able to eat now, and Dr. Daughtery said I could go home Saturday morning, after I'd had a long talk with him. I dreaded that, for I didn't want to be scolded. From the tone of his voice, I knew I would be. I didn't know it would be about Bob.

Dr. Daughtery did bawl me out. The first thing he said was, "You starved yourself almost to death! What made you do a thing like that?"

How do you answer a question like that, when you don't know yourself what happened? I tried to explain I got worried about my school work.

Dr. Daughtery wasn't impressed. He said my starving myself into the state I was in had to start much earlier than the last week or two. I tried to tell him I didn't eat because I just wasn't hungry, but he kept asking me what else I was worrying about. No matter how much I insisted it was just my school work, he kept asking questions. Finally, he blurted out, "What about that young man you're going with—Dr. Howard's son, Robert? Are you in love with him? Are you trying to starve because of him?"

I said, "For the love of mud! How did you know anything about him, anyway? How did you know I was going with him?"

He gave me a long speech about my being the daughter that he'd like to have. He'd known me so long and known my grandmother and mother so long he felt as if he were part of the family; and it was very important that I tell him the truth because, whether I knew it or not, I'd been very, very sick; I had practically starved to death.

I appreciated his personal interest in my family and me, but I couldn't see what my going with Robert Howard had to do with it. I told him I thought I had seen Bob outside my door while I was sick. He didn't say I hadn't, but he said Dr. Howard gave orders I was not to have any men visitors. Dr. Daughtery agreed with that. He and Dr. Howard talked a long time.

"Frankly," Dr. Daughtery said, "a girl can starve herself to death if she loves a man but thinks he doesn't love her."

What I wanted to say was one of Bob's good, healthy damns, but I didn't.

I tried to impress upon Dr. Daughtery that my illness didn't have a thing to do with grieving over Bob. I also said, quite honestly, I was very sorry I didn't love Bob. In fact, I felt guilty that I didn't care for him. He was the only man I'd ever met who was doing something I'd only dreamed about—writing stories that sold. Bob was making a good living at it, too, which was exactly what I would like to do. I told him some of Bob's ideas were for the birds, but I enjoyed talking with him more than with any other man I'd ever known.

I looked Dr. Daughtery straight in the eye, and I said, "Dr. Daughtery, I am going to say this again and don't you forget it. I am sorry, very sorry I don't love Bob Howard. When a girl gets twenty-seven years old and isn't married, all the good men she meets are either married like Nat Williams, or they're jackasses like Bob Howard."

It was Dr. Daughtery who blinked, not I. Then he started telling me why he was worried. He knew Dr. Howard very well, had talked with him several times about his family problems of which Bob seemed to be an important part. He had tried to get Dr. Howard to come to Brownwood and practice with him, thinking it would be beneficial for both of them. But when I asked him why Dr. Howard hadn't come, he stopped, toyed with a paper weight on his desk for a minute, put it down and looked at me. "I'm not sure I know."

He picked up the paper weight again and turned it round and round in his hands as if examining it carefully.

Then he said, "Has Robert ever said to you that he didn't want to live after his mother dies?"

I shrugged that off. "Dr. Daughtery, when I was a kid and got mad at Mother, I thought about killing myself to make her sorry. Bob still makes stupid remarks like that once in a while, but it's all baloney. He just wants me to sympathize with him and try to talk him out of it. I used to do that; but the last time he said anything like that I agreed it might be a good idea, and he shut up about it mighty quick."

I shook my head, thinking about Bob, seeing him as he rode along, enthusiastic about so many things, sorry about so many things. Aloud, I said, "He's a good writer. Very good. I think the world will know it, too, if he ever writes the novel he wants to write."

"He seems very attached to his mother," Dr. Daughtery said.

"So are all of us," I snapped. Then because there was something about Bob's affection for his mother that had always bothered me, and because Dr. Daughtery was a dear friend and a good listener to my thoughts, I leaned toward him. "I don't think it's all affection," I said slowly.

Then I told him what I thought about Bob, his mother, and the almost fanatical way Bob took care of her. Dr. Daughtery didn't say anything. He sat, holding the paper weight, and stared at me. When I finished, he gave a low whistle. "You may be right," he said. He nodded his head and said it again.

"You may be right. Either way, I hope you won't get serious about him."

I was aggravated. Again, I tried to explain that Bob was very well read and interesting to talk with. I said that, although Bob didn't like psychologists or their brothers who wrote psychological novels, we did talk a lot about William and Henry James as well as Bacon, Voltaire, and Roosevelt.

"There are other men in the world to talk with about those things," Dr. Daughtery said firmly.

As patiently as I could, I explained that you didn't meet that kind of man but once in a lifetime.

I was almost angry with Dr. Daughtery, and I didn't want to be. He'd been too good to my family and me. He'd stayed at the hospital every night while I was so sick, always right there to take care of me. He loved my grandmother and my mother. I had to remember that.

But he knew Bob, too, it turned out; knew about his writing, his affection for his mother, everything. He'd met him, talked with him, seen him a good many times, and he definitely didn't like him. He did like Dr. Howard, although he didn't have too much admiration for Mrs. Howard. He thought it was time for me to think about going with someone else.

I was beginning to feel frustrated; I was trying so hard to explain to Dr. Daughtery that I knew in my heart I'd never meet another writer like Bob, one I'd enjoy talking with the way I liked to talk with Bob. Dr. Daughtery wouldn't listen. He asked me if I had ever read any of Hegel's writings. I said I had read about Hegel, but I'd never read anything he'd written and that Bob never talked about him.

Dr. Daughtery had a point to make. When he was a young man in college, he and a group of his fellow students used to get together to discuss philosophy. Hegel was his favorite. Not that he could understand him, but the fun of reading Hegel was in trying to understand him. Then he made his big point. "In all my years of being married, I've never talked to my wife about Hegel's philosophy, not even one time. You don't talk about those things when you're married. You have other, more important things to discuss."

His point fell flat. I wasn't thinking about marrying Bob for one thing. For another, I knew Mrs. Daughtery. She was a sweet, unattractive, wonderful, German-speaking little hausfrau, not like me.

When I didn't say anything, Dr. Daughtery began to talk of his prescription for me. Recently, he'd read something in a paper about the University of Wisconsin and their professional speech department. It had made him think of me. Part of my prescription would be for me to look it up and go to school there; get out of Brown County; get out of Texas; go somewhere else. People who lived all their lives in one state and one section of the country became stagnant. Provincial. All of us, especially me, needed to get away from where we'd grown up, meet new people, people who wanted to talk about philosophy and things of that type.

Go to school in Wisconsin! Impossible! It would be easier to try to go to Europe in a tub. For some unknown reason, he was trying to get me away from Cross Plains and Bob.

Patiently, I explained that I couldn't go to the University of Wisconsin. But the idea of going to a new place was exciting. Getting away from the things I knew would also be exciting. Stimulating. As I explained why I couldn't go to Wisconsin, I told him I'd just bought a book on speech, written by two Louisiana State University professors, and I'd read a lot about them in speech journals. I said maybe I could save my money for a year and go to Louisiana. Dr. Daughtery got very excited about that. To him, it was settled.

The rest of his prescription was dumb in a way. He gave me a tonic which I expected him to do. I was to eat three meals a day, whether I was hungry or not, go to bed at nine o'clock every night, and go to Louisiana State University next summer. I was also to stop seeing Bob Howard!

I agreed to take the medicine he gave me. I'd eat. I never wanted to be that sick again. I would go to bed before midnight. If possible, before eleven. At least before twelve!

Not to see Bob? I enjoyed talking with Bob and being with him too much to stop, especially since I wasn't in love with him. Besides, I felt guilty sitting here in a doctor's office talking about him. It wouldn't be long until school was out; and I doubted that I'd see very much of him during the summer. He was too concerned about his mother's health to leave her alone much of the time.

I also agreed to write to Louisiana State University, as soon as I got back to Cross Plains. Finally, I promised, on my honor, to spend the summer of 1936, attending Louisiana State University.

Back in Cross Plains . . .
After my sojourn in the hospital . . .

Mother always brings me back to Cross Plains early Sunday afternoon, because she must hurry home to milk the cows and do the night work about the farm. Mrs. Hemphill said she would have a late supper tonight. Ethel went home for the weekend and isn't coming in until late. Mr. Hemphill has gone to a meeting that is expected to last until almost seven.

I had a long afternoon ahead of me.

Mrs. Hemphill told me that Bob had called several times. I saw Mother frown, and she said very quickly that I should lie down and rest until supper. She knew I was still weak and needed rest. I listened without protest or argument. I sat down on the bed, turned on the radio, and avoided her eyes. On the street, some kids were playing ball. The wind moved the curtains, and I watched the ballgame indifferently.

I thought: I really am weak and tired. All the way to Cross Plains, when Mother tried to reinforce Dr. Daughtery's prescription for me to eat and rest, I had not said a word. I was sorry for Mother. During the past week, I suffered pain, but the anxiety and worry had been hers. It didn't seem quite fair to me.

After Mother left, I sat for a few minutes, just watching the boys. Mrs. Hemphill went back to her part of the house, assuring me that if I needed anything, she would be happy to help.

I thought of Bob.

It had been a month since I had seen him. So many things had happened, it didn't seem just one month. Suddenly, I wanted to see him. I wanted to talk with him, listen to him weave fantastic yarns of early Texas or of some prehistoric age. But it wasn't just yarns I wanted to hear. I wanted to see Bob. I wanted to be with him. His presence filled a vacuum in my life.

It occurred to me that I could sit here on the side of this bed and do nothing until I began to feel worse than ever. I could rest, or I could get up and make an effort toward putting things in my life in order.

A thousand silly, romantic thoughts rushed happily over me as I started for the telephone. Bob and I were right for each other. I had lied to Mother and Dr. Daughtery when I said I didn't care for him. I had lied to myself. I loved Bob.

He answered the telephone and his voice sounded as glad to hear from me as I was to hear from him. His words poured out rapidly. How was I? God. Didn't I know that I had scared the devil out of him? When did I get back to town? It hadn't been more than thirty minutes since he'd tried to call me. By God, he was coming right over.

I laughed happily, beginning to tremble. "I've got to be home for supper."

There was a slight pause. "I want to see you, damn it."

He was there almost before I could powder my face and tell a disapproving Mrs. Hemphill I was going for a ride.

He came in and we greeted each other, as though we had not seen each other in ages. A month? It had been a thousand years, in an illimitable reach of time! I leaned against him, laughing, hoping he would not notice how shaky my laughter was. I thought wildly: I am in love. I am in love.

Although he did not have on a coat and tie, Bob looked great; better to me than he'd ever looked. He had on a blue shirt, a pair of dark gray pants that reached well down around his ankles. He dressed like that now to please me.

"Let's ride a while," he said, and we went outside to the car.

Going down the walk, he hovered over me, talking rapidly. How did I feel? Would I like to ride out the highway toward Coleman? By God, what happened? Worked myself to death, that was what. He'd known I was going to do that. Wouldn't listen to ol' Bob when he tried to tell me.

The way he was fussing over me pleased me, made me feel important, the way a man should make a woman feel.

I said I was all right and Dr. Daughtery had greatly exaggerated when he said I had almost starved myself to death. Bob said he wasn't sure about that. His father had told him the same thing.

As he started the engine, he turned and looked at me, and I realized something was bothering him. I could see it in the tenseness of his body, the way he moved his hands in jerky, quick motions. I could see it more plainly in his troubled, question-filled eyes.

He guided the car slowly past the ballgame. It doesn't take long to drive through Cross Plains and out the Coleman highway past his home. As we neared the place, I saw him glance uneasily toward the house.

"How is your mother?" I asked.

That set him off. It was his mother and his responsibility toward her that he was worried about. Not me. Not really. He ran his hand through his hair and shook his head.

"She's so-so! I wish I could report a much better recovery then she's had. I'd like to have her well again. There's so much I want to do."

I wanted to show my concern. I asked him if the operation had been as successful as he had hoped it would be. He shook his head as if in anger. It seemed to me his eyes were becoming more agitated, more questioning.

"She's suffered so much," he said harshly, "and she has tried to keep it from interfering with my life." He took out his handkerchief and wiped his face. "She's very brave."

I couldn't say anything. Suddenly, the beautiful day was drab. I began to hurt inside.

Bob whirled toward me, his eyes begging me to understand something I would probably never understand. His voice sounded hoarse. "You know, don't you, that as long as my mother needs me, I'm not free?"

I didn't say a word.

He explained, then, that the wound from her operation had abcessed, and he was taking her to Coleman two or three times a week to have it dressed because his father didn't have the proper facilities to take care of it.

As gruff as Dr. Howard is, I felt sorry for him, working as he did without the proper tools—doing his best against the odds. In spite of Bob's worry about his mother, it was his father I felt sorry for.

I knew I must change the subject, get Bob's mind off his mother to something less emotional for him.

"By-the-way. Congratulations on your father's being chosen Man-of-the-Year."

I didn't expect Bob's reaction to be a burst of sudden anger.

"Yeah. I suppose they were trying to make up to him for the long hours and little pay he gets." He hit the steering wheel with his fist; then he ran his fingers through his hair. As he struggled to control his anger, he began again. "You're proud of an honor when you're part of the town, when you're at peace with your neighbors." He paused and his voice became less harsh. "Though I suppose you appreciate an honor any time you receive it, damn it, buying food is even more important."

Again, I wanted to change the subject. "Bob, you're always saying you'd like to live in a larger town than Cross Plains. What about Brownwood?"

"I've lived there," he said indifferently. "I like it. It doesn't have too much to offer, but I have some good friends there. I think I could write in Brownwood, without having people call me a lazy, good-for-nothing bastard." He paused. "My mother would enjoy living there more than she does living in Cross Plains or any other small town."

"Dr. Daughtery told me he asked your dad to come to Brownwood to practice," I said. "I'm surprised he didn't go."

Since Dr. Howard had a chance to go to a larger place and didn't, was he, too, afraid of something . . . something intangible? Did he, like Bob, know some secret fear that kept him from going on to bigger and better things?

Bob shook his head. "You don't know my father very well."

He tried to explain it to me. His father damn sure wasn't as interested in money as he himself was. Part of the trouble was that his dad felt he had a mission to perform in a small town. Mission, hell! Did I think for one minute he'd slave long hours at the typewriter, if there weren't any money in it? If there weren't always the chance and the hope he'd make bigger money?

He looked boyish then, and I felt sorry for him. "You can't fool me," I said. "You love sitting in there at the typewriter and shouting fantastic stories to the top of your voice. You were born to write. It's the only thing you want to do."

He smiled, and I could see he was beginning to relax. "You're right. You're damn right. I wouldn't spend an hour doing anything else. Hack that I am."

"You're no hack." I shrugged my shoulders. "You'll write that novel some day—the one even the critics are going to like—the one about Texas you're always talking about. It'll bring you fame and prestige as well as money."

He laughed. "I wish I could be as sure of it as you seem to be. I'd take my mother away from this place."

Always back to his mother! It didn't matter that I didn't want to talk about Mrs. Howard. She was there. Right between us, as big as life. If I turned my head, I could see her slightly disapproving look. It left me completely without self-confidence. I tried to settle myself more comfortably and clasped my hands to make sure they didn't begin their silly shaking again.

When he spoke, his voice was quiet as if his anger at life and fate had gone from him. "My dad has a great talent, more than a place like Cross Plains realizes; Brownwood would have been much better; but if he were to leave here, he'd settle for some place no bigger and no better than Cross Plains."

I said lamely, "I like small towns."

Bob seemed to be feeling better now. He began his good-humored, breezy caballero act then. He started that old tune of his about a woman tying a man down, keeping him from being free.

I knew he was trying to be funny, but I didn't laugh when I said, "Is that the way your dad feels about your mother?"

That shut him up. He took a deep breath and began defending his father. He said when his father was young, he got this crazy idea—like some of mine—that he had to try to save the world. His father could have been a great doctor if he had only tried.

But it was his mother he really wanted to talk about. His responsibility to her and to himself. It's a problem all of us face, but it was more serious to him then to a lot of other people.

He talked, and I listened. The joke, I told myself, was on me, and I needed to laugh at myself. He was not going to say the words I wanted to hear. Not today. He could make no commitment of himself.

He said, "I suppose the truth is that as good a man as my father is, he doesn't always appreciate how helpful and good Mother has been to him. If he'd gone to a larger place like Brownwood, he might have been able to be at home more; then Mother and I wouldn't have been left alone so much at night. Mother was afraid, afraid to leave a window shade up." He smiled ruefully. "I guess she was always afraid of Indians."

He meant that as a teasing joke to me, calling me an Indian.

After a short silence, he spoke again. "I can never do enough to repay Mother for all she's done for me. You know that, don't you?"

I didn't say anything, and he repeated himself. "You've got to understand that, Novalyne. My mother needs me, and I've got to give her the best I can, even when it interferes with my dating, or writing, or anything else."

For a minute, I just looked at him. He realizes how weak and unhappy I am today and that I want more than friendship from him. But his problem is in the way. What he doesn't know . . . and can't see . . . is that this problem is as old as the history he loves to talk about, and every man and woman has to decide what he owes his mother and what he owes himself. I had ideas on the subject—definite ideas. I began to try to make Bob see how other people solved this same problem. I believed he could take care of his mother without denying himself love and success.

"Bob," I said, "No man or woman can repay his mother for all she's done for him, but we also have our own lives to lead. Our mothers—"

"I live my own life," Bob interrupted quickly. "I am free. I come and go as I please. My mother never interferes with that."

He began to turn the car around. Evidently aware of my unbelieving look, he spoke again with a little more force. "My mother wants me to have friends who are interested in the same things I am, and there's damn few of those. She'd never interfere with my life in any way. If we lived in a larger place, she'd—"

I interrupted him. "What I don't understand is if your mother wasn't happy in small towns, why didn't she leave your dad?"

He was shocked. "What in the name of God are you saying?"

"When I was little, my mother realized her marriage was not the way she wanted it to be; she and my father separated."

Bob did not seem able to speak. He glared at me.

My hands were clenched so tightly, they were moist. I was trembling again. But I told him my family story—how we solved the problem. I told him my father was a good man, a hard worker, but he was restless and wanted to roam. Mother was not like that. She wanted to stay in one place and try to own the little plot of ground her house was on. They separated. He'd been gone twenty-three years, and I'd only seen him twice. But Mother and I had gotten along all right. We'd made it okay.

I didn't see in Bob's eyes what I wanted to see.

"My mother always felt that once you got married, that was it. You stayed married." He sounded disapproving of my mother and me.

"My mother married again." I said defiantly.

I told him that she married a good man the second time, too, a man whose family once had a lot of money. Then things went wrong. His mother and father didn't seem to like me. They thought Mother ought to give me to my grandmother.

"One trouble with my stepfather was that he was tied to his mother's apron strings," I said, and I could hear my voice accusing Bob of being tied to his mother's apron strings. "Every time anything went wrong between him and mother, he ran to tell his mother about it. A marriage should be between two people. It—"

"My mother would never interfere with my marriage." Bob was emphatic. "She'd never do anything to hurt anybody, especially the woman I married."

"No marriage is all bad or all good," I said wearily. "While Mother was married to my stepfather, I knew the happiest time of my life, and I also knew the biggest hurt I ever had—one that has stayed with me always."

"How in the hell—" Bob began.

"The best, most carefree-being-young-girl-time I ever had in my life was at my stepfather's sister's house—Nina's. I'll never forget that."

I looked past Bob to the green trees bowing in the wind. Why, on a pretty day like this, did I have to hurt so much? Why did I have to remember the other time? Why did I have to try to explain something to Bob?

"But the thing that hurt so happened before that," I said. "Soon after my mother's second marriage, I had an operation that my stepfather's mother and father didn't think I needed. Afterwards, my step-grandfather and Mother had a big argument in which both of them said harsh things. He had on a pair of gloves. As he took them off, he said, 'I wash my hands of this whole affair, and I want you to know we don't care anymore for that kid in there, than we would about any other little waif we'd pick up off the street.' "

"My God," Bob said.

"After he left," I said, "I went outside and stood at the gate in our back yard and looked in the direction of my grandmother's house. I said out loud, 'Mammy, I'm not a waif. No grandchild of yours could ever be a waif.' "

"Did you tell your grandmother what happened?" Bob's eyes were kind, but I didn't want sympathy. Not as a substitute for love.

I shook my head. "No. It would have hurt her, and I knew I could take it. I learned that day that no matter how much words hurt you, you can hold your head up and keep right on going."

I looked at the barbed wire fence along the side of the road. Usually, along here, Bob began some of his stories about the wire cutting episodes of the 1890's—the war between cattle growers and the farmers moving in. Today, he was intent on other things.

"Is it possible you broke up your mother's second marriage?"

I didn't want to think that. No part of the conversation had gone the way I wanted it to. "I suppose so. I did everything my stepfather didn't want me to do. Yes, I'm sure I helped break it up."

Bob was shocked. "You made things worse for your mother?"

I wondered how you could start out with one idea and wind up with one that was just its opposite.

"I didn't mean to. He objected to my having friends out to the house, and I had them anyway. When I got into my teens, he objected to my driving the car. Once, I made enough money from my expression classes to pay off a note on the car, and so I drove it anyway. When it was time for me to go to college, I got a scholarship to Daniel Baker. He and all his family had gone to Howard Payne. I hated Howard Payne."

Bob didn't say anything. If you're going to kill yourself, I thought, do it all the way. I went on. "One semester, I enrolled and got a job working for my room and meals. I wasn't making enough to buy textbooks, and so I got discouraged. I went into the office and resigned. About an hour later, Mother came to see me. She said, very sadly, my stepfather wanted her to ask me to drop out of college, continue working, save my money, and wait a year before trying it again."

Bob nodded. "Sounds reasonable."

"It was," I admitted, "but I didn't tell Mother I had just resigned. As soon as she left, I went back up to the college and got myself reinstated. I finished the semester."

"Without any textbooks?"

"It was the only way," I said miserably.

Bob shook his head. "I believe you're the stubbornest woman in the United States. I suppose all it takes to get you to do something is just tell you you can't do it."

I couldn't answer. Bob moved restlessly, frowning. Suddenly, he whirled toward me, his eyes dark and troubled. "I have to ask you this: You do love your mother, don't you?"

I stared at him. "Certainly. I love my mother very much, but I want to live a life that's completely free and independent from her."

"You owe her everything," he said vehemently.

"Not my life," I insisted just as vehemently. "I want Mother to get married again. I don't want her to be the least bit dependent on me for happiness or anything else. I wouldn't interfere with her marriage now, because I'm grown and out on my own. She'd have a chance for happiness."

"Your mother is a lot younger than my mother," Bob said thoughtfully. "It might be all right for her to marry again. But my mother is already free and independent of me."

We rode without talking; I told myself that this was over, and in a few days I would stop hurting. We were closer to Cross Plains now, almost to the "Peaks" where he usually wove stories of Spanish gold and Indian massacres.

When Bob spoke, he was not weaving stories of Spanish gold. "What would you do if your mother were old and sick? An invalid? Would you want to live your own life so much you'd leave her?"

"Certainly not!" I said heatedly. "But I would keep on working. I don't know how to take care of sick people. I'd work myself to death to hire someone else to take care of her."

"God, I don't understand you," was all he said.

We were almost home. I pressed my fingers against my temples to ease their throbbing.

The boys were still playing ball in the street and still arguing. The sun was setting, and the sky was rose colored. Bob walked beside me to the door, trying vainly to be cheerful now. "What about my coming over some afternoon when you get off from school. We could ride around, and I'd shoot my mouth off . . . as usual."

I managed a smile. "I'll be trying to get my children's theatre going at school. Helen Grace has been by herself for a couple of weeks now. I was working on County meet before I got sick and couldn't help her. Beatrice

Minton is supposed to direct a one-act play for the freshman dramatic club. I'll be awfully busy trying to catch up with that and my classes. I'd better not plan on doing anything but working."

"You're going to make yourself sick again," he complained. "All right, how about Friday night?" He paused, then, and his eyes were dark with questions. "You will go with me again, won't you?"

"Of course," I said. "Why not? Friday night is fine."

He went down the walk and I stood, looking at the sunset. Suddenly, he turned to me, trying to be humorous. "Look, girl. That's a beautiful sunset if I do say so myself."

I smiled weakly. "Thank you. I appreciate it."

He was gone. I stood looking at the sky, fighting another feeling of nausea and weakness. The boys attracted my attention. Two of them were fighting. The larger one knocked the smaller one down. The fight was over. The little boy got to his feet, crying, beaten, and accepting it. Out of his rage and helplessness, he called out, "I hope you stomp your toe and break your neck!"

I didn't laugh. I knew how he felt, and I shared his defeat. Bob's car was out of sight now, but I looked at the empty street and thought: I hope the time comes, Bob, when you want me to say "I love you," as much as I wanted you to say it to me today. But I'll never say it. I hope you hurt as much as I hurt now.

Friday night . . .
After a happy date with Bob . . .

This week at school had its ups and downs. Mostly ups. When I was sick, I knew that in spite of it all, everything would turn out all right. It did. I worked like mad all week. By Friday night, I was glad Bob was coming, for I wanted to get away from the house—to get out and ride around.

Ethel said, "Oh, my, my. Going to a show?"

I said, "Yes." But I knew darn well we were not; we'd ride around and talk—but not about the things we talked about last Sunday. I'd see to that.

The good thing about seeing Bob tonight was that he was in just as good a mood as I was. He was exuberant. Vital. Interested in talking. A yarn he was working on had gone right. "They don't always do that," he said, enthusiastically, "but, sometimes, like this one, they write themselves without any effort on my part. A western." He ran his hand through his hair. "Did you ever read any of Ring Lardner's baseball stories?"

"A few."

"Well, I'll tell you," Bob said, "what he did for the baseball players ought to be done for the American cowboy. It would be very different, of course, as to content. There should be yarns about a cowboy who ain't just riding the range. One who's big, dumb, and helpful to settlers moving in, depending on the kind of help they need. The cowboy had his lighter moments; his fun; sometimes bustin' up a whole village was fun."

We talked about cowboys. Then Bob volunteered that he wasn't through writing Conan stories. I was sorry about that, for I don't care much for Conan, what little I've scanned through.

Bob said he had an idea for a Conan yarn that was about to jell. Hadn't got to the place where he was ready to write it. All he'd done so far was make a few notes, put it aside to let it lie there in his subconscious till it was fully built up.

"What's this one about?" I asked.

"I think this time I'm going to make it one of the sexiest, goriest yarns I've ever written. I don't think you'd care for it."

"Not if it's gory." I looked at him a little puzzled. "What do you mean 'sexy stories?' "

"My God. My Conan yarns are filled with sex."

The thought passed through my mind that sex in stories was a peculiar subject for a young man and woman to be discussing. However, I put it aside. After all, for heaven's sake, here we are in the year of our Lord, 1935, and we know a few things about life. We know there's been a lot of sex around in the last five thousand years of civilization, and so I suppose it doesn't hurt to talk about it as it is in stories. But I couldn't see that the Conan yarns Bob had brought me to read had any sex in them. Gore, yes. Sex, no.

"You have sex in the Conan yarns?" I said unbelievingly.

"Hell, yes. That's what he did—drinking, whoring, fighting. What else was there in life?"

I thought of a story he'd brought me a couple of months ago. I couldn't think of the name of it, and I hadn't read it closely. If he got technical and asked me what was in it, I wouldn't be able to tell him. About the only thing I remembered was there'd been a naked woman in it.

"I don't see anything sexy about a naked woman dancing around on a ship."

"You don't? For God's sake!" Bob barked the words out.

"No," I said, and it was all I could do to keep from laughing.

He took an audible breath. "My God, she danced the mating dance. What could be more sexy?"

"I thought she was crazy," I said. "There she was captain of a pirate ship, and running around naked. Naked in front of all those slaves or whatever you call them—soldiers, sailors. Anyway, those black men around her."

Question his story and Bob becomes belligerent. "What you don't understand was they were black."

"All eunuchs, I suppose," I said. That struck me as being so funny I began to laugh and couldn't stop.

Bob seemed stunned at first. He said that in such a situation the black slaves thought of the girl as a goddess. He explained, emphatically, that when people were dedicated to a particular belief, the belief makes the impossible normal.

"What do you think would be a sexy story?" he asked. "If you don't think naked women are sexy, what would be? Would a naked man be sexy?"

I pride myself that I can keep my mouth shut when I have to. I wondered what Mrs. Howard would say to a question like that. It occurred to me what she would answer, and so I folded my hands in my lap, drew my lips in a pious line, and said sweetly, "I would turn my head and look the other way."

Bob whirled and looked at me so quickly, I felt as though the car might leave the road. Did I imitate his mother so perfectly? I have imitated someone before and other people knew who it was. I decided to drop the imitation then and there.

"You probably would," Bob grunted. He gave his attention to his driving. "Go on. Tell me what you'd consider a sexy story."

During my last year in college, I'd read several of D. H. Lawrence's books. I could see they were sexy. I didn't know whether to tell Bob about reading them or not. Maybe it would be best to change the subject, and I did.

"I haven't written very much lately," I said. "Just a few conversations I've had with people."

Bob, too, seemed willing to drop the subject of sex and talk about all the different subjects we could find to talk about.

"You waste a lot of time copying conversations, I think," he said. "I don't mean to be giving you advice, but it seems to me while you're writing down conversations you have had, you could use them just as a basis for a yarn. What conversations have you been writing down this time?"

"One I had with Nat not long ago. It would be absolutely perfect as the beginning for a one-act play."

"At times, I've written down things friends have said," Bob admitted. "I may have used something similar in a yarn, but I doubt very seriously that you can take a real life conversation and transcribe it directly into a yarn."

"Let me explain it to you," I said, borrowing one of his expressions. "Let me give you the background, and you'll see how it could be used word for word as I have it."

"Give me the background," Bob said with mock resignation. "I want to hear it."

"Some time ago in my history classes, I said that the Catholic Church was the oldest organized church in existence, and that to be a Protestant was to protest against the Catholic Church."

"Nothing about that is unusual," Bob said. "That's not exactly a world shaking statement; however, it could be here in this town."

"It was unusual in this town," I said. "Immediately, one of my students said, 'It's not the oldest church in the world. The Church of Christ is the oldest church in the world.' Then, of course, I explained that John Campbell established the Church of Christ, which is why they are sometimes referred to as Campbellites. That didn't satisfy him. He insisted that Christ established his church. I was all set to argue, and I said emphatically that Christ did not establish any church. It was St. Paul who established the first church. About that time, another kid said that his church was established by John the Baptist. I tried to explain to both of them that the Baptist Church was based upon what the Baptist's *believed* were the teaching of John the Baptist, and that the Church of Christ was based upon what other people felt were the *real* teachings of Christ."

"I see nothing wrong with what you told them," Bob said, "but you may lose your job over something like that. Suppose the whole Campbellite congregation were to come up to see Nat about the heresy you're teaching their children?"

"For several days, I half expected them," I admitted. "If not the Campbellites, then the Baptists."

"Exactly. It wouldn't surprise me either," Bob said. "If you want to keep your job, and for some damn reason, I hope you do, I think you'd—uh—better keep your mouth shut."

"Nat agrees that I'd better shut up about religion," I said. "I will from now on. My conversation with him put a different light on the whole thing."

Bob was all interest. "What did Nat say? Did he back you or the kids?"

"It wasn't a question of 'backing' either one exactly," I said. "He explained to me that you don't destroy a child's faith in his religion. I had a right to teach the truth as I saw it, but I didn't have the right to make an issue out of something that might hurt a youngster."

"Isn't education supposed to weed out erroneous beliefs?" Bob asked dryly.

I didn't say anything for a minute. "I'll be sure to use that sentence when I write my play," I said lightly. "The play will concern a teacher who wants to teach the truth, regardless of the consequences. I can see it all on a brilliantly lighted stage. There is Nat sitting at his desk, and I walk into the room. I—"

"You throw your arms around him and kiss him," Bob interrupted.

"No. Damn it," I said. "But my point is that the conversation we had—word for word—as I have it written down, would fit right into my play. It would explain the action that went before—antecedent action. It would begin the action—inciting incident."

Bob grinned. "You may be right. You make it sound right; but it wouldn't work for me. What kind of story would you use this conversation in?"

"Simple enough," I said, trying to think of something. "I see great possibilities in it."

He laughed. I thought: "Here we are changing the subject again."

"You're always talking about going into old houses and old, old castles; down into labryinthine passages. Deep things," I said, remembering one of Henry James' short novels. "Suppose there was a lost manuscript. Suppose the manuscript dealt with something important like—"

"Like where we hid the body." Bob shook his head.

"Of course," I said lightly, "the world is sitting there, waiting; then the manuscript is found."

"I don't see it," Bob said. We laughed. "Speaking of lost manuscripts— and you were, you know. In the late 1800's, a lost manuscript of one of Shakespeare's plays was found, only it had Francis Bacon's initials on it."

"Oh, good heavens," I said. "What are you talking about?"

"I'm saying that this great Shakespeare whom we love, revere, was or may have been Francis Bacon."

"Oh, Clyde told me something like that once," I said. "but I didn't believe it then, and I don't now. Francis Bacon wrote essays and scientific stuff. I've read some of his essays. I think they're great essays, but I can't see them being turned into plays by Shakespeare."

"Now, girl," Bob said, getting enthusiastic, "that's where you're wrong. The thinking in those essays could very well have been in Shakespeare's plays. Read *Hamlet*. In it, you get something that was bothering the Elizabethans. Bacon especially. They still held to the old belief in blood revenge. You kill my father, and I'll kill your father."

Bob was excited enough to gesture with his hand. I watched him, amused, hoping he wouldn't take both hands off the steering wheel at once.

"Another idea was growing too, the idea of the responsibility of the State." He settled himself and began again. "Can't you just see those old Elizabethans sitting around talking, trying to decide whether revenge should be done by the next of kin or by the State? Bacon was especially interested in things like that. That's why he wrote his essay on revenge."

"You're crazy," I said, trying to remember just what Bacon's essay on revenge had been about.

"You read that essay and then read *Hamlet,*" Bob said. "See if you don't think that was one of Hamlet's problems."

"Don't worry," I said. "I've got a book that has a few of Bacon's essays in it. When I go home, I'll read it."

Bob was in his heaven on that subject. He kept on enthusiastically and exuberantly, telling me that William Shakespeare was an ignorant actor. How the only letters that had survived were about hops and grain and not about plays and acting. I listened, not believing, and not sure that he wanted me to believe. I was as fascinated by the story as he was. But, finally, when he said an actor couldn't have written the plays, I couldn't keep still.

"An actor could have written the plays," I said positively. "A good actor understands the human heart, not the human intellect always, but the human heart. In college, when I took a course in Shakespeare from Mrs. Wright, she stressed, over and over, that the plays were about people and their problems."

"William Shakespeare, the actor," Bob said, "was an unlettered man, who couldn't even write his name."

"You just said he wrote some letters!" I said, triumphantly.

"Don't bring that up," Bob laughed. "What I mean is that he was so ignorant he couldn't have written the plays, not while he was thinking of hops and beer."

"Baloney," I said scornfully. "Let me tell you what's going to happen to all these things you're writing. Someday, people will begin taking one of your stories apart. Like the one you say is coming out in *Weird Tales*—the one you like about the Picts—"

"Yeah," Bob said. "The triumph of a dog and the barbarian."

"Someday, some biographer will come along, and when he reads that story, he'll say, 'Who was this Robert E. Howard? He couldn't have written these stories. Why he was not college bred! Remember, when he went to Howard Payne, all he did was sit around writing yarns, trying to break into *Weird Tales*. He didn't even try to get a college degree! But isn't it written somewhere that he dated a school teacher who dreamed of being a writer?' "

Bob was listening with a broad grin on his face.

"He'll say: 'That school teacher wrote those yarns, every single one of them. Wrote 'em and didn't have nightmares at all.' "

"By God, you may have it right." Bob ran his fingers through his hair. "I wouldn't be a damn bit surprised. Trouble is they won't know that the school teacher only wanted to write things that are all sweetness and light. Nobody has any trouble. Nobody has a hard time. Everything works out. She marries a handsome superintendent—"

"How does she get rid of his wife and seven kids?" I bantered.

"Easy," Bob said. "She destroys her rivals with words. She even destroys poor innocent children's religion."

It was a great and wonderful night. We'd talked about a lot of different things. Along with the talk, the fun of being young and happy was there too. You laughed a lot and looked at the stars shining and far away. You saw the houses around you, but, somehow, in an unreal world: who knew where you were going or what came next?

Sunday . . . A near disaster . . .

"Mankind is on the edge of disaster." Bob has said that a thousand times. Today's date was almost a disaster.

He didn't come last night because, yesterday, he took his mother to Coleman for a treatment, and she didn't feel well when they came home. This afternoon, he was supposed to come at 1:30, but it was closer to 4:30, when he came. Neither of us was in a good humor. I resented his being late. He was restless, blue, and discouraged. When he gets in a mood like that, he talks about our rotting civilization and of imminent catastrophe. It was the main topic of his conversation the minute we got in the car to drive around.

"Suppose you're right," I said. "Suppose we are facing a cataclysmic disaster? What can we do? Why not get busy and trust in the Lord?"

Bob shook his head.

Then I tried to cheer him up. "Things are going to work out all right. You just wait and see. You've always said that man pulled himself up from the abyss. Well, he will again!"

"Oh, God," Bob groaned. "You remind me of Voltaire's Candide. No matter what had happened to Candide, whether he was beaten, robbed, turned into a jackass or what, he always remembered that Pangloss, the philosopher, had called this the best of all possible worlds."

I didn't say a word.

"What I'm talking about," Bob said patiently, "is that civilizations rise and fall. We've had our day. We face a new kind of cataclysm, one we're building ourselves. We're doomed and haven't got sense enough to know it."

"How are we building our doom?"

"Every way. We're tearing up nature and destroying it." He put his hand over his eyes and rubbed his head. "The earth has known cataclysms before. It was a great earthquake or a gigantic tidal wave that destroyed Atlantis and reduced it to the bed of the ocean. Thousands of years ago, ice settled over the land and destroyed life and vegetation. Those were things man had no control over. It's not that way today."

I didn't know what to say, for these were things I didn't like to think about.

He raised his arm and made a sweeping gesture toward the fields we were passing. "See those fields? Fifty years ago, this was a semi-tropical country. Trees. Vegetation. Grass as high as wheat today. Rains came. Then, what happened?" He answered his own question. "Men came in and began to destroy the trees, to plow up the land. When the winds came again, they blew the top soil away. Even the postoaks are having a hard time of it. Mesquites are going to take over. They've already taken over in Brown County. They'll get us here, too. Mesquites run their roots out a hundred feet in all directions, trying to suck up water that ain't there anymore."

"It looks like rain," I said, and felt awfully stupid.

Bob ignored me. "Man has destroyed this land. A man-made cataclysm." He turned and looked at me, an unhappy smile on his face. "You're right. No use to blame God with this one."

I tried to think of something else to talk about. "Roosevelt won a victory. It's now illegal to keep workers from joining a union."

It was another subject he liked to discuss. "I doubt it will work. Big industry will continue to squeeze the life blood out of the workers."

I am a labor sympathizer, but I was caught in a stubborn streak today. "These labor unions you praise so highly will be just as bad as industry, once they get in control," I said glibly. "With the law on their side now, you just watch what they do."

"The little man is nothing. He doesn't have a chance. Even the law won't protect him."

"Yes, it will," I insisted. "Everything will work out right. You'll see."

It was the first time today Bob had laughed. He began to turn the car around to go back to town. "Yeah." He laughed again. " 'The best of all possible worlds.' I'm going by the house and get *Candide* for you. Voltaire was a smart old devil. I want you to read that book; then tell me if you think this is the best of all possible worlds."

I waited in the car while he went into his house to get the book. I was beginning to feel depressed, for I didn't like to talk about the things we'd talked about today. I was also provoked with myself. I hadn't said a thing to help Bob, and many times, when I am blue and discouraged, he says the right thing to make me feel good again.

He was smiling when he brought the book to the car and gave it to me. "Be sure to read it," he said.

Our date was rather short today, for he brought me straight to Mrs. Hemphill's, after we left his house. When we got to the steps, he said, "I'll call you next week sometime. I'll write or call."

"I'm going home next Friday," I said. "I have to go back to see Dr. Daughtery. I'll be in Brownwood all weekend."

"I can't promise to come after you. I don't know how Mother will be feeling."

"I don't know what time I'll get back next Sunday."

He said, "I'll call you."

I didn't go into the house. I stood on the steps to enjoy the long Texas twilight, with all the sounds a little town makes getting ready to go inside its house and close its doors.

I watched Bob drive away. He didn't look back. He had a problem he couldn't solve. He had spent all of yesterday and most of today taking care of his mother. Usually, that doesn't keep him from being happy. But, today, he kept wiping his hands across his forehead as if his head hurt. But he denied it when I asked him if he had a headache. He moved constantly, but without the exuberance and vitality with which he usually moved. Something was wrong; yet he had talked of everything, except whatever it was that troubled him. Just before we got to town, he said he was not ready to go back home to work on a damn yarn. He might never write anything else as long as he lived.

I wondered if that meant he was thinking of leaving here and going to some far-off country, as he sometimes talked of doing. Maybe in some other place, he would feel like writing again, but I would hate for him to leave here.

A wave of sadness settled over me. Things would change. I loved this town, but things would change! Enid was writing letters now, trying to find a new job with more pay. She deserved it. And Nat. Nat would not stay here forever. Other places wanted him now.

Bob was right. Things change. But I didn't want them to change. I could not imagine this town without Enid. Nat. And Bob. Without all of them. Especially Bob.

"The art of storytelling," Bob said,
"is in knowing which is the end and
which is the beginning."

It happened!

Truett Vinson is Bob's best friend. I had a date with Truett last Saturday night!

One of Bob's favorite reincarnation stories is that in every previous life he has lived, his best friend always steals his best girl from him. This same devastating thing keeps happening over and over again.

My date with Truett just happened. It was not planned. I had never even thought about dating Truett Vinson!

Saturday morning, I went to town to keep my appointment with Dr. Daughtery and to shop a little. It began to rain, and I hurried into the bookstore, not only to get out of the rain, but to look for a book I wanted. Truett was there; we talked a few minutes about books, where I was teaching, and where he was working. He asked me if I wanted to go to the show that night, and I said yes.

All the way home, I kept telling myself how glad Bob would be about it.

Bob would be glad for both of us. After all, I didn't have to be smart to know Bob wasn't really interested in me. There was his obligation to his mother, and a woman ties a man down! Don't forget that!

I reminded myself that if Bob had cared anything about me, he would have shown it the Sunday I got back to Cross Plains after my stay in the hospital. That day, he had made it clear that his obligations to his mother came *first* in his life. The silly thing I had thought about, hoping someday he would hurt as much as I hurt, was ridiculous. I was sorry I had even allowed myself to think something like that.

Clyde Smith, Robert Howard, and Truett Vinson. Three close friends. Three friends who liked to read, talk, and try to solve the problems of the world. Now, when I dated Truett, I will have dated all three!

Clyde and I had known each other from our grammar school days and through high school. I knew Truett slightly in high school, but even though Bob was there I didn't know him. Clyde introduced me to Bob, but when Bob and I started going together, Clyde was already married. Everything was fine. No problem at all!

When Truett came into my life, things were not over with Bob, but there was no problem. The three of us would be good friends. The three of us might get together some time and talk and argue about books and writing.

Truett. Definitely the best looking one of the three. Black hair, blue eyes. He's as good looking as Nat Williams, and no doubt as brilliant as Clyde and Bob. Truett is tall. More than six feet. Six-feet-four, and he weighs close to two hundred pounds. On him, two hundred pounds look great. I kept thinking: Is this the beginning of the story, or the end of the story?

One's impression of Truett is that he is a very quiet man. You will probably never know what he is thinking. With Clyde and Bob, you know what they're thinking, because they tell you in no uncertain terms.

Truett seems different. Clyde respects him. Bob calls him an ascetic. I thought of that several times during the movie, but I always dismissed it quickly. I could see no problem with Bob Howard about my dating Truett Vinson or anyone else. Why, then, I asked myself, should I feel any sense of guilt about dating Truett? It was none of Bob's business whom I went with.

Being with Truett was so pleasant, I could take time to enjoy the slow falling rain. After the show, we talked about books and found that we liked many of the same ones. We talked about authors of books, and the conversation was stimulating. At my home, we stood on our front porch a few minutes, listening to the rain falling off the house, and he asked me for a date the next time I was in Brownwood. That, I thought, would make those two-week trips home more enjoyable. I didn't have long to feel happy. It was Truett who mentioned Bob.

"Are you still going with Bob?"

Instantly, I was on the defensive. I wanted to lie and couldn't. I wanted to say, "It's none of your business." And didn't.

"Yes," I said.

Truett Vinson

Truett Vinson, Tevis Clyde Smith and Robert E. Howard were close friends. They became acquainted when Howard attended Brownwood High School in 1922-1923.

Truett didn't say anything for a minute. He just stood still, looking off into the night.

"Are you going to tell Bob you had a date with me?"

At that moment, I wasn't sure. All I could think of was that two weeks from now, I was going to have another date with Truett. Was this the beginning or the end of the story? I had no way of knowing whether he or I would want to continue the relationship two weeks or two months from now.

Neither am I married to, nor engaged to Bob.

Reluctantly, I said, "I suppose so. I—I—I certainly don't think Bob will care."

"Why not?"

"Because," I said, "it really—"

I stopped. What could I say to Truett? Could I say, "A girl gets damn tired of having a man's mother for a rival?" For God's sake, no! I tried to explain how I felt.

"Bob and I are just friends. Nothing more."

And that was the truth. *Let it drop, Truett!*

"I'll tell him myself," Truett said, and laughed. "I don't know how he'll take it. He's funny."

"Yes," I agreed hastily. "He does have some funny ideas. He's always talking about being born over and over throughout the ages, and every time—" My sentence broke off in mid air; yet I was expected to finish, "his best friend always takes his girl away from him."

Truett laughed. "He still tells stories like that?"

"Oh, yes. That along with a lot of others."

We laughed. The slow dripping of the rain off the house was music.

"I know." Truett turned and looked at me. "I wouldn't want to do anything to hurt Bob."

That upset me. What about me? There were more than two sides to this question. School would soon be over. I'd have a long summer ahead of me. I would stay pretty much at home, study for next year's classes, write some, but there'd be times when I'd want to go to a picture show or just talk about books and writers. How often would Mrs. Howard be feeling upset and Bob wouldn't be able to come over?

I didn't want to marry anybody. I just wanted to date Truett while I was in Brownwood, and Bob while I was in Cross Plains. I didn't want any complications.

"Don't worry," I said flatly. "I'm not in love with Bob, and Bob doesn't care for me either. I like him as a friend. Nothing more."

And it was the truth. And it was not the truth. I didn't know what the truth was. Not anymore.

What was lost is found . . .
What is found is lost forever . . .

Bob had said he was going to call me late Sunday afternoon when I got back from Brownwood. He did not. He came Monday afternoon the minute school was out. Before I could get into the house to take off my hat, Bob was there. No date. No word. Just came.

The first thought that flashed through my mind was, "I'll tell him about my date with Truett." But another thought came almost immediately. "Why? If he'd had a date with someone else, he wouldn't tell me. Men never do."

"Just dropped over," he said, "to see if you might like to ride around for a while before supper."

I said I would, but I was neither enthusiastic nor unenthusiastic. I'd tell him, of course. I'd told Truett I would.

Bob headed the car toward Coleman.

"We had some rain last week. Did it rain in Brownwood?"

I remembered the rain falling off the house Saturday night as Truett and I talked. "Some," I said. "When I got back to Cross Plains yesterday, Mr. Hemphill called it a million dollar rain."

Bob nodded. "That's what they're calling it. I suppose it was worth a million to the farmers. It rains so little these days."

There was an irony in this if you wanted to laugh about it. Here we were talking about the rain! Everybody in this country talks about the rain. Why should we be an exception? It's a good, safe subject. Let's talk about the rain!

"Now, a long time ago," Bob began.

Suddenly, I didn't want to hear about conditions fifty or a hundred years ago. Right now, 1935, bothered me. To live your life fully, you can't get stuck in time a hundred, a thousand or ten million years ago.

"I saw Truett this weekend when I was home," I said. "Truett Vinson."

"That's good," Bob said indifferently. "How is he getting along?"

I hesitated a moment, fighting that darn sense of guilt. I started to say, "I had a date with him." But I didn't.

"I suppose he's okay," I said.

I was willing to let it end there.

Bob wasn't. He started talking about Truett and Clyde and all the things they used to do. I interrupted. "You do talk about books and writing, don't you?"

"Hell," he said. "We talk about everything. Name it. We talk about it. Mostly we talk about girls, about getting drunk, and about girls."

I ignored that. They were intellectuals. I was interested in what they talked about. It would prove something to me.

"Do you ever talk about Plato? Truth? Do you try to figure out what life is all about?"

Bob grinned and looked closely at me before he answered. "Well, I'll tell you. Ol' Truett and Clyde and I talk about nearly anything, but, mostly, where we're going to get the next case of beer."

I settled back in my seat. Things must be right for him today. He makes jokes about everything.

"I've got to see ol' Truett pretty soon," he went on. "We've talked about a trip to New Mexico this summer when he has some time off. We just may do that."

"Good," I said indifferently.

There must have been something in the tone of my voice that made Bob turn quickly and look at me. "You don't seem in too good a humor today. What's wrong? Tell ol' Bob."

"Everything is fine," I said laconically. An inner voice said, "Now, you can tell him."

I said, "Enid told me she had a letter from a superintendent somewhere in North Texas. She's going to apply at some school. I know she'll leave, and I hate to see it."

"They still haven't agreed to pay her as much as they pay the football coach?" Bob asked.

I shook my head dismally.

"I thought not," Bob grinned. "What do you expect? After all, we've got to have a good football coach. He may be a damn fool and a jackass, but he's important."

"Enid is the best English teacher they'll ever have."

"Good English teachers are a dime a dozen."

"Oh, no," I insisted. "Not Enid."

"You've told me she's the best dozens of times," Bob said. "Just what is it about cousin Enid that makes her the best in the United States?"

I get enthusiastic about the way Enid teaches, and I wanted to tell him. Never have I wanted to talk about it so much. One thing I didn't want to talk about was my date with Truett, but it was the only thing I could think about!

"It's the way she coordinates her English classes," I said enthusiastically. "She makes the kids write themes all the time, and from the mistakes they have on their papers, she builds an English course to correct those errors. The textbook is only used as a reference book; it is not the whole course."

"Sounds all right. I don't think I had an English teacher like that."

"I'm sure you didn't. Enid is the only teacher I know who builds a course for a particular group of kids. I've been saving themes all year. I'm going to take them home with me this summer, and I'm going to plan a course built on student mistakes, the way Enid does." *I'll work on that when I'm not dating Truett.*

"What about your writing?" Bob asked.

I sighed. *I love to talk about writing. Anything but Truett.* "I want to write some, but I'll have to teach next year to make a living. Kline slammed my favorite short story—the one about the high school kid the other kids pick on—back to me. He's like the editors. He thought the kid's mother was unbelievable. But I like that story. I'm definitely going to rewrite it this summer."

Bob didn't say anything about the story, and I didn't press the point, even though he would not recognize himself as an overgrown high school kid tied to his mother's apron strings.

Evidently, Bob was still thinking about the way Enid teaches English. "What about books? Do you still read books in English classes these days?"

"Oh, yes," I said quickly. "Enid takes time out from the story to call attention to the author's way of describing things, or his way of achieving effects. She compares and contrasts that with student writing, and shows them how they, too, could achieve good writing. I read the stories and plays for pure pleasure."

"Pleasure!" He gave a short, sardonic laugh. "Do you still read the *Vicar of Wakefield?*"

"In my classes, we read *Silas Marner.*"

Bob turned and put his arm on the back of the seat behind me. "There's something I want to ask you," he said, "and I want you to tell me the truth."

I tensed up. "Okay. I'll admit it. I'll tell you the truth."

"Have you ever read that book—the *Vicar of Wakefield?*"

I took a deep breath. "Yes. A long time ago."

"I think it's the sorriest damn book I ever read," Bob said emphatically, "and I wonder what you would do, or what cousin Enid would do, if you had a student tell you something like that about it."

You could have knocked me over with a feather! "You mean, what would I do if a student told me I didn't know what I was talking about? Told me what I considered a good book was stupid?"

"Hell. Not exactly that way. But suppose you said to write a theme about the *Vicar of Wakefield* or *Silas Marner,* and the student wrote he thought it was the sorriest damn book he'd ever read. What would you do? And what would cousin Enid do?"

I thought a minute. "I don't know, and I don't know what Enid would do." He had made cheap jokes today. I decided to do the same thing. "I just might take my trusted scimitar and cut him to pieces."

Bob didn't laugh, and I went on. "I suppose the kid's attitude would have some influence on me. If it were his honest opinion, I could accept it, I think. If he were trying to be smart, I'd get upset."

Bob nodded knowingly. His lips twisted into a sort of sneer. "What do you think about that book," he demanded.

"It's been so long—" I evaded.

"I'll tell you what I think," he interrupted. "I think the Vicar was a lousy old bastard. The villain seduced and raped his daughters, and the damned old fool took it piously."

It was easy to get me riled up today. "That's not the way I remember it. I think the old man was kinda dumb, but he had a sweet and generous nature. He's like the rest of us. He does dumb things and knows it. Sure, he forgives easily; he repents of his mistakes, and, in spite of everything, he comes out all right. I don't think the Vicar was a sorry old bastard."

"I expected something like that," Bob said accusingly. "You swallow everything they tell you, hook, line, and sinker. I know what you'd do if a kid disagreed with you, and cousin Enid would do the same thing. You'd bawl the kid out and—"

"You're darn right I would."

"Sure, you would!" Bob's eyes were angry. "There's no place for individual thought in the schools."

I raised my voice. "There is a place for an honest difference of opinion. I mean an *honest* difference of opinion. You don't expect kids to parrot back everything you say, but you don't expect them to be rude either. If you don't teach some kids politeness and consideration for other people's feelings in school, they'll never learn it."

Bob began to move about and act as if he didn't want me to get more upset than I already was. He started to say something, but I didn't let him.

"Besides," I roared, "maybe someday in school, some kid will read one of your Conan stories, which the teacher tells him is a good example of the way a barbarian would act in those circumstances, yet the kid is adamant. He says, 'I think old Conan was a son-of-a-bitch.' "

Bob looked shocked. "Girl, you talk like that, and I'm going to wash your mouth out with soap."

That made me even madder. "You say things like that."

Bob ran his fingers through his hair. "Hell, girl, I'm just a sorry old man in my sere and yellow leaf. I can say things like that, but a pretty young woman is not supposed to talk that way."

I felt dumb. I hated myself. I had told Bob about everything except my date with Truett. But the more my silly conscience bothered me, the more I ranted. I told him that men made me tired, as far as I was concerned they could all go to hell.

Bob made a peculiar sound, and I looked at him. His eyes weren't angry.

They weren't questioning. They were amused. Amused! The rat was pretending to be very shocked at what I'd said, but he was enjoying it! Men!

I relaxed and began to laugh at my own foolishness, at his foolishness, at everybody's.

I still didn't tell Bob about my date with Truett. I couldn't. When things got all right between us again, I didn't want to take a chance on ruining it. I would tell him, though. I'd promised Truett I would. However, it wouldn't bother Bob. Not a bit. I'd be sure to tell him . . . next time.

Harsh wind . . . Soft wind . . .

This was a long Saturday. We're beginning to round up the school year, and the rush is killing me. There is so much to do; however, late this afternoon, I put it all aside and went downtown for a while.

In the drugstore, Dr. Howard was leaning against a counter. He barked out his usual "Good afternoon," and I said, "Hello." I waved to Mrs. Smith, who was busy in another part of the drugstore. I leaned against the other end of the counter, opposite from Dr. Howard.

He said it was a nice day, and I agreed it was. He said that Robert took his mother to Brownwood today. I knew that, but I didn't tell him. When I asked how Mrs. Howard was getting along, he hesitated but said he thought she was getting much better. He didn't sound too convincing.

"I don't know how Robert will take it," he said.

I didn't answer. Maybe I'm not yet convinced that Mrs. Howard is really sick. But suppose she is? Though I can't imagine what it would be like to lose one's mother, I know that people do lose their mothers and keep on going.

Dr. Howard was staring out at the street. I followed his gaze and watched the wind pick up a small paper bag and blow it about. It is late spring, and the wind blows hard.

We talked of other things then. Dr. Howard spoke of the old days when he used to make his rounds over the countryside in a horse and buggy, and sometimes Robert went with him.

While we were talking, Bob stopped his car in front of the post office, said something to his mother, got out and went inside. I didn't say anything to Dr. Howard, and he didn't say anything to me. We just stood and watched as though it were a drama unfolding.

Bob came out of the post office with a bunch of letters in his hand. "I guess he got a lot of fan mail," I said.

"Probably," Dr. Howard said proudly. "He gets mail from everywhere— England. Everywhere." He paused as Bob started the car and drove off. Mrs. Howard was sitting very straight, looking neither to the right nor left.

"Robert ought to travel," Dr. Howard went on. "He'd like England. Ireland." He paused and sighed. "Maybe it's the place for him."

I didn't know what to say. Poor Bob, I thought. Born in the wrong century, living in the wrong place where friends are few and fun is limited.

Other people were coming and going in the drugstore now. Dr. Howard tipped his hat to the ladies, spoke briefly to the men, and nervously got ready to leave. I needed to get home and get dressed for the evening, and so I wasn't sorry to end the conversation.

When I walked into the house, the telephone rang. It was Bob. He was still planning to come over tonight, he said, if I would let him. "What's wrong?" I thought. "He doesn't usually telephone, if he already has a date."

Something in his tone of voice warned me of one of his dark moods. The wind had blown hard today, maybe he was restless. He'd been to Brownwood. Maybe he'd talked to Truett!

I said, as cheerfully as I could, I'd be happy to have him come over. He asked if I wanted to see a show, but I felt he would prefer just riding around.

It was a pleasant night. The wind was down now, and there was a soft, cool breeze. From the open car windows, you could smell the freshness of the land.

Bob was restless. He seemed to regret his Black Irish mood, as he referred to it. He made a half hearted attempt to apologize. He said the trees were heavy with birds and leaves, the grass and crops green, flowers blooming; yet, he felt the same restlessness and melancholy he always felt in the fall of the year. "My God," he said wearily, "if I feel this melancholy in the spring, what will I feel like in the fall?"

As if trying to throw off his dark mood, he asked me about school. Recently, he has this new thing about schools. "Schools suppress rather than educate." He's going to talk and argue until he finds an answer that suits him. I'm glad to talk about this topic; it's vital to me, and it's not about Truett.

Bob said one of the things he didn't like about school was discipline—the eternal rules and regulations.

"But, Bob," I said, "if there were no rules and no discipline . . . if kids can come to class when they want to, read what they want to, or do anything else they want to do, they'll never learn anything."

To my surprise, Bob said, "You're probably right. I guess when you go to school, you sacrifice creativeness in order to learn."

During the last few months, I'd thought a lot about that subject. "In a way, I agree schools lose creativeness," I said. "In my dramatic work, I find some very talented students, fifteen or sixteen years old, who are as stiff as if bound. When we do pantomimes or make up stories to act out in class, they have a hard time breaking those bonds. They're ungainly and self-conscious, not creative. Little children are not that way."

He began to warm up to the subject. "That's right. The school has taken creativeness out of them."

"Think of Ethel's first grade," I said. "A whole room of little kids, whom she has to teach to read, to write, to count. All sorts of things. If they can't read and write as first graders should by the end of the school year, Nat will tell Ethel if she can't do the job, he'll get someone who can."

"There ought to be some way to preserve talent and teach kids something too," Bob said.

I waved my hand airily to brush that aside. "Ethel does the best she can. She works with the kids in groups. While she's working with one group, some children color pictures, read or draw. They have the freedom to be creative, but she can't let them stand on their heads just because they may want to."

Bob scratched his head. "You may be right," he admitted. "You have a way of making things I don't like sound right. But what do you do with a kid that's talented, brilliant, and a little 'different' from the rest?"

I wondered how his teachers had treated him. What do you do with the 'different' child? I tried to remember what I'd heard Mrs. Trapp say in education classes. "Most of the students in anybody's class fall into that great big medium group. Very few have far above average minds."

Bob leaned against his door. "From you, I'm learning things about teachers I never knew before. If all of them work as many hours a day as you do, they don't have much time to spend on anybody. But can teachers recognize the very brilliant, talented child? Edison's teachers thought he was dumb, didn't they?"

"You can't always recognize the genius, I suppose," I said.

I explained the difficulty by saying there was another kind of student who was hard to distinguish from the genius—the brilliant student who did beautiful work, did his work on time, and deserved the highest grades; however, he seemed to lack the uniqueness belonging to the genius. I said that, among the students I taught—good, medium, or all of them—I thought perhaps Beatrice Minton had a good chance of being an actress or artist—someone important.

Bob looked at me as if I'd lost my mind. "I know her when I see her, but she doesn't impress me."

I laughed. "See there. You wouldn't be a very good teacher. You can't tell the really talented from the run of the mill."

Bob grinned and shook his head. "You win," he said. He was quiet a few minutes. "I guess you're right. The climate, the situation, our mediocre civilization doesn't contribute to genius. You say most of your class are just run of the mill students. A friend of mine calls them the 'common herd.' I've never called them that because I didn't want to insult the herd." He shook his head morosely. "But that's your average man for you, able to make a success, do the right things, say the right things, but anybody who is really different is the one who is picked on by the herd."

"I haven't seen much of that in our school," I said, "and that's because Nat is the fine superintendent he is. The right kind of discipline keeps the kids in line. No harmful teasing."

I told him of an incident I'd witnessed as a freshman or sophomore in Brownwood High School. One day, I saw a group of boys standing around a puny little boy, teasing him. He was real smart and he took piano lessons. No self-respecting boy did that in Brownwood High. When I walked out into the hall, the kid turned and looked at me, and I'll never forget that look as long as I live. I felt sorry for him, and, as I told Bob, the irony was that the boys tormenting him and calling him sissy and worse were the third-rate football players who weren't good enough to make the team, the dumb clucks, who thought it was smart to try to make someone else feel bad.

"The goddam dirty devils," Bob rasped through gritted teeth. "That kid got a hurt that will stay with him the rest of his life. He'll hate those bastards—"

"Oh, probably not," I interrupted emphatically. "As he gets older and accomplishes something, he'll be too interested in his own life to bother with hating those kids. They aren't worth it."

"I'd hate them, no matter what I accomplished," Bob said grimly. "When I was a kid, I had a few overgrown bullies make me miserable. If I were to meet one of them today and he made any kind of move, I'd crush his damn head between my fists the way I would a cantalope."

That didn't sound good to me. "I guess most of us have things bad happen to us," I said briskly. "But, as St. Paul says, when we grow up, we put away childish things."

"You talk like a Sunday School teacher who's never known the harsh, black world," Bob said. He reached out his hand and tangled my hair, which I hate for him to do because my hair never stays in place anyway. "You've had your troubles, I admit that, but you don't know what it is to get beat up in a fight every day."

I pulled one foot up under me and leaned back against my door. "Oh, I got beat up in fights when I was a kid. Once, real bad," I said and laughed.

Bob was shocked. "You can laugh about it?"

"Why not?" I said lightly. "I did the best I could. We lived a little over a mile from Clear Creek school. A number of kids who went to school there lived all around us. I guess none of them liked me very well. The fact that I could get up in front of an audience and say poems and other readings caused them to think I was smart. I thought so, too, which may have been another reason I was disliked. One afternoon, as we were coming home from school, a couple of boys—one my age and one a little younger but a lot bigger—ran up, hit me, pulled my hair and knocked my books out of my hands, and—"

"The little bastards," Bob barked savagely. He seemed more upset than I'd ever been. Certainly, he was more upset than I meant him to be when I told him.

"The thing I hated most," I tried to explain, "was that I had a new Zane Grey book that I didn't want to get dirty. They hit me, knocked me down and kicked my book. When I tried to kick and scratch them, they hit me harder and ran."

"Weren't there any older students along to help you?" Bob sounded incredulous.

"There were a couple of girls about sixteen or seventeen, but I guess they hated me too. They walked real fast to get away from us." I laughed again.

"I don't see how you can laugh about that," Bob said angrily. "Everyone of them should have had their heads beat in."

"I thought so too, at the time," I said. "But that was kid stuff."

"God," Bob groaned. "What did you do?"

"One thing for sure, I didn't cry. I wanted to, but I wouldn't. I didn't run either. I picked up my books and went right down that road toward home."

"Did they let you alone?"

"Oh, no," I said. "The older girls were way, way down the road by that time. The two boys waited for me. As soon as I got to where they were, they hit me in the eye and knocked my books out of my hands, but, believe me, I got in some mighty good licks too. I scratched their faces until they had bloody streaks. I tore their shirts. The trouble was they could hold me off at arm's length, and I couldn't do too much to them, but I tried."

Bob was alert and moving now, moving with the old vigor and energy. He lunged against the steering wheel. "Wasn't there a house where you could have gotten help?"

I shrugged my shoulders. "My stepfather's brother lived about a mile from us, but I didn't go in and ask for help. That road was as much my road as it was theirs. My home was down that road, and I was going home."

Bob put his arm around me as if to protect me at this late date. "Honey," he said kindly. "I think you had more guts than common sense. You should have gotten help."

"Heavens, no. I fought it out. They'd hit me, then run down the road about a hundred yards, wait until I got close enough to hit again."

Bob lunged angrily. "My God. How many times did that happen?"

"How many hundred yards are there in a mile?"

Bob swore. Then, suddenly, he choked, took his arm quickly from around my shoulders, wiped his hand across his mouth and snorted.

"You—you—" He sputtered. He was trying to keep from laughing. He tried to say something, and then gave up and laughed. When he could get his breath, he gasped out, "I'm—I'm sorry," and went off into another peal of laughter.

"I'm sorry," he said contritely when he could get his breath, "but I could just see you getting up and walking down that road, knowing you'd get beat up, but marching straight on. Reminded me of Tennyson's poem 'The Charge of the Light Brigade.' No strategy. No planning. No finesse. Only one idea—go straight on. I wasn't laughing at you, and I damn sure don't think it was funny. It was just so damn ridiculous that I couldn't do anything but laugh." He paused, got his handkerchief and wiped his face. "I'd go right this day and beat 'em up if you wanted me to. What happened when you got home?"

"Oh, I cried then. Mother called their mothers and told them that I was going to walk down that road to and from school every day, and she didn't want anything like that to happen again." I added complacently, "The next day, I went to school with one eye shut, a clean dress, and nobody but nobody bothered me."

"And now you hate those two boys," Bob said, "and if you were to meet them on the sidewalk, you'd turn your head?"

I tossed my head. "I've seen them dozens of times since then. I didn't go to school at Clear Creek the next year. I went to school in Brownwood. True, we were never close friends. We never mentioned the incident again. Maybe they were a little ashamed that it took both of them to whip one puny little girl. I didn't have anything to be ashamed of. I did the best I could against the odds, and I didn't cry."

The thing that amazed Bob was that I talked to the boys after that. I tried to explain that we went to country parties during our teens and played a country game called "snap." He'd never heard of that, but when I explained it, he got a big kick out of it.

I told him how country parties differed from town parties. "Nobody invites just a few people," I said. "Everybody is invited. You meet a neighbor and he'll say, 'Hey, there's a party Saturday night at Bob Childers's. You all come.' Or somebody telephones you and tells you about a party some place. And everybody says, 'You all come.'"

"And everybody goes?" Bob was beginning to laugh and enjoy my stories of the simple parties and the games we played.

"At country parties, you played snap with the boys you fought with as a kid." His voice sounded unbelieving, but there was no anger in it now.

"At country parties, I never did snap either of them," I said, "but once in a while, one of them would snap me. We were grown up. At least, we thought we were. No use worrying over what had happened when we were crazy kids."

Bob shook his head, laughing. "I don't know whether you're the dumbest or the most courageous girl I've ever seen. But in a fair fight, you'd probably get the best of an old cowboy friend of mine—Breckenridge Elkins." He laughed jovially. "It's true, you know, the female of the species is more deadly than the male. But I guess she's also the most forgiving."

His dark and somber mood was gone, vanished with the laughter and the cool night breeze. We didn't talk anymore about schools and how they suppressed creativeness. We didn't talk anymore about fighting and hate. But Bob did talk about the way he studied Jenghiz Khan and Alexander the Great's lives and battles, so that he'd be able to make some of the things his main characters got involved with sound more like honest happenings. He made it plain that you couldn't just take one of their battles, for example, and let another character fight it all over again, because different people, in different lands, would act and even fight differently.

He told me about a story that he had either written, or was going to write. It sounded better than a Conan story to me. Alexander the Great had established colonies in the territory he conquered. As he had marched through the territory, capturing it, he established Greek cities and kingdoms which were to be the bearers of Greek art, culture, and civilization in the conquered territories.

Bob thought that if one of those old Greek cities had somehow lasted to the present time and maintained its Greek language and customs, it would make a "hell of a yarn." It interested me because I'd read a short novel, "The Aspern Papers" by Henry James, in which there were lost letters. A lost city, I thought, might be even better.

One thing worries me about Bob's writing. He hasn't started his novel about Texas he wants to write. The reason, he says, is that the right Texan hasn't come along yet. Another thing, too, he has to pound out yarns fast in order to make a living.

Almost every time I'm with him, Bob gets enthusiastic about the early days of Texas when men came searching for lost gold mines. Gold mines, some of which, Bob insists, had to be near San Saba or somewhere in that territory; some, maybe as far south as Guadalupe, and there, now, that is real country for you!

It's great to be with Bob when he gets out of a dark mood and begins laughing and talking and is vitally interested in everything around him, even old party games like snap and things that happened to me when I was just a kid.

I don't know why it is, but the *right* time to tell him about my date with Truett just doesn't seem to come around.

Sunday night . . . Time out from the hectic pace . . .

I don't know whether to say that Bob was in a jovial humor tonight, or what. Certainly there was much of the old exuberance, but there was also a touch of the usual melancholy about him. He seemed preoccupied with the end of civilization. He talked at length about the story that's coming out in *Weird*

Tales, the one he likes so much. He predicted that civilizations, as he had written, would rise and fall; and once again the barbarian would triumph.

"You see," he said, warming to his subject, "that part of man which is part barbarian and untamed will never die." He whirled and looked at me. "Throughout every vicissitude of time, the barbarian survives; civilized man forgets *how* to survive. There will always be the triumph of the barbarian over civilized man."

If there was anything I was not interested in tonight, it was the survival of the barbarian. All I wanted to do was survive the end of school. "I doubt you and I will live to see it," I said dryly.

Bob said that he wouldn't say this to anybody else, but there were moments now when he wished he could devote time to being just a common, every day man of the town.

"Some of the things you've said to me," he said, half shyly, half bantering, "make me believe in myself as I've never believed before."

I became a little uncomfortable and made a protesting sound to stop his talk, but he either didn't hear me or wanted to speak his mind while the mood was upon him. He said I had made him believe that it was possible for him to stand on the street corners and talk with other men about the rains and the crops, and all the ordinary things of life. Maybe talk with people the way Nat Williams does.

He said he thought he might even, and he laughed self-consciously, go back to church. He used to go to church, he assured me, even went to the Epworth League, and all that tomfoolery. Well, he thought he might go back again and not sit arguing with the preacher, but listen to him instead.

I laughed and said that might be a good idea. Going to church was good for the soul.

"It might be," he said, running his fingers through his hair. "Some of these preachers just might know something about the mysterious Yahwey that has somehow escaped me, though I've looked for it many times, by God."

When I tried to encourage the church attendance, he wondered if he could be a writer and live like that.

"Of course, you could," I said emphatically. "You finish stories and go places before you start a new one."

He shook his head. "At a cent a word and less, it takes so damn many words to buy food for the table."

I was greatly heartened by the fact that at long last he would talk of church, that he would think of living just a plain, ordinary life of a man in a small town. I thought he could be a successful writer and be part of the church, the school, and even take part in the life of the community. It might give a new depth and breadth to his stories—yarns, as he called them. I suggested, tactfully and very obliquely, that such stories might indicate a new growing up and maturity.

I looked at him in the dim light, yet seeing vividly his big overgrown boyishness. In the half light of the car and night, I could not see the shadows in his eyes.

I didn't say so, but I thought to myself what an irony it was that he would finally say what he had tonight . . . just after I'd had a date with Truett.

> *One minute, the summer looks beautiful . . .*
> *The next . . . Not so beautiful . . .*

School ended a week ago. Last Saturday morning, Mother came for me. That night, I had a date with Truett. Sunday, Bob came. During this past week, I had four dates with Truett. No word from Bob. Everything looks great for a beautiful summer. . . .

That is not true.

I still haven't told Bob I'm dating Truett. I have tried. But I haven't said flatly, "I had a date with Truett last night." I don't know why not.

Is it just because I want to be friends with everybody, or do I have some fear? Fear? What is there to fear? There's nothing to worry about. Bob wouldn't harm anyone. Still, sometimes, he displays a quick, wild temper and wants to crush somebody's head in. But that's all talk. Bob can't stand the sight of blood, even though it flows in his "yarns." Those grisly heroes, unafraid of blood and gore, are what he thinks he *ought* to be, not what he *is*. But I tell myself I don't want to put him to the test.

On the other hand, my conscience bothers me. When I'm with Bob, I keep thinking: "I'll tell him about Truett." I say something to the effect that "Truett thinks this" or "Truett thinks that." I have said, "I am going to date Truett this summer."

Bob ignores the remarks. I expect him to ask me about Truett, but he doesn't say a word. Why?

Truett speaks out. Last Saturday night, the first thing he said was, "Did you tell Bob we're dating now?"

Then I did what I tell my speech students not to do. I stammered, and in a confused way, said, "I—I—No. I didn't." Then I said quite frankly, "It really is none of Bob's business whom I go with."

Truett agreed with that. Then I thought, "At the same time, what about next year? Will I want to date Bob again? I probably will, for I enjoy being with him most of the time. Will I hate to tell you?"

I don't know. While Bob was here Sunday, he picked up one of Sinclair Lewis's books that Truett had given me. It had Truett's and my name in it. When Bob picked it up, I held my breath. He opened it, but didn't say a word.

Yet I'd swear he read Truett's name! It seems to me that if he really cared, he would have said, "What's Truett Vinson's book doing here?"

And I would have said, "He brought it."

Then Bob would have said, "What's he doing coming out here and leaving his books lying around?"

What happened? Bob read the page and began talking about what a damn fool Sinclair Lewis was! Said he'd call Lewis a jackass, if he were sure my grandmother was out of earshot. He talked about Sinclair Lewis! That was all. He suggested we ride around, for he wanted to ride past the Cheatham place and look at the old log cabin still standing behind their house and still used by the Cheatham's for storage. He also wanted to ride down toward the Brook Smith community, because he'd heard "some pretty important things happened there . . . things important to hack writers."

When we walked out on the porch, Bob stopped and listened. Mammy was in the back yard singing an old song she had sung when she was a girl: "Barbara Allen." Bob listened, smiling. Her song, he said, was a favorite of his, because he'd heard it as a child. I told him I liked another one of the Alabama hill country songs she sang: "Lord Thomas's Wedding."

Bob was so interested, I told him those old English and Scottish ballads still hadn't been written down when Mammy was a girl, though I supposed they were by now. At the time she learned them, they were still handed down by word of mouth by descendants of English and Scottish people.

Bob spent the next hour talking about them, wanting me to write them down exactly as Mammy sang them. But he was especially interested in the old ghost and witch stories she told. Those were a gold mine, he thought. Another reason those witch stories interested him was that he believed such myths were based upon facts and real happenings.

All that led eventually to a discussion of the folk tales and ghost stories of the early days of Texas. Those were great days, he said, why even preachers carried guns as they traveled to church on Sunday mornings. They leaned their guns against the pulpits and preached against killing. "It wasn't a sin to shoot Indians." He laughed.

As I listened to Texas history and ghost stories, and to the exploits of "Francis X" in Afghanistan, I kept thinking of all the things that worried me this summer. Not just Bob and Truett! A good summer doesn't just depend on men. I had lost something valuable.

When Mother had come after me, she was, as usual, in a hurry. Bless her heart, she's always in a hurry! I lost a stack of papers, important and valuable to me.

That stack of papers! In it, were some of those cute little three line letters Bob had written me, calling me names of vegetables; several manuscripts; play scripts; poems I'd written for my students, and a stack of English themes I'd saved in order to plan an English course the way Enid does.

Then just before the end of school, Kline sent one of my stories back to me with a two and a half page, single spaced letter of criticism. I didn't take time to read it. I put it on the stack of manuscripts, themes, and letters I was bringing home. I told myself that, when I got home, I'd be able to take my time to read and digest it. I put the forty or fifty themes I'd saved on top of the stack of letters and scripts.

I put my books in the suitcase I use to carry books in, trying to keep Mother from seeing the Pierre Louÿs book Bob had given me for Christmas. The papers were in my way, and so I had taken the whole stack and put them on the floor beside the waste basket, which was full. I don't know why I put them on the floor, except that I was trying to get things off the table in a hurry.

We loaded everything else I had—typewriter, books, clothes, radio, gifts from the kids, and knick-knacks that I love to collect. We walked out of the house and left that valuable stack of papers by the waste basket!

When I got home, I was still in a hurry, unpacking, cleaning house, trying to get ready for my date with Truett. Sunday morning, when I realized I had left the papers, I almost died. We don't have a telephone, and so I rushed down to Brownwood to telephone Mrs. Hemphill to find out if she had found them. I planned to ask her to give them to Bob and let him bring them to me that afternoon. I would telephone Bob later and ask him to get them for me.

Mrs. Hemphill said she hadn't found anything valuable. The only thing she saw was a bunch of old themes that had already been graded! She just assumed I didn't want them, and had put them on the floor beside the waste basket to be thrown away. When I left, she straightened up the room and burned all the papers.

"The whole stack?" I managed to gasp out.

"Yes, of course," she said. "I just assumed you had put things there to be burned."

There wasn't any use blaming Mrs. Hemphill. But she had just driven one of Bob's scimitars through my heart. Now, I'll never know what Kline said. I've lost the cute letters Bob wrote me, and some manuscripts for which I don't have carbons. Furthermore, I'm stuck at home, trying to plan an English course the way Enid plans one, and I don't have the kid's papers to guide me. I don't know which of those things hurts the most!

When I listened to what Bob was saying, he was telling me how sorry he was that he forgot to bring me a copy of the *Weird Tales* story he likes so much, but he was writing another one, and when it comes out, he really wants me to read it! Now, there, girl! There's a story for you! But from now on, he hoped to devote his time to westerns, maybe a few historical yarns, and he sure wanted to get to that Texas novel he keeps researching!

He didn't talk too much about reincarnation on this date, but he did say he felt keenly the sharp, blood-pain of the man whose love proves false. I sat still and didn't move, or laugh, or question. He looked straight ahead at the road. I watched him, waiting for him to talk about Truett, or about the best friend who stole his girl in some other life.

He talked about the early days of Texas, about the fields and the crops beside the road.

Bob and Truett are planning to go to New Mexico together in a week or two. I wonder if *they* will get around to talking about my dating both of them.

> *Though fathoms deep you sink me in the mould,*
> *Locked in with thick-lapped lead and bolted wood,*
> *Yet rest not easy in your lover's arms;*
> *Let him beware to stand where I have stood.*
> *. . . Robert E. Howard . . .*

It happened. It was inevitable. Bob would have to find out, or, rather, face the fact that Truett and I were dating. The thing that surprised me was the explosion. It surprised Truett too.

Although I had not said plainly, "I had a date with Truett last week," I had tried to talk with Bob about Truett. I had told him I was going to date Truett, but he simply didn't pay any attention to me. When he and Truett came back from New Mexico and Truett came to see me, I asked, "Did you tell Bob that we were dating?"

Truett shook his head. "I tried to, but he always passed it over as if I hadn't said a word." He frowned. "I don't know what to think of him anymore. He does some crazy things. You can talk to him, but he doesn't listen to a word you say."

That was all we said, then.

While they were in New Mexico, I got two cards from Bob, and I thought they were delightful. The first one was from Roswell. The picture on the front was of the famous potters of Tonala, Mexico. The card said—

Roswell

Dear Novalyne, The weather is good but the beer is lousy. Hoping you are the same.

Bob

I laughed like everything when I got it. It was so typical of Bob's trying to make a funny joke—his kind of humor. I liked it too.

The next day, I got another card. The picture on that one was gruesome, and I would have liked to hit Bob hard when I saw it. It was an actual photograph of a rattlesnake swallowing a rabbit. He had done that to horrify me. And it did. There was no message on the card. . . . Just "hello" and "goodbye." I thought the card was hilarious, not the rattlesnake swallowing the rabbit.

> Sante Fe, N. Mex.
> 19/6/35

Dear Novalyne,

> Cordially,
>
> Bob

I didn't hear from Truett, but he brought me a small table cover, a miniature Navajo Indian blanket with the vivid blue and red of Indian colors. I like it very much.

I wrote to Bob in Cross Plains a very short note, telling him that I had gotten his cards and enjoyed them, except for the snake swallowing the rabbit, but that, as the explanation on the card said, "was one of the tragedies of the Southwest."

The note I wrote was friendly, nothing more nor less. On July sixth, I got another letter from him, and he mentioned Truett for the first time, as if aware of our dating. It had a subtle cut or two, but it wasn't too bad.

> Cross Plains, Texas,
> July 4, 1935

Dear Novalyne:

I take my typewriter in hand to write you a letter on this grand and suspicious—I mean auspicious occasion—when the zoom of the horse-race and the rodeo is heard in the land, punctuated by the flap of waving flags, the rumble of patriotic speeches, and the howls of patriots getting their scalps burnt off by premature fire-crackers.

For many years now, I've been planning to attend the annual rodeo at Stamford, but each year I postpone it. Indeed, days of leisure are as rare and unusual as candid friends. My time is divided between trying to make new markets to replace defaulting old ones and trying to persuade old ones to pay me what they owe me. Concerning these, my popularity in some quarters seems to be falling off, and I suppose the editors feel they can do without me—forgetting that this has happened repeatedly in the past, and that I've always built myself up again with the readers. But this time I don't think I'll go to the trouble of a rebuild. I'll devote my time into breaking into new pastures. I'm neither smart nor subtle, but I have sense enough to know when I'm being played for a sucker.

I trust you and Truett had a good time at the Brady races.

Bob

I wasn't quite sure how to answer the letter or even whether I should answer. The more I thought about it, the more I wanted to write him and be very sweet and cut him as he had cut at Truett and me. It began to irritate me as I thought about his looking at books with Truett's name in them and ignoring it. It irritated me that Truett had tried to tell him, in fact, had told him that we were dating; yet he always ignored it. Why, now, was he acting like this?

If the remarks I had made, the remarks Truett had made, and the books did not get across to Bob, then who had told him? Was it Clyde? I doubted that. Clyde was too busy tending to his own business. Then who? Who was there from Cross Plains? I couldn't remember seeing anyone. Dave Lee? Lindsey Tyson? I didn't remember seeing either of them.

One other thought bothered me. No matter how irritated I became with Bob, I had enjoyed being with him, and I thought Cross Plains without him might be pretty dull.

Finally, I wrote him a short letter, and I tried to be as casual as I could possibly be. I even told him I was looking forward to seeing him again. His answer to that made me so mad I couldn't see straight.

Cross Plains, Texas
July 9, 1935

Dear Novalyne:

Thank you for your invitation to call; but you honestly can't expect me to enjoy ridicule and contempt so much that I come back for another dose.

You understand me, I think, but I'll make myself clear so there won't be any chance of misunderstanding. It's simply that you and Truett haven't played fair with me, in concealing the fact that you were going together—and you know you haven't. There wasn't any need for such secrecy, and the only motive for it was to make a fool out of me. It's none of my business who you go with, or who

Truett goes with; but if either of you had had any consideration whatever for me, you'd have at least casually mentioned the fact that you were going together. If you'd merely told me, I wouldn't have thought anything about it. If you'd even neglected to tell me through carelessness, I'd have overlooked it. But both of you had plenty of opportunity to mention it to me, and instead you concealed the fact, made a secret of it—and no doubt laughed at me because of it.

I understand now why you laughed at me so much the last time I was with you, though I still fail to see the joke. Why you thought it was such a hilarious joke on me for me to be kept ignorant of the fact that you were going with Truett, is something I can not fathom. Nor shall I try to fathom it; the knowledge that the slight was intentional is quite enough for me. Taking advantage of a friend's trust, respect and consideration to try to make a fool out of him seems a poor triumph.

Very truly yours,

Robert E. Howard

I had to read that letter twice to believe it. I was furious. Just exactly what was he trying to do—play the part of the injured, innocent, unsuspecting lover? Where was his scimitar? Truett and I making fun of him? Well, no more than the people we meet on the street who, he thinks, are laughing at him. No more than the people in the drugstore are laughing at him when we go in for a coke.

My first impulse was to tear the letter up and go throw it in his face. I sat down at the typewriter and wrote him a letter, telling him to go to hell and take his mother with him! I told him that no other woman in the world but me would have put up with him, and that the only reason I did was because I could appreciate a person who had talent and a profession which he worked at hard enough to make the kind of success he had made. I told him I never wanted to see or speak to him again.

After I wrote it, I read it to Mother and Mammy. Mother kept busy at the sink and didn't look at me, even when I finished. Mammy sat in a cane-bottomed chair beside the churn and watched me. I waited for one of them to speak.

"Well," I said a little impatiently. "Why don't you say something?"

"He seemed like such a nice man," Mammy said. "I'm sorry he won't be coming over anymore to hear those old stories of mine."

Mother's back was straight. Her silence bothered me. I waited a minute. Mammy began to churn the milk, looking down at the softly rattling churn lid. Mother finished washing the milk pails and hung them up.

"What do you think, Mother?" I asked.

"You've said it now," she said quietly. "Tear it up."

In my heart, I knew I should do that, but I couldn't give up without some kind of fight. "Well, after that hateful letter he wrote me, I certainly do want to tell him to go to hell."

Mammy looked up from the churn, smiling. "Once, when I was a girl, I thought about telling a man to go to hell. If he had gone, I would have been glad, or at least, I thought I would be glad."

"Did you tell him?" I asked.

She shook her head. "No. I decided it wasn't ladylike. I hurt him worse, though. I made him think what I'd done was his fault, that he'd brought it on himself. Later on, we were friends again, and I was glad I hadn't told him where to go. It's better to have the good will of a dog than it is to bite him."

Mother turned and looked at me for the first time. "Either don't write him at all or write in such a way that you don't end the friendship altogether. He has been a good friend. That's all you want him to be. I'm not telling you to make up with him. I'd just as soon you didn't. I don't like him. I don't like him at all. He's not the kind of man I'd want you to marry. He's too tied to his mother's apron strings."

"A man who's nice to his mother—" Mammy began.

"A man who'll put taking care of his mother, who is not seriously sick, above dating a girl, when he's got a father who can take care of her as well or better than he can, is so tied to her apron strings that he'd be a poor excuse for a husband." Mother's voice was firm.

I tore up the letter and put it in the stove with the wood to be burned. The best thing to do, I decided, was go for a walk. Outside, the birds were singing, untouched by human bickering. Strength comes from the earth.

The large rock at the back of our pasture is a place to sit and listen to the birds and the soft drone of hidden nature. There a deep peace grows inside you, and you hear an inner voice, the voice of the strong, understanding person you want to be.

I remembered the day Bob and I had sat here, weaving stories of the people who had once lived in this old log house. I remembered how he tapped the stick against the ground, looking in the direction where the last Indian was killed in Brown County. I thought of the whimsical tone of his voice as he poked goodnatured fun at all the different versions of the story. I remembered the rain, and our laughter as we walked in the rain together.

I did not hate Bob.

I was angry at him, as I'd never been before. But I didn't hate him. Not yet. Not because of Truett.

The birds quarreled at me, eyeing me first with one eye and turning their heads to see me better with the other. A squirrel chattered angrily, and a silent rabbit hopped by. The cows milled around, disdainfully ignoring me. Gradually, my anger lessened, and I went back to the house to write Bob a letter.

July 12, 1935.

Dear Bob,

Although you leave nothing for me to say, being a woman, I'll say something anyway. You said that you didn't care whom I went with. I know that, Bob. During the time that I went with you, I realized perfectly how you felt about women. Women chain a man down. You always wanted to be free and independent. Such an idea as being chained to a woman was obnoxious to you. Self-preservation was the first law which you recognize. Strange as it may seem, I, too, demand my freedom; self-preservation is also a law of my life. I'll do anything which gives me pleasure and consider myself under no obligation to tell my friends my personal business.

I did tell you that I wanted to go with Truett when I came home. Once when you were over, and I mentioned that I had seen Truett, you said, "You're trying to make me believe that you've had a date with him, but I don't believe it." I said, "I am certainly going with him this summer." You chose to think that I expected to go with him in the future. You said, "You may do it, but you haven't yet." So I dropped the subject. Later (the last time you were over), you picked up a book that he had given me, and on the first page are his initials and mine. I saw you look at the page, and when you ignored the matter, I mentally applauded you. "Well," I said to myself, "he intends to put one over on me by not mentioning the fact. He wants further to impress upon me that he is not in love with me nor the least bit jealous of me. He's pretty clever." I thought that you were laughing at me because you thought that I thought I was putting something by and I wasn't. You remember that you were always careful to let me know that I was just a friend, and I was careful to let you know that I knew that that was all there was between us.

Clyde and I went together four years. Two weeks before he married, I had a date with him and he didn't tell me that he was fixing to marry. When he did, I was utterly dumbfounded. All my friends in Brownwood offered me sympathy. Was that easy to take? I considered that his affair and I didn't say a word to him nor about him for not telling me. And today I like Clyde as well as I ever did. I still think of him as a real friend, and I don't think he did not play fair with me.

I have always considered you head and shoulders above the average man. I didn't believe that you'd resort to middle-class melodrama and I can't believe that you really in your heart think that Truett and I have not played fair. You know both of us well enough to know that we haven't been untrue to your friendship. I can't help but think that you were tired of wasting your time with me and this is an opportunity of getting rid of me for next year. I could not help but know that I sometimes interfered with your work, and the well-ordered routine of your life. You might have told me in a nice way that you could not spare me anymore of your time.

In my last letter, I took it for granted that we were still friends and I invited you to call, assuming that our friendship would continue as it had been in the past. I apologize for having made that mistake.

Please know that you will always have my sincere wishes for your continued success and happiness.

Novalyne

I read the letter over and corrected some of the typing errors, thought about it for a minute or two, put it in the envelope to mail. I would not try to do what Mammy had done with her friend. I did not care to try to turn things around to make it his fault. Friendship should be stronger than that. It seems to me that if you have a real friend, the friendship should last forever.

Bob and Truett are so different. If I were to say to Truett, "Bob says—" he would immediately ask me when I'd seen and been with Bob. If I were to say to Truett, "I am going with Bob next year," he would not ignore it. Bob hears and sees the ingredients for a story with a complicated plot.

I put Bob and all his affairs out of my mind and began to get ready for a date with Truett. We will probably see a show, though sometimes I feel bad to think that going to a show and getting a coke or milkshake to drink afterwards, probably costs a man between two and three dollars. In these days, that adds up.

What a relief it is to be around a man like Truett. I have no intention of ever seeing or being with Bob again. I will not even think of him again!

. . .but this is a world of sweets and sours;
E. A. Poe . . .

That Bob Howard! That great, big, overgrown, round-faced, stinking Bob Howard! He does the most unexpected things in the world. You never know what he will do next!

When I went to the mailbox this morning, I found an envelope with Bob's name on it. I frowned. It really didn't seem to me that my letter had had time to get to Cross Plains, yet here was a letter back from Bob, or else, I thought, as I walked slowly toward the house, this one had been written before he got mine.

I didn't open it at once, for I wanted to get myself completely under control. Every step I took, I warned myself that no matter what Bob said or did, I would not let it upset me. I was careful with the rest of the mail—magazines, a couple of papers, a bill for Mammy. I took it all into the house, took off my bonnet, laid the mail carefully on the table, reached for my letter from Bob and opened it.

Surprise! It was not a letter from Bob! It was my letter, the one I wrote last Friday! My letter was in the envelope; he had sent it back to me! There was not a single word or line from Bob . . . just my letter!

My face grew hot, and I felt anger surge up in me. Had he even read it! I could reason that he probably had or else he would have returned it unopened. What message was I to get from this? That he doesn't care a continental about me? Then why didn't he throw my letter away and not spend three cents on a stamp? If he didn't care a damn for either Truett or me, then why this injured lover act?

Was something like this Mrs. Howard's suggestion? Did he show her my letter and talk with her about it? I can't get mad about that. I'd read his letter and my answer to Mother and Mammy.

Bob said once that a barbarian could be cold, ruthless and uncaring. Well, he's not a barbarian. He wouldn't last one day in Conan's bloody world, and he knows it! That's part of what ails him.

Mammy came into the room where I was sitting and wanted to know why I was so still and quiet. I told her what had happened, and she began to laugh. That made me see the ridiculousness of the whole thing and I joined in.

A good laugh not only chases the blues away, but it also drives away anger. I got up and put my returned letter in the envelope with the one Bob had written me and began to sing as I worked on my English lesson plans; even without the graded themes, I liked what I was doing.

This was going to be a beautiful day, and Bob couldn't spoil it for me. Truett would be here at seven tonight. We'd enjoy the twilight, read and discuss another book. We would not talk about an unpredictable man at a typewriter in Cross Plains, weaving fantastic and gruesome yarns about a world that never was and never could be.

I could laugh and sing about my work and not think about Bob's eyes, begging me for understanding when he said some foolish something such as "My life wouldn't be worth a shot in the dark, if it weren't for my mother."

In spite of my staunch resolution otherwise, I felt a stab of pity for Bob. I could not see where he was trying to go. In a way, he did not live in my world at all. All he could do was complain loudly about the world we live in, disparage it. He was determined not to try to find companionship and happiness apart from his mother.

Still, there was one thing I didn't want. He and Truett had been real good friends. They had liked each other. I wanted to be friends with both of them.

Summer is hurrying by . . .

The letter lying there in the mailbox looked innocent enough. I opened it. One line! One single, solitary line, and it made me furious!

Not one word had I heard from Bob since he sent my letter back to me. Now this! "I'll be over Thursday evening between seven and seven-thirty. Bob."

The sun was hot but no hotter than my anger. I didn't even want to think about Bob Howard; certainly, I didn't want to see him Thursday night.

"The unmitigated gall of that man," I practically shouted as I slapped the letter down on the kitchen table where Mother and Mammy were sitting, shelling peas. "I could absolutely shoot him!" I snarled. "Look at that. Not will it be convenient for you if I come over Thursday night! No. Not one word to the effect that if you don't have a date—or I'd like to come if it's all right. Just that one, arrogant, smart aleck, 'I'll be over Thursday night.' "

Mother and Mammy stopped what they were doing and stared at me. "Well, I won't be here Thursday night," I raged. "After dinner, I'm going to get in that car out there and go to Brownwood and telephone Mr. Bob Howard and tell him to go straight to hell."

Mother got her breath back and began shelling peas again. "Is Truett coming tomorrow—Thursday night?" she asked.

"No," I said shortly. "He'll be here Friday night."

"When I was a girl," Mammy said, "I went to a dance with Jim Shelly on Saturday night and to church with Francis Reed on Sunday morning. I married Francis Reed."

"I wouldn't marry the last man on God's green earth," I said contemptuously. "You see this letter, don't you? Well, this is what I think of Bob Howard and his letter." I stuffed it in the stove to be burned.

Mother and Mammy watched me, saying nothing. Though Mammy did look as if she didn't quite know what to make of it. I got the water buckets off the shelf. We have to bring water from the tank about two hundred yards away. "I'll get some water," I snapped and went out the door.

* * * * * * * * *

In spite of the uncertain beginning, the summer had been almost perfect. Truett had made it perfect! I enjoy being with him. He likes to talk about the same things I do—books, the stars, and why things happen as they do—the ethereal, intangible problems I love to think about whether they can be solved or not. Although Truett's been here every Saturday and Sunday and two or three times a week, I've accomplished a lot of work. I've planned a new speech course for next year, and have almost finished my English course. In addition, I've rewritten some of the stories that are now ashes in Mrs. Hemphill's back yard.

Only now and then have I had a nagging thought of Bob. Some insignificant happening will cause me to think about him, and I begin to wonder about him and what he is doing. Has he really begun to write something besides the Conan stories? I hope so.

When you're with Truett Vinson, you don't really have time to think about Bob Howard. Only you do. A couple of Sundays ago, Truett and I had been coming home from a baseball game in Ft. Worth. The moon was so bright it turned the empty land beside the road into an unreal world.

It had been a delightful day. I had loved every minute of it.

As we were riding along, I had looked at Truett through the filtered moonlight. He is handsome, but, most of all, he's quiet. He doesn't seem to be worried about people around him, because he knows he can manage his life and be happy. Happy! He's not afraid of happiness. He seems to carry no sense of guilt.

"It's a beautiful night," I had said idly, dreamily.

And Truett had smiled. "Yes it is. That moon is almost bright enough to make the car lights unnecessary."

I had turned, then, to look out the window across the wide expanse of country, lighted by a bright moon. I thought, "This night—this beauty thrills me so much it hurts." Suddenly, at that moment, unbidden, unwanted, Bob was there beside me. His voice was clear and distinct. "Now, look out there, girl. That's a beautiful moon, if I do say so myself."

Quickly, I had turned back to Truett, giving my undivided attention to the baseball players he was talking about, willing all other thoughts from my mind.

Robert E. Howard

This photograph of Robert E. Howard was taken at the same time as the profile photograph reproduced on page 109, and Howard gave a copy of it to Novalyne Price. Mrs. Howard preferred this photograph, as did Dr. Howard, who presented another copy to Miss Price in the fall of 1936.

Has it been over two weeks since that happened? It didn't matter. Today, I could see it as a forewarning or a foreshadowing of events to come.

At the tank, the mockingbirds put on a great show, flying up out of the oaks across the way, singing with their hearts in their songs. I filled the buckets with water and sat down beneath the oak near me, wondering what to do.

There isn't time to mail Bob a letter to tell him not to come. I will not go to Brownwood this afternoon to call him.

Tomorrow night! He'll be here tomorrow night!

"Don't listen to the whip-poor-will—"

A faint touch of rose still lighted the sky as I put the last egg in my basket and started toward the house. It was then I saw Bob's car cross the railroad and cover the last few yards to stop at our front gate. He got out of the car and came toward me.

My feet were leaden, and my heart was loud in my ears. Then I got a good look at Bob.

Dear God! He was changed! He didn't look like himself tonight. Usually, when he comes to see me, he dresses carefully, neatly. Not tonight. He had on those everlasting old brown pants of his, the ones cut short to come just above his shoe tops. His fighting pants, he called them, which he said wouldn't trip him up if he got into a fight.

He had a mustache too. A mustache! Not a small, sophisticated mustache, such as some of the movie stars wore and which made a man look dashing. No. This one hung over his upper lip and drooped at the sides. He was like something from an old tintype photograph of a man in the late or middle 1800s. He came toward me.

I had to force myself to be still. Not to run.

"Howdy," he said cheerfully. He was so close now I could see his eyes, his questioning, shadow-filled eyes. He was putting on a show, but he was more ill at ease than I was. "Been getting the eggs?"

"Yes," I said. "I'll put them away. How are you?"

"Fine," he said. "Everything is fine."

I was going to ignore the mustache and the clothes. He was determined not to let me ignore the mustache.

"Well, how do you like my new buttermilk catcher?" he chortled. "Remember the Kipling yarn you used to tell me about?"

I managed to laugh. "Yes. I remember."

"What was it the girl said?"

"She said kissing a man without a mustache was like eating an egg without salt."

"That's what I thought. You know I've never read that yarn, but if you say it's there, I'll go along." He walked beside me toward the house. "What do you think? You like salt on your eggs, don't you?"

"No," I said flatly. "I'll take mine fresh, without salt."

There were some chairs on the porch, a cane-bottomed chair or two, a table, and a rocker.

"Have a chair," I said, politely, gaining more self-control all the time. "I have to put away the eggs."

The screen door closed behind me, and I hummed a little tune in a voice that was steady. I went to the kitchen, put away the eggs, washed my hands, and came back to the front porch. He was not sitting in either of the chairs. He was standing, leaning on one of the pillars around the porch. He didn't speak for a minute. He just stood there, resting his arms on the little cement ledge around the pillar. I walked over to another pillar and stood by it.

Even in the hottest part of the summer, there is always a cool breeze on our front porch. It is the most pleasant place in the world to be. I was grateful for the breeze tonight.

"I like this place," Bob said softly. "I'm almost tempted to ask your grandmother to sell it to me."

I leaned against my pillar and didn't answer.

"Yeah," he went on, "I like it here on the farm. It's quiet and peaceful." he paused. "Listen. Listen to the night sounds. I tell you, girl, in sound is reality. As long as you can hear sound, you're alive. Yes, sir, in sound is reality."

I listened. The night was full of sound, the everyday, common sounds of the farm: a cow bawled, chickens made chicken noises, and across the way from our house, a neighbor's dog barked. At another neighbor's house, Mrs. Guyer called to her husband. "Did you find Old Bessie?" Old Bessie, the cow, was forever breaking out of the pasture.

Bob was intent on the sounds, listening to the faint chirping of birds, the sound of the bull-bats, flying low. Then from the trees, another bird began its song—a low mournful cry of "Whip-poor-will."

Bob didn't turn to look at me. "Hear that?" he whispered. "Hear that whip-poor-will?"

"Yes," I said softly, keeping my voice down, hushed, not knowing why.

"Do you know how the whip-poor-will got its song?" he asked, his eyes still on the clump of trees from where the song came.

"No," I said. "I've never heard it."

"A good yarn."

"I'm sure it is."

He whirled toward me, suddenly, his eyes bright with an intensity I had not seen in them before. "I'll tell it to you," he said bluntly.

I tried to say I wanted to hear that story as much as I wanted to hear my death-knell, but my words were mumbled and meaningless.

Bob was in a strange and unusual mood tonight. It was more than simple jealousy. I was trying to understand it.

"Years, ago," he began and turned back to stare into the darkness of the trees, "before there was even a log cabin in this part of the country, your ancestors, the Indians, roamed about hunting buffalo and deer for food."

"I remember," I said lightly, trying to be funny.

He ignored me. "Among the Indians was a beautiful Indian maiden. Beautiful? Hell. That doesn't describe her. Some of the time, she was beautiful; some of the time she was just pretty, and some of the time she was downright ugly. You never knew what she'd be. They called her Little Fox. There was a brave, broad shoulders, trim waist, with—"

"With the corded muscles of the barbarian race," I interrupted.

Bob barely glanced at me. "Like a fool, he loved the girl. Loved her and didn't know why, didn't care why, and didn't want to know why." He paused again. "Well, the Indian warrior was a fool in more ways than one, a softhearted bastard, always trying to help somebody. That's why the Indians called him Sheep's Heart."

I could not stop the story even if I tried. I concentrated on Bob's voice, soft above the night sounds.

"Settlers began pouring in, and Sheep's Heart tried to help them," Bob went on, slowly. "He didn't know that the civilized white man will always take the help of a savage, but, then, he will turn and shoot the one who helped him. Shoot him in the back."

I stepped off the porch into the yard and picked up a chicken feather lying there. I twirled the feather in my fingers, watching Bob.

He knew the story was not going over, but he was determined to tell it. "One of the settlers was a young man, tall, black headed, keen-eyed. Will, they called him. When the settlers decided to stay in the country, Sheep's Heart brought them food and showed them how to build their cabins facing south to catch the winter sun."

I knew, of course, where the story was leading. "I suppose Little Fox fell in love with Will?"

Bob's body lurched. He was trying to be a ruthless strong man, but his eyes were not the cold, icy blue of a barbarian's. "Sheep's Heart wanted to kill them both," he rasped out. "He took the girl by the hair of her head and tied her to a tree. He took his whip—his long, plaited, buffalo hide whip, knotted and greased, and he whipped Will. He whipped him until the blood poured out of every cut the whip made. Little Fox began to cry and beg: 'Don't whip poor

Will.' Some of the birds in the forest, who didn't have a song of their own, began to sing it with her, but all the birds could sing was 'Whip-poor-will. Whip-poor-will.' Sheep's Heart turned away and left them there to live or die, his curse upon them."

"What a wonderful story," I lied. I stepped back onto the porch with a forced smile. "Have you written it down?"

Bob didn't answer; he didn't even turn to look at me.

"You must write it," I went on. "I think you could sell it." I offered him the rocker. "Won't you sit down?"

He was more ill at ease now. My act had disconcerted him. I had seemed too unconcerned with his bloody story, and he found himself not at his typewriter where he was comfortable.

"No," he said. "I—uh—Well, your grandmother is not here. I guess I'd better be going. I—" He hesitated. "Would you like to see a show?"

"Tonight?"

"Or we might ride around," he said lamely.

Some inner voice warned me not to go to a show, for this was a new Bob Howard. Yet I knew that with all his bravado, he was an uncertain Bob Howard.

"Yes," I said. "I'd like to see a show." I suppose I was beginning to feel sorry for him.

As he was buying the tickets, it occurred to me that he had brought me here, hoping to run into Truett! Perhaps to let Truett know that all was not over between us. At that moment, I hated Bob. I hated myself even more.

He must have known on which side of the theatre Truett usually sat, for he chose the down front right section, and we took our places. Silently swearing at myself for having come, I looked at the screen for a minute without seeing it. Then my eyes went instinctively down three or four rows ahead of me. There was Truett. I wanted to die. I wanted to crawl under the seat. But I knew that if I said anything, I would start Bob off; then I didn't know what he might say or do.

I sat still, and I could feel the perspiration beginning to break out on me. I kept my eyes resolutely on the screen, even though I could not see it, did not know or care what it was all about. Over and over, Bob's story of the whip-poor-will came back to me. Over and over, I swore at myself for my foolishness in coming. Only Bob seemed at ease, and Truett was unaware that we were in the theatre.

Suddenly, Truett got up from his seat and moved toward the aisle. I held my breath, keeping my face turned toward the screen, letting only my eyes wander to the side to watch as Truett went by. Bob sat perfectly still. He made no move to get up, though I thought I could tell that he turned his head and watched Truett; but he did not say a word.

Still, I could not relax. I was too tense. Now and then, I wiped my handkerchief across my face and thought of a thousand things I might do. Every woman who has ever dated a man has, at some time or other, thought of getting up and walking out on him. When I was sure Truett had had time to get out of the theatre, I thought of getting up and going outside. Whom could I call?

Clyde, I thought, was still my friend. I could call him. He understood Bob. He would be able to reason with him. Clyde was, perhaps, closer to Bob than any of his other friends. But I would not call Clyde. I could not.

The show ended. It was a relief to get up and leave! Usually, Bob hovered over me the way he hovered over his mother. Tonight, he stalked beside me as if he walked by himself. He didn't ask me if I wanted to go somewhere to get a coke. Instead, he said, "Let's go to the drugstore. I'm thirsty."

There wasn't much for me to do but go along. I ordered a coke; he, a strawberry milk shake.

I sat across the table watching him. A cool breeze from a ceiling fan near our table helped to dry the moisture from my forehead and body.

Bob began to talk about stories he'd sold—to *Action Stories, Top-Notch,* and to *Weird Tales.* But he didn't just talk about magazines he'd sold to, he began a long, detailed description of a Conan novel that would be published soon.

It occurred to me that he was bragging on himself and his writing. He was talking to get attention! Bob had never done that before, and it shocked me. He had much to be proud of with teaching himself to write. He could be proud of the sales he was making. I appreciated his accomplishments. But not tonight. I could not pay attention to his success because he was talking so loud. He was not shouting, far from it, but his voice carried and people turned to look at him and me.

It embarrassed me to be stared at in public like that! One man had the audacity to stand and stare at us.

I have my problems too. I sat at the table, hardly touching my coke, so embarrassed I wanted to scream. I said to myself, "I will not stand for this. I will get up and walk out of here, holding my head high. No man can make a fool of himself and of me in such a way. I am going home!"

But how? From Brownwood, it is seven miles to my home. Seven miles of walking in high heels, through pastures, over rocky hills, among trees and shrubs. Even if I walked the railroad tracks, it would be bad. I could easily walk seven miles. That was not the problem. I would need someone to take me home. But who?

I could not let Truett know. I didn't know whether he and Bob would ever be close friends again or not. On the trip they had taken the first of the summer, I think Truett had become disenchanted with Bob, and I was sorry about that. I could not go to Truett. I could not call Clyde, nor my aunt, because she had a family and would not understand.

But there was one person I could call! My cousin—Jack Pike. He was a policeman, and he dealt with all kinds of people and all kinds of situations. I could go to Jack and he would see to it that I got home.

I looked at Bob with as much anger as I could put into the look. Suddenly, I saw more than this supercilious rambling, his bravado, his bragging. Now, he was caught in a web of his own making, and he didn't know how to extricate himself from his own trap.

I took a deep breath. I would not walk out. I would stay there. Let people stare. They would not stare long. They would go about their business, more intent on their own thoughts than upon a drama in a drugstore. Even the man who had seemed interested in the bloody story of Conan, where a long dead man had been brought back to life and proved to be a ferocious enemy, was not interested now. He walked away.

I looked at Bob, trying to be the unconcerned, carefree man who did not care for the trappings of civilization. He was not having fun. His eyes were not cold and calculating.

I still felt some embarrassment, but now I felt another emotion—a deep pity for Bob. I think he realized it. He didn't know how men and women acted in real life. He was "different" from other people. He was talented, and his mind ran to worlds created on paper. When he was young, he could have learned how to cope with ordinary life situations, but he had been more interested in books than in people.

His mother? She had played a part in this—innocent or not. Had she understood his talent, his genius, or had she only understood his love for books? She knew how to encourage that. If he stayed home and read, he was not out somewhere away from her getting into trouble! She had felt safe to have him there at home, reading. He had been safe. What a price he had paid for safety!

If Truett ever became angry with me, he would not do the things Bob had tried to do tonight. He would simply turn coldly away, but Truett would never lose his dignity.

Poor Bob! He had told me so many times that civilization was an unhappy accident of fate. He had said that the barbarian was superior to civilized man. He had not yet realized that the barbarian could not compete in any area with a civilized man. It was the civilized man who would triumph, not the barbarian.

The story ended. He finished the milk shake with a deep pull on the straw that made a small gurgling sound which well-bred people think is crude. I had reached the place where I would no longer let it faze me.

"It's time I was getting home," I said very quietly. "You've sat here tonight and told the whole world one of your Conan stories, and I haven't said a word;

but I'm ready to go now."

He looked at me quickly, and a dark flush spread over his face. His eyes took on that haunted, fear-filled look that had always baffled and hurt me.

I got up and he followed me. I walked outside into the cool night air and took a deep breath. He caught up with me. "I'll take you home," he said.

He opened the car door for me and got into his seat, reached to start the engine, then stopped. I didn't say a word.

"I think you pay too much attention to what people say and do and think," he said slowly. "What the hell's the difference what people think? As long as they don't feed you or buy your clothes, what they say or think is not worth a damn."

He was right. I cared too much. "I care," I admitted. "I do care what people think. Good or bad, I care."

"I don't give a goddam what they think of me, or say about me. I want you to know that. I don't give a damn what you and Truett or anybody else says or thinks about me. I'm no great writer, but, by God, I've made as much of a success at what I've done as anybody else has."

"I know that," I said simply.

"I've made a living, not much of one by your standards, perhaps, but, damn it to hell, I pay my bills, earn my own bread, and I do it at something I want to do."

"I think you've made that perfectly clear," I said. "You've also made it clear that you don't give a damn about—about other people."

We didn't say another word during the seven miles to my home. He stopped the car in front of the house, and I began to get out, not waiting for him to come around to open the door for me. He joined me at the front of the car and walked to the steps with me.

When I got to the steps, I turned and looked at him, trying to think of something to say. I could not find the proper words.

The night was soft and lovely. The stars, which Truett had talked to me about, shone over Bob and me. From millions of light years away, they cast a dim, ethereal glow around us; but I could see nothing familiar to me, not even the stars. The world was not yet real. This night had not been real. It was a dream, and I would wake from it soon, feel the cool night breeze on my face, and know that I was home.

"I cannot believe this night," I said reluctantly, from a hurt in my heart.

Without warning, he grabbed me in his arms and kissed me as I had never been kissed before by him or any other man. It had all the careless possessiveness of a barbarian who is here for one moment and is gone the next. It had something of the tenderness of a man's love for a woman.

When it was over, his eyes searched my face. "Don't listen to the whip-poor-will with—"

His voice was low, husky, filled with emotion. He dropped his arms from around me, turned, and walked rapidly back to his car.

I stood where he left me and watched as he got into his car, started the engine, turned the car around, and drove away. I looked back at the sky, rich with stars, but I knew that the lights of his car cut the darkness. I knew when he turned from our place onto the highway and the lights gleamed down the road. I knew when the darkness swallowed up the light.

I was not thinking or dreaming. I stood still. Waiting. Waiting for something. *In sound is reality,* Bob had said. In the distance, I could hear a train begin its long upward pull as it struggled up the hill between Brownwood and our place.

Standing there, everything became clear to me. Bob had not meant to make a fool of himself tonight. He was trying to say something he believed intensely. He was saying that a man who earns success by his own effort and sweat deserves to be taken as he is—a plain and common man. The accoutrements of society do not make the man. Bob wanted to be honored for his accomplishments. He had been trying to say, "Look at me, the man."

Why does it always take me so long to understand? I had been aware of something deeper than the outward show, yet it had taken me this long to understand!

A train makes a lonesome sound as it lumbers, rattles, and groans over the tracks. This one did too. A star fell. For an instant, there was a brilliant flash of light across the sky, like a white light turned on and off quickly in a dark room.

"It is not over between us," I thought. "Not yet."

Pain was in my heart for a shadow lay between Truett and me.

Then on the night breeze came a voice, husky with emotion: "Don't listen to the whip-poor-will with—" It came again in the sound of the train, dying away, "Don't listen to the whip-poor-will."

"Don't listen to the whip-poor-will."

The fall of 1935 . . .
School begins with a bang . . . Bob is a bang . . .

It was Nat Williams who made me aware that Bob was still proclaiming to the world that a man who is "different" should capitalize on that difference. But he didn't tell me what to expect. All he did was make it hard for me to pay attention to what was being said in faculty meeting.

Teachers congregated in the hall to talk. Shortly before we began to move toward the study hall where we were to have the faculty meeting, I went to my classroom to see how much trouble I'd have to get it ready for classes. I hurried back so that I wouldn't be late.

I saw Nat, his arms full of books, on his way into the study hall. He looked over the books, smiling devilishly. "Have you seen your old boy friend since you got back?"

Naturally, the first thing I thought of was Bob's mustache. "You mean he still has that crazy mustache?" I said with a touch of irritation.

Nat laughed. "Well, the mustache is part of it." He grinned. "You'll see him. Go to town. You'll see him."

Louise Nelson walked up. "El gran vaquero," she said. She and Nat laughed as if she'd just said something very funny.

Immediately, I was on the defensive. "He's not a cowboy; he's a writer," I said, trying to make him sound important.

Nat and Louise laughed. Lewis Norman joined us. He wanted to know what was so funny, and Nat, still teasing me, told him they were laughing about my good-looking boy friend. Lewis laughed.

He didn't say anything about Bob. He wanted to know if I'd be able to make it without Enid this year, since she'd taken a job in north Texas. When he introduced me to the new football coach, Claude Daniels, he called me the best speech teacher in Texas. I felt good about that.

As I sat down in the study hall, I began my inevitable comparing Bob with other men. Nat, for example, has the ability to tease teachers or students in a friendly way, without malice; yet he keeps a wall between himself and them. You never forget that he's the boss, and you respect him for it. In my heart, I wished Bob could be more like Nat, instead of being jealous of Nat. He was jealous of Nat, both as a person and as a successful man, who knows how to associate with other people.

Nat took his place, and we settled down quietly. Although I tried to listen, my mind strayed to Bob. It's too bad he can't enjoy the comaraderie we teachers enjoy. Our conversations were not profound. Actually, we'd made inane remarks. "What did you do this summer?" "Ready for school?" "Did you have a nice summer?"

Ethel and I greeted each other like long lost sisters. She said, "Oh, my, my. You're back at Mrs. Hemphill's?"

Then I said nice things to her, such as I missed her and that it wasn't fun to be by myself. I crossed my fingers on that one, for I enjoy rooming alone.

Nat seemed even more enthusiastic this year than last, not so many rules and regulations to tell us about. He had more time to make us know what a privilege it was to be a teacher. I knew it was not only great to be a teacher, but it was also great to be on his "team." I tried hard to listen, but, inevitably, I found myself wondering what was so funny about Bob.

His mustache? None of the men his age had big walrus mustaches. Was he still trying to say to the world: "I've made a success of my work. Very few men in Cross Plains make more money than I do. Accept me for what I am, not my mustache!"

In August, when he came to see me, I didn't realize until too late that he was asking to be admired for his ability. I didn't want to be so long to understand again. I tried to prepare myself.

After faculty meeting, I spent more time in my room than I had intended to. Everybody was gone when I came out to go to the post office. I had kept my box all summer. I decided to see if the rent was due, before I ran over to see Mrs. Smith to give her a message from Enid.

As I started out the door of the post office, I bumped into Bob. It wasn't the collision that almost knocked me flat! What a Bob Howard that was! Nat had said the mustache was part of it. He was right! Louise had said, "El gran vaquero." And she was right. The way he was dressed! I nearly dropped dead.

The first thing that startled me was the black sombrero he had on. It was a real Mexican sombrero with little balls dangling from its rim. The chin strap was a thin little strip of leather attached to the hat. It came down and was tied under his chin. The vaqueros used the chin strap to keep their hats from being blown off by the incessant winds that swept the plains. But the flat crown and chin strap made Bob's face look rounder than ever.

He didn't look like a vaquero, but he'd gone all the way to dress like one! The red bandana around his neck was tied in the back. He didn't have on those old short, brown pants. Not this year! He had on short, *black* pants that came to the top of his black shoes.

His mustache was longer and droopier than ever. I gasped and stared at him. I couldn't say a thing. I couldn't even say a careless, "Hi, Bob." I just gurgled.

He swept off his sombrero, bowed low, and said, "Miss Price, imagine meeting you here! How do you do? What about a—"

I didn't wait to hear the rest of the sentence. I got my breath, the breath to run, not to talk. I literally ran across that wide, wide street!

Dr. Howard was coming out of the drugstore when I reached the door. I glanced quickly back toward Bob. To Dr. Howard, I gasped out, *sotto voce,* "What is he trying to prove?"

Dr. Howard shook his head. "I don't know," he said softly. "I really don't know."

What mighty contests rise from trivial things . . .
. . . Pope . . .

Everywhere I go, someone asks me if I've seen Bob lately. If I happen to be in the hall at school when Nat steps out of the office, he begins to imitate Bob's lunging walk. I pretend to throw something at Nat and get out of the hall as quickly as I can.

Bob's dressing peculiarly should not be new to the people in Cross Plains, though I think his reason is new. He's always worn his pants only to the tops of his high-topped buttoned shoes.

I'll never forget one day after he'd gotten his good-looking brown suit; he stopped the car on the street in front of the post office. I watched him, thinking how nice he looked. I asked him why he didn't get some nice shoes, and he said, "Look, girl, I'll wear a damn coat and tie and this fancy hat for you, but my ankles are weak, and I'm not going to try to walk in those sawed off shoes you're talking about."

But after that, I noticed his shoes were high-topped-laced shoes instead of the buttoned ones. That was some improvement. I settled for that.

This year, however, he has gone all out for peculiar clothes. Everywhere you see him, he has on the black sombrero tied under his chin, and a bandana around his neck.

He hasn't been by the house, but I've seen him when I go to town after school or on any Saturday morning that I'm in town. If I'm in Smith's drugstore, or some other store, and see him stop his car and go into the post office, I stay out of sight until I'm sure he has gone.

Last year, I seldom saw him in town; this year, he seems to go to town every time I do. If I'm not working after school, I try to slip downtown for a coke or a cup of coffee. I look up and down the street or duck into the post office to avoid him, but I always see him. He is either coming out of the post office as I go in, or else he's going in as I'm coming out.

He bows, sweeps off his sombrero, and says, "Well, Miss Price! How do you do?"

I speak pleasantly, but I don't stop to chat. I say, "Hi, Bob," and throw "How are you?" over my shoulder at him.

Bob is not likely to come around me, wearing that hat and dressed like that, but I wonder what I'll say if he does. I will say something, and he knows it. To go with me, he can not dress silly like that.

But, doggone his ornery hide! In spite of all his foolishness, I miss him.

I miss riding around after school. I miss riding all over this part of Texas and talking about the world and the state of civilization. I'd like to know if he's given up writing those blood and thunder Conan stories, as he said he had, and gone on to more modern things. I wonder if he's started on his novel about the early days of Texas. And I even miss the arguments we had. I'd like to argue with him again about psychological stories, which I like and he doesn't. The truth is I miss him, and I hate myself for it.

There is a new man in town, Pat Allen. The other night, I was at a party, and Pat and another man came in. Pat dresses as nicely as Bob does sloppily. Pat is a little over six feet tall, has green eyes, real light hair and is as Irish as they come. When he was introduced as Mr. Allen, he held out his hand, grinning, and said, "My name's Pat. I'm a Jew."

That got a laugh. I've had a few dates with him, but nothing serious will develop there. He is pleasant company; I enjoy talking with him, even though he doesn't try to solve the ills of the world as Bob does. Pat can be serious or fun. I won't fall in love with him for two reasons: First, I love Truett. Second, Pat is also dating my beautiful cousin, Jimmie Lou.

I am angry at Bob because of the way he acts and dresses. It seems impossible for me not to compare him with other men. I have to keep reminding myself that he is a brilliant man who makes a decent living and corresponds with men and women from all over the United States and some foreign countries. But he lives in a small Texas town where a lot of people don't understand him, just because he is a writer, not a shoe clerk. Writers, as Enid used to say, are proud, intelligent people who live somewhere else and probably don't do crazy things. They don't dress crazily either.

And I, myself, keep wondering why he is dressing and acting as he is doing.

Surely my heart cried out that it was thou
When first I saw thee; and thy heart spoke too,
I know it! but fate trod those promptings down
Under its iron heel . . .
                                . . . Arnold . . .

You never know what Bob Howard will do next!

After school started and I saw Bob about town, I could not believe my eyes—that sombrero, bandana, and those other silly clothes. But the thing I didn't really believe was that I would come home from school one afternoon, and Bob would appear at the curb in front of Mrs. Hemphill's.

It has rained this fall, and I was picking my way slowly toward the house today. I looked up just as Bob's car stopped in front of the house. The uncanny way he can foretell events leaves me speechless!

My heart began to beat faster, but not with joy and anticipation. I kept

---

thinking, "I will not go anywhere with him with that hat on, and he ought to know it."

Before I got to the car, he stepped out. Although his mustache seemed to leap out at me, the sombrero was not on his head nor was the bandana around his neck! He had on a blue shirt and the short brown pants. But that was better than the other costume.

He was smiling. "Like to ride around a little while?" he asked.

"Sure," I said and wondered why in the world I'd said it.

I got in the car, put my books on the back seat. His sombrero was not even in the car! I breathed easier.

We talked of this and that. Nothing important. He had been working hard he said, and he thought he'd like to relax a minute; figured I'd been working hard and maybe I'd like to relax too; thought we'd just ride around, and he'd shoot off his mouth.

It was pleasant, and I began to feel that maybe things were all right again. Not that I really wanted to re-open an old friendship.

I asked, politely, about his mother. He said she seemed to be doing much better. I didn't tell him that I had talked with Dr. Howard a couple of days ago, and that Dr. Howard just shook his head. I knew the poor old man was awfully uneasy about her.

Then I said that it was a pretty day, and Bob said yes it was but here it was the fall of the year again and he was in his sere and yellow leaf and worrying about the desire he had to wander all over the world. He wanted just to chuck it all and roam.

"If it weren't for my parents," he said, "I wouldn't stay here for a minute! Fall is the time of year to wander. Someday, I'll roam the deserts and hills where Jenghiz Khan roved. I'd like to follow Alexander the Great's trail and see if it's true that there is a lost colony somewhere, some vestige left of the Old Greek civilization in a colony that Alexander started. I'd like to go down into Egypt and follow the Nile." He smiled at me from faraway places.

He settled himself comfortably and began again. He hadn't expected an answer to his ramblings.

"Archaelogists have a good life," he said. "They go all over the world, seeking lost and forgotten civilizations. Now, there, girl, that's a profession for you. Instead of being chained to a typewriter, you could wander the world over, digging into lost cities, finding the artifacts of past civilizations. That would tell you louder than words the kind of life men lived."

He sighed; his voice was melancholy. "The fall of the year awakens the wanderlust in me and makes me want to go as far away as my ship will carry me."

"You could go," I said, and I sincerely wanted him to. I forgave him his silly dress, his striving for a place of his own and being ridiculous.

At that moment, I became angry with Mrs. Howard. It was not the typewriter but she who had chained him. It seemed such a shame that a young man, who dreamed so fervently of faraway places, was chained to a way of life in a small, prosaic, and, sometimes, hostile town.

He shrugged his shoulders, and turned to smile at me. "Mark graduated, didn't he? Got any more pupils like him that you want to thrust greatness upon?"

I refused to let that bother me. I was a year smarter, too. We had another pupil in school who was destined for greatness, a kid who had transferred there for his senior year. It made me realize that God sends teachers wonderful pupils year after year. I knew I had to be careful the way I told Bob about him, or he'd think I'd fallen for another not-dry-behind-the-ears kid.

"Do you know Weezy Lane—Rosa's younger sister?" I asked.

"I know her when I see her," Bob said. "Is—"

"She has a new boyfriend who started to school this year—Durwood Varner. All of us teachers are talking about him. One of the most brilliant boys we have. Has a great personality too. Weezy's such a cute girl, I'm glad for her."

I waited. Bob nodded his head as if approving Weezy's boyfriend too. I laughed to myself. There's more than one way of hawg-tying a calf.

This afternoon was pleasant enough in spite of the barrier between us. He didn't ask for a date, for which I was glad. While we were riding around, I thought a lot about Bob and Truett.

Truett and I had been to Ft. Worth to ball games; we'd been to Brady; we'd even ridden once to San Angelo, but he had never suggested he come to Cross Plains for me, or that he bring me back to Cross Plains. He always wants to know when I'm coming home. When I do, he comes right out to see me, and we read books and talk for hours.

I remembered how Bob and I used to ride around—almost to Abilene, to Coleman, Ballinger, and almost to Mineral Wells. Last year, he had taken me home to Brownwood and talked about going on to San Saba. I am getting to know this country pretty well if not the two friends who are my friends too.

Bob didn't ask about Truett. But the next time I see Truett, he'll say, "Have you seen Bob?"

What will I say to that?

Far from the madding crowd's ignoble strife . . .
. . . Gray . . .

No matter what I do or say, Bob finds out about it!

Last Saturday, several of us went to Brownwood shopping, and I found a beautiful white pigskin jacket. When I saw it, I knew I had to have it. This was the first time in my life I felt I could afford something like it. I have a black sweater with a high neck, and a black skirt to go with it. In that black and white outfit, I look dramatic! It's the way I want to look.

Pat Allen called me and wanted to know if I'd like to go to Brownwood to see a football game. On the way, a car passed us. It wasn't going too fast, but a couple of hundred yards down the road, all of a sudden, the car simply turned over.

Pat stopped his car and we got out to see what we could do to help.

By the time we were out of our car, they were out of theirs, standing around, asking each other what had happened. No one was badly hurt. We stood there another fifteen minutes before it was decided that Pat and I would take the two girls and one of the boys to Brownwood with us. We'd take them to the hospital to make sure there were no serious injuries and to get patched up, if that was needed.

While I wanted to help the people, I saw no reason why I should crowd into that coupe and let them bleed on my new white pigskin jacket. I suggested to Pat that we put my jacket in the back so there wouldn't be any danger of getting blood on it. One of the girls said they certainly didn't want to bleed on my jacket, and I said I certainly didn't want them to, for I had worked pretty hard to pay for it.

Pat and I were too late for the ball game, and so we went to a show.

I thought that was the last of it.

But today, I decided I'd come home early after school and organize myself before going back to play practice. I was already at the steps when Bob drove up. I looked at him and saw the black shirt, but it didn't warn me. When he asked me if I wanted to ride around for a while, I agreed.

Bob gets to the point quickly. "I hear you've been saving lives," he said.

I gasped. "What do you mean?"

"They tell me that you and your friend, Pat Allen, saw a car wreck the other night," Bob said with seeming sweetness. "Pat, being an Irish gentleman, a man of great sympathy and consideration for the less fortunate, as all good Irishmen are, agreed to take some of the people down to Brownwood to the hospital—"

"That's true," I said, wondering how in the world he knew about it.

"I also understand you took off your white pigskin jacket and put it in the back, so that nobody would bleed on it." He looked at me with a smile I didn't understand.

"Why not?" I said. "That jacket cost almost as much as a coat. I wasn't about to get it ruined."

"That's what I'm talking about," Bob said, his eyes filled with sardonic humor. "I always say we are really advancing in civilization when we're so willing to save lives we endanger our white pigskin jackets."

When I got my breath, I said, "I don't see why that necessarily indicates a rotting civilization. Should I have been foolish enough to say: 'Come on; you're not badly hurt, but you're bleeding; bleed on my new jacket and ruin it?' If I could help them, fine. At the same time, I didn't think I had to sacrifice my jacket to do it if it wasn't necessary."

It didn't occur to me until too late that I had foolishly gotten myself into an argument with a writer who used words to paint any kind of picture he wanted to paint.

"You're absolutely right, girl," Bob said in the mockingly serious tone. "You didn't owe it to them to ruin your jacket. As I always say, the more advanced we become in civilization, the more we talk about our understanding of God's word. But do we throw down our lives for a brother? No. Let the man bleed to death, as long as he doesn't touch my white pigskin jacket."

He did exactly what he wanted to do. He made me furious.

"You make me sound terrible," I snapped. "I'm not a mean person, just because I didn't want somebody who wasn't hurt badly bleeding all over me."

"If he was bleeding," Bob said piously, "he must have been hurt."

"Not bad." I raised my voice. "None of them was hurt badly. They were just skinned a little. One had a small gash on his forehead, but it wasn't bad either."

"I know," Bob said still in the pious manner. "We have to justify ourselves, don't we?"

By that time, I didn't know whether I was coming or going. He didn't give me time to answer. He launched into a tirade about modern sophisticates who make fun of torn and bleeding bodies. He talked of human beings and their pitiful attempts to hide their wounded hearts from the world. When they knew sorrow and agony, they should not be analyzed by some two-bit psychologist who scorned the man who earned his bread by the sweat of his brow.

I took all I could before I put a stop to it. "Bob," I said angrily. "You're talking sentimental nonsense!"

He shook his head and said that all sophisticates were like me. All of them prattled about sentimentality while they laughed and scorned a man's bleeding soul.

"Those people we took to Brownwood didn't have bleeding souls," I blurted out. "Your soul isn't bleeding and neither is mine. You don't know anybody whose soul is bleeding. I'm not going to listen to you. I still think I did the right thing. To me, it would have been stupid if I had told them to get in the car and bleed on my jacket."

Bob laughed smugly. I was glad that we were near Mrs. Hemphill's. Bob didn't have any more to say except that it was peculiar to see the way sophisticates could always find an excuse for whatever they wanted to do and never find an excuse for what a poor troubled soul was struggling to accomplish.

I admitted I was beaten by a man with a superior use of words.

"All of your talk—fluent, beautiful—means nothing. It does not make me cry."

And he asked, suddenly quite solemn. "Could I do anything that would make you cry?"

And I said, emphatically, "No."

The leaves and grass are turning brown . . .

It has rained a lot this fall. Two months ago, farmers were searing the stickers off prickly pears in order to feed them to the cows for moisture. Now, there's so much mud it threatens the harvesting of the crops. But that's not all that's different.

I didn't go home last weekend, and Truett didn't come over here to see me either. That bothers me. He has not been over to Cross Plains to see me, or to take me home since school started. At least Bob took me home or came after me. What Truett's reasons are for not coming, I don't know.

Last weekend, I wanted terribly to see him. I felt downhearted and lonesome, even though everything was going nicely. The play I'm working on is coming along. Things at school are wonderful. On the surface, everything is beautiful; on the inside of me, I'm not exactly happy.

Sunday, when I got home from church, it looked like a very long, tiresome afternoon. I had already studied my lessons for next week, and I'd graded a few papers. It looked as if all I'd do would be sit around and wish I could be with Truett.

Mrs. Hemphill called me to the telephone. I hadn't even heard it ring.

To my surprise, it was Bob. He asked me if I wanted to go to Brownwood to see a show. I hesitated, thinking about his mustache and those awful clothes. Could I take going to Brownwood to a picture show with that mustache and sombrero?

"Wel-l-l," I stammered. "I—I guess I should study awhile or work on a story I'm trying to write."

Bob broke in. "Well, girl, I just took my brown suit out of moth balls, and I'm all dressed up. I've even got that idiot hat out of the bottom of the closet—"

I laughed. He was assuring me that he was going to act like a normal red-blooded he-man, but I couldn't resist saying, "Have you shaved your mustache?"

There was a silence on the other end of the line. "No," he said slowly. "Love me; love my mustache."

I did some mental gymnastics and decided I could go with the mustache. I could not forget the many times I had enjoyed talking and being with Bob.

I was dressed in my black and white when he came.

"Is that the white pigskin jacket?" Bob asked when I opened the door. "The jacket nobody can bleed on?" He grinned, but his voice was not mocking today. His eyes seemed worried and questioning.

"Yes, it is," I said, trying to be cheerful.

"Mighty pretty," he said. "I don't reckon I blame you for not letting people bleed on it. I mean, let the fools die, let 'em bleed to death, but protect your jacket."

This was not a good beginning.

"If you're going to start that again," I said firmly. "I just won't go to the show."

He laughed and said he guessed he wouldn't say anymore about it, though he did admit it would be mighty hard not to.

On the way to Brownwood, we passed a stopped car where someone was trying to fix a flat tire. Bob slowed down and asked if he could be any help.

They didn't need any help, but they thanked us just the same.

When we drove on, Bob said you had to be very careful, because you never knew when people like that might be pretending to have a flat but who would be intent on robbery. I remembered another day he had speeded up and driven so fast past a car I had barely been able to hold on. I didn't mention it. Whether or not he asked if he could help depended upon his mood at the moment.

He talked about some of the desperadoes who had settled in this country. He told me about a man in Brownwood who had risen to a place of high esteem, but people whispered he'd been a fast gun with some outlaw gang. Didn't believe the story himself, but that's the way they told it to him. He said he himself had to be careful whom he helped, because a man with as many enemies as he had needed to be careful.

Amused, I said, "Bob, you talk about enemies. How many enemies do you really have?"

He grinned. "Anybody who is not your friend is your enemy," he explained pleasantly.

We argued about that for a while. I said a person who was not your friend probably didn't care enough about you to be your enemy. Bob insisted that in this dog-eat-dog civilization of ours, any man who wasn't your friend might stick a knife in your back without a second thought.

The show was all right, but I spent my time looking at the people around me to see whether or not anyone I knew was there. Truett was not. For that, I was glad.

After the show, we went to a drugstore for cokes. Things had been very pleasant, and I was feeling carefree and happy.

It was as we came out of the drugstore and started to the car that the pleasant afternoon almost dissolved into thin air.

On the corner of Center and East Baker streets was a little preacher, trying to preach a sermon. A few people, who didn't seem to have anything else to do, were gathered around him. He was a small, nondescript looking fellow, and he may or may not have been a good preacher. It did not affect me one way or the other.

Seeing him there made Bob angry. For a minute, I was afraid he was going to say something to him. I began to pull at Bob's arm. "For heaven's sake, come on," I groaned.

He came, reluctantly, grumbling all the way to the car. He kept saying it reminded him of Theodore Dreiser's book, *An American Tragedy*. Bob said men like that, who got out on the street corner and tried to preach, were tragic, inarticulate fools. He thought they ought to be locked up, so that they could not insult people's intelligence.

It irritated me. I preached a good sermon to him. I said that this country had been settled for the purpose of letting any man, woman, or child worship God as he wanted to. "If that little man back there feels he was called to stand on the street corner and preach a sermon here in the United States of America," I said emphatically, "then I believe with all my heart and soul he has a right to do it."

Basically, I believe Bob agreed with me, but he was obstinate. He said half-baked preachers did not have a right to stand on street corners and preach the gospel to him. That was not the kind of gospel he wanted to hear. He said there was a Catholic church just down the next street, and when he wanted to hear priests, who did not shout down hell fire and brimstone, he could go to it and hear the gospel. Otherwise, he would thank people for staying off the streets to do their preaching.

I continued my sermon. "That's not the point. That poor little man back there wasn't preaching just to you. He was preaching in order to pay what he considers to be his debt to God; if he wants to stand there and preach to hard-hearted beings like you, he has a right to. Stop up your ears if you don't want to hear him. It's as simple as that. Besides, what have you got against religion? No one makes you go to church. You're free. At least, you always claim to be free."

Bob glared at me, knocked around against the steering wheel a time or two.

"I haven't got anything against religion," he said shortly. "Religion is all right. I just want to straighten out a few bastards who try to practice it and don't know how."

"Going to church has always been a big thing to me," I said slowly, trying to get myself under control. "I went when I was a kid, and I just think it's part of life."

Bob slowed the car down, and settled himself against his door. "I went to church, too, when I was a kid. I believed it all, even though some of the things they told me didn't work out the way they said they would."

I took the bait. "What things didn't work out?"

"Well, girl, they told me in Sunday School not to take the Lord's name in vain. I sure as hell didn't, because I was afraid if I did, something awful would happen."

He was off on one of his "yarns," and I sat back, looked at him, listened, and smiled.

"One Sunday afternoon . . . after church and Sunday School, too, by damn, a kid came over to my house to play. There we were in my back yard playing cowboys and Indians . . . I was the Indian. All of a sudden, this crazy damn kid said, 'goddam.' Well, I jumped back away from him because I expected a bolt of lightning to come down out of the sky and strike that little bastard dead."

I laughed. "It didn't, of course."

"Hell, no. It just didn't seem right to me it didn't. But, after that, I figured if he could say it and not get struck by lightning, so could I. I've been saying it ever since. You don't see any lightning, do you?"

"I'm sure there is some," I said, "You'd better be careful how you talk."

Whether the little preacher had caused it or not, Bob was interested in religion and ready to talk more about it today than usual.

"Man created God in his own image." He launched into a description of the lonely Hebrew, tending his flocks, a small dot on the wide reaches of the desert. "From out of his loneliness, while he watched the flocks, the shepherd began to meditate on God or Yahweh. To him, God became a manlike creature, bigger and more powerful, of course, able to defend man against his enemies. But, however you look at it: Man created God in his own image."

"I think you're leaving out something," I said. "Maybe we'd better talk of other things."

He grinned and told me I ought to listen to him and learn something. We drove home slowly, talking, then, of other things. We talked of Shakespeare and Hamlet, safe subjects; we talked about writers of today who lacked the fervor, the gusto, and the human understanding of Shakespeare. Bob talks and writes with gusto, but I'm not sure about the human understanding.

It was almost sundown when we got back to Mrs. Hemphill's.

"This has been a good day, if I do say so myself," he said, "and that's a beautiful sunset to top it off."

He was right. The day had had its moments of uncertainty and fear, but it had also had its moments of beauty.

Christmas is here again . . .

Since that Sunday in November when Bob and I went to the show in Brownwood, I haven't seen much of him. I've been too busy to go to town in the afternoons; that is probably why. So I couldn't believe it when Bob came over, the day before the holidays began, and brought me a box of candy and a Christmas card.

He gave me the candy and said he knew I liked chocolate candy, and he thought I might like something to chew on during the holidays since I wouldn't have him around to chew on. He looked at me strangely.

I laughed and thanked him. It's a nice Christmas card and the candy is delicious. It was sweet of Bob!

Why do things like that tear at one's heart?

Early January 1936 . . .

It's January and school has started again! I'm glad. I had a pleasant vacation. I was with Truett a lot during the holidays and enjoyed every minute of it. He gave me a book for Christmas. I love it.

Only one thing is wrong with the new year, and that wouldn't be bad if I weren't who I am. A new teacher had to be added to the faculty. She's a young lady from Cisco, Mary Beth Langston. She teaches in the lower grades.

She's real nice, and it was inevitable that she should go to the Hemphill's to find out if she could get a room there. Mrs. Hemphill asked me if I would object to having a roommate, and I told her, very cheerfully, I was so glad to be staying at her house myself, I wouldn't do anything that would upset her. If I had to have a roommate, I would gladly room with Mary Beth.

I saw Ethel at school one morning after Mary Beth moved in and began teaching. Ethel said, "Oh, my, my. Miss Langston is your new roommate."

I don't know whether or not Ethel thought about my books and papers all over the room and felt sorry for a roommate of mine. I wouldn't blame her.

I said, "Yes, I have a new roommate. I'm very lucky. I always seem to have nice roommates."

It was the only way I could let Ethel know I appreciated her, too.

Mary Beth is quiet. She listens well. That's too bad for her sake. I've told her my life story. I've told her all about Bob, what a nice person he is, in spite of the crazy way he dresses these days. I told her he was a very brilliant and a very interesting man. I also told her about Truett, and Clyde, who had introduced me to Bob. "Three interesting men," I said, "and I've had the pleasure of dating all three."

She laughed. "This Truett. You like him, don't you?"

"I love him," I said and thought that settled it.

She looked doubtful. She wanted to know how I liked Bob. It's easy to say, "I like him a lot." I told her I could get very angry about things he does, the way he dresses.

"He just will dress some crazy way," I repeated sighing. "I hate it, even though I know why he's doing it. He's trying to tell people he's a writer and writers have a right to be odd. Since they think he's crazy, anyway, he'll show them just how crazy he can be."

Mary Beth shook her head and sighed. "It's too bad."

I nodded. "In a way, I understand him. He's trying to say he doesn't care in order to hide how much he cares, because he thinks people don't like him. I understand that. I do the wrong thing at times, too."

February 13, 1936

"The way to interest a writer," I said to my roommate, "is to ask him about his writing. After you find out what he's doing and selling, you ask him to help you with your writing."

Mary Beth laughed. "That will work, will it?"

"Without fail!" I said. "You can have him eating out of your hand with those tactics."

Then I mentioned Bob, and said that, in spite of his mustache and the crazy clothes he was wearing these days, I enjoyed talking with him, and I missed him very much.

"So you're going to ask him about his writing?" she laughed.

"The letter is written and mailed. I asked him where and how much he was selling these days. Then I asked if he had any suggestions about markets I might sell to."

He answered so promptly Mary Beth put her hand to her mouth and began munching away—to show me I had him eating out of my hand.

Cross Plains, Texas,
February 14, 1936.

Dear Novalyne:

I heard yesterday you had the mumps; now you tell me it's the itch. I wish you'd make up your mind. In either event, you have my sympathy.

I noticed your sinister insinuation regarding my whiskers. Shave, in this weather? Do you want to expose me in a practically nude condition to the icy blasts of the Arctic blizzards? They say the Lord tempers the wind to the shorn lamb, but they don't say anything about Him temporing the wind to the shorn jackass. Perhaps when the gentle heifers—or maybe it's zephyrs—of summer gambol and frolic lightly through the post oaks I may employ the shears on my rugged countenance, but not in this weather.

Yes, Kline's still my agent, and I'm doing a little business with a fellow named Kofoed, of Philadelphia, former editor of Fight Stories, and now editor of Day Book, who does a little agenting for me on the side, much to Kline's disgust, I fear. The tales of Sam Walser (a rugged, upright, forthright, typical American name, even if the original was a Dane from Skaggerack) appear—or will appear when they start publishing them—in a magazine called Spicy Adventure Stories. They pay one cent a word, on acceptance, and report fairly promptly. I've sold them four yarns so far, and fondly hope to sell regularly, if they ever start publishing my stuff and get a reaction from the readers, who, I feel, are cultured and scholarly gentlemen, who wax enthusiastic over meritous artistic efforts, he remarked with characteristic modesty. The main handicap is the necessity of keeping the wordage down—they take nothing over 5500 words, this being their limit not only for Spicy Adventures, but also for Spicy Mysteries and Spicy Detectives, which I hope to make also. A nice balance must be maintained— the stuff must be hot enough to make the readers bat their eyes, but not too hot to get the censors on them. They have some definite taboos. No degeneracy, for instance. No sadism or masochism. Though extremely fond of almost-nude ladies, they prefer her to retain some garment ordinarily—like a coyly revealing chemise.

However this taboo isn't iron-clad, for I've violated it in nearly every story I've sold them. I've found a good formula is to strip the heroine gradually—she loses part of her clothes in one episode, some more in the next, and so on until the climax finds her in a state of tantalizing innocence. Certain words are taboo, also, though up to a certain point considerable frankness in discussing the female anatomy is allowed. The hero should be an American, and the action should take place in some exotic clime. I've laid my yarns in the South Seas, in Tebessa in Algeria, in Shanghai, and in Singapore. Laid one yarn in Kentucky but they said it was too hot for them to handle. The hero doesn't have to be a model of virtue. In fact, a favorite formula is for the hero to accomplish what only the villain attempts in conventional yarns. My character is Wild Bill Clanton, a pirate, gun-runner, smuggler, a pearl-thief and slaver, and carefully avoids all moral scruples in his dealings with the ladies. These magazines were the object of a rather bitter attack in the *Author & Journalist* not long ago, but some of the most prominent writers rose up and fought back lustily, notably my friend E. Hoffman Price, who has been making a good living off them for some time.

If you'd like to try a rap at it, there's nothing to keep you from it. While the magazines cater mainly to masculine readers, I don't think there's any objection or prejudice against women writers. Indeed, I have an idea the editor might like to see some yarns from the feminine viewpoint, providing they were sufficiently lusty and bawdy. Plots should be rather complicated, action fast moving. The handicaps of stories that are short are obvious. Little space for character development or for subtle unfolding of plots; the narration must be dynamic, clear-cut, vivid. Cynicism and humor have their place, but not too much humor. It isn't always necessary for the hero to rush in and save the heroine's virtue at the proper moment. Indeed, in most of my yarns, the heroine's virtue is in more danger from the hero than from anybody else. Price uses a good formula—triumph of the villain, forcibly, over the heroine, and triumph, in turn of the hero over the villain, generally by shooting the hell out of him.

This is a brief sketch, of course, but enough to give you a general idea of the requirements of the Trojan Publishing Company, whose magazines, I might add, though considered somewhat as outlaws in the more conventional circles, seem to be prospering.

You ask how my mother is getting along. I hardly know what to say. Some days she seems to be improving a little, and other days she seems to be worse. I frankly don't know.

This being Valentine Day, I suppose I should make the conventional request for you to go and join the army. That may sound a bit wobbly, but look: Valentine comes from the same word from which "gallant" is derived; a gallant may be a suitor, but is also a cavalier; a cavalier is a knight; a knight is a cavalryman; a cavalryman is a soldier. To ask one to be one's Valentine is equivalent to asking him, or her, to be a soldier. And one can't be a soldier without joining the army. So, a request to become a Valentine is approximately a demand to go and join the army.

I learn with interest your struggles with Cabell. Hold on to it for a few days, until I can get over there. I've never read that particular book, and I'd like to look it over with you.

I'll be seeing you, I hope.

Your bearded friend,

To me, the letter is as delightful as the big gump himself. I'm looking forward to seeing him, talking foolishly, and seriously, with him. I'll look up one of these days, and he'll be parking in front of Mrs. Hemphill's.

I'll have the scissors ready and trim that mustache down to the proper, sophisticated size!

Monday, February 24, 1936

It isn't that I pretend or even believe I am psychic, but there are times when I seem to have a premonition of impending disaster, a disaster I am powerless to stop.

I was walking slowly toward Mrs. Hemphill's this afternoon, avoiding the little puddles of water in the road and thinking thoughts far away from Cross Plains and all the people in it. A fancy daydream, in which Truett played a hero's role, but Bob was not in it at all.

The sun shone brightly, now and then, from behind a cloud. I looked up. Bob's car stopped in front of Mrs. Hemphill's. My first thought was, "I don't want to see Bob today." Then a momentary fear and a desire to run flashed over me. But I pushed the thought from me, remembering that Bob had filled a vacuum in my life here in Cross Plains. When I was a few yards from him, he got out of the car and stood beside it. He was not smiling.

"Howdy," I called with more cheerfulness than I felt. "I see you've still got your mustache."

He managed a weak smile, "Yeah. I've got to keep it as long as this cool weather keeps up. You wouldn't want me to catch my death, would you?"

He was making an effort at humor, and I laughed. "He needs to joke," I thought. "He's down and out." I was at the car now, close enough to get a full view of the drooping shoulders, the uneasy mouth, and I could read the questions in his eyes today! They concerned me, along with whatever other worries he might have.

He had on his good brown suit, and I should have appreciated it and stopped my silliness there. "The rain is over and the sun is out," I laughed. "I'll borrow Mr. Hemphill's razor for you."

Bob frowned slightly. "I thought you might like to ride around a little while. There's something I've got to say to you."

Again that fear, almost panic, engulfed me. Memories crowded in on me. All I could think of was that almost a year ago, when I felt weighted down by fear and illness, I wanted him to say, "I love you." When he didn't, in a fit of hurt pride and anger, I'd thought, "I hope the day comes when you want me to say those words to you and I won't do it."

Had that day come? "Oh, God," I prayed silently, "don't let him talk of love." Again that silly thought came to me, "I must make jokes."

I looked at my watch. "Sure. I'd like to ride around with you, mustache and all."

The depth and reality of his own dark emotion exploded in his half angry, half fearful voice, "For God's sake, forget about the mustache, can't you?"

That idiot thought blazed again in my brain, "Make jokes. Keep him from getting serious." With laughter, I said, "I can't forget it. It's too big."

He paused beside the door he'd opened for me and looked at me. I crawled into the car quickly to hide from the hurt written so plainly in his eyes. On the outside, Bob is bluff, like his father, but inside, also like his father, he is scholarly, tender; he shrinks from any semblance of brutality in his personal life. I knew that. I felt it. I didn't know what to do. It was as if I were hurtling through the stars, unable to change direction. I didn't want to see hurt in Bob's eyes. I wanted to laugh and to have him laugh with me as we had laughed before I started dating Truett.

We drove toward Rising Star.

"What have you been up to?" he asked, not really interested but trying for some atmosphere he wanted to achieve.

I talked fast. "Teaching. The kids were bad today. Restless, I suppose, is a better name for it. Anyway, they didn't want to be educated."

Bob shrugged his shoulders and didn't look at me. "Most people don't want to be educated. When you're young, you feel the lust for the age-old adventures buried in your subconscious. You don't want to be bothered with dreary things like school."

We'd talked before about young people being close to racial memories and we'd disagreed about it. No need to talk of that today. I thought of his mother. Had she gotten worse? I dreaded mentioning her, but I took a deep breath and plunged in. "How's your mother?"

Her worsening condition and his own fear was in his answer. "She's not doing at all well. Everything is falling in on me at once. I'm going to do all I can to get her to hang on and get well."

"I saw your dad last week," I said. "He mentioned something about your taking her to Marlin."

Bob nodded. "My plans are to take her day after tomorrow." He turned then to look at me. "I can't write or do anything else but take care of her. A week or so in Marlin may straighten us both out."

"What do you mean you can't write?" I asked, worried because I wanted him to be happy and content *if* and *when* his mother passed on. Furthermore, he was getting away from those Conan yarns now, and I was sure he'd be able to do some really good things about the early days of Texas.

"Mother requires almost constant care night and day. I couldn't sleep last night or the night before." He shook his head and rubbed his hand across his forehead. "God knows how many nights I haven't slept. She has these terrible night sweats. Her nightgown and bed get wet, really wet. I changed her bed and gown three times last night."

I don't know why that simple statement nauseated me. "You change her gown and bed? Where is your dad? For God's sake, Bob, that's not your job."

"I do it because I have to." He whirled toward me, his eyes begging for understanding. "It's my job. Damn it, you do what needs to be done. You can't let her stay there, wet and uncomfortable. You do the damn best you can."

Why couldn't I accept that and let it go? "You could get a nurse who is trained to do the job better than you can," I said, the horror and anger I felt goading me on. "You've got the money. Your dad makes money too. He certainly makes enough to take care of your living expenses, and you know it. You keep saving your money. For what? To take her away somewhere? Well, that's fine, but what about you? You've got to save yourself and keep working to pay for nurses to take care of her. My God, Bob, you're not required to give up your whole life for her, your writing and everything."

"I'm required to give up anything and do whatever she needs to have done." He pounded the steering wheel.

"Not your life. A man's work is his life."

Bob slammed the car onto a sandy side road, speeded up until we were in the midst of farm country away from the highway. He threw on the brakes so fast, I almost fell out of my seat. He grabbed my arm in a vise-like grip. "What's work? A man can do any kind of work." He sounded desperate. "Work is not worth a damn, unless you work for somebody you love. All my life I've loved and needed her. I'm losing her. I know that. Damn it to hell, I know that. I want to live. You hear that?" He shook me, and it angered me. "I want to live! I want a woman to love, a woman to share my life and believe in me, to want me and love me. Don't you know that? My God, my God. Can't you see that? I want to live and to love."

I panicked. I thought of Truett. No matter what happened in the future between Truett and me, I loved him in a way I could never love Bob. I was frightened at the intensity of Bob's emotion, and I said the foolish thing.

"Well, shave your mustache and maybe you'll find one."

"My God, you say a thing like that when everything has crashed around me?" He grabbed both my arms and pulled me to him. "If you don't love me, say so, damn it. I know you loved me once. Is it over?"

He held me so tight and kissed me so hard, I felt miserable and frightened. I tried to push away from him.

"Bob," I gasped. "Your work. I do believe in you. I know you're brilliant, and you've got a great talent." I was rattling, talking as I would have to an upset student who needed encouragement. "I want to see you make something of that talent. I don't want your work to be interfered with. I'm glad you've stopped writing for *Weird Tales*. They didn't pay you anyway, and you're better than that. Much better than that. You—"

"Are you in love with Truett?" he insisted, harshly. "I want to know. I've got to know. If it's Truett you love, say it. Say it, damn it."

"I don't love anybody," I said, half crying. "Not anybody at all."

His arms went suddenly slack, and I moved away from him. I kept on talking. "I'm going to Louisiana State University this summer to begin work on my master's degree. I've already been accepted. I got a letter from Dr. Wise, head of the speech department, just the other day. I'm going there this summer. You've made good with your writing; I'm going to make good at something too. I'm going to teach. I've made up my mind definitely about that. I'm always going to work harder than any other teacher on the faculty. Teaching is what I want to do. It's not writing I want. Oh, maybe a story now and then, or maybe a book or two. I don't know. All I know is that teaching is my field."

Bob sank back on his side of the car and ran his hand over his face. His shoulders drooped, and I tried not to look into his eyes, but I couldn't help myself. He sat staring at me, his eyes filled with hurt, anger, and some deeper wound. I looked at him, wanting to help him; scared, not wanting him to talk of love and afraid he would bring it up again. I thought of Truett. Never. Never did I want Truett to know what Bob had said this afternoon. I didn't want Truett to know how panicky I felt, not wanting to hurt Bob, and not wanting to do anything to encourage him.

"You'll make a good teacher." Bob's voice was flat and emotionless. "You'll do anything you set your mind to." Still, he didn't take his eyes off my face.

I talked on, trying to think of something to say to break the mood of despondency hanging over both of us. I wanted to cheer Bob up, to have him laugh and joke the way we used to do. But I spoke only of the serious thing I thought and felt.

"I may never be anything but a small town teacher, but that's not the important thing. It doesn't matter if it's a small town. I may not do anything worthwhile myself, but maybe some student I teach will be able to do great things."

Bob turned his head away from me, and I sighed with relief. A bird settled on top of the fence near by. Bob seemed to be watching it too.

"You'll dedicate your life to kids in a small, apathetic town," he said despondently. "And what will you get out of it? Not even a thank you."

"If I teach to be thanked," I said, above the hurt and pain I felt for both of us, "I might as well quit now. I'm not doing it to be thanked, Bob. You're probably right. Maybe the very one I help the most will be the most indifferent. I don't know, but I have to do the best I can. Work the best I can. I'll never ask for thanks from any kid I teach or from anybody else."

"Your missionary zeal is showing itself again," Bob said with an attempt at his old way of poking fun at me. "Are you sure teaching means that much to you?"

I swallowed hard. I wanted to be a good teacher, and more than that, I wanted a man to love, and a child to love. I wanted it all. But it was also true that I loved teaching. At times, I felt it must come first before love . . . even before Truett. Bob had a career. There was something he wanted to do. Surely, he could understand how I felt. I tried to choose my words carefully to make him understand.

"Some people are called to preach the gospel," I said, slowly. "I was not called to preach, but I feel in my heart I am called to be a teacher."

Bob was silent again, watching the bird sitting on top of the fence. It flew. Slowly, as if with a great effort, he turned to me. "You have a great cause. For life to be worth living, a man—a man or woman—must have a great love or a great cause. I have neither."

I tried to be breezy, to make jokes. "Shave your mustache, and love will come."

I laughed. But he didn't. He looked at me, moved heavily, and reached to start the engine. We drove home slowly. Bob was silent, and I talked glibly, telling him how wonderful he was as a writer, telling him that I appreciated his talent, and urging him to shave his mustache and get out a little more, find some recreation . . . find a girl.

We were nearly home, when he turned to look at me. "Don't talk anymore. Please. Don't say another word."

I hushed. I began to make an effort to get my own tumultuous emotions under control.

Bob stopped the car in front of Mrs. Hemphill's. He made a sluggish move to open his door and get out.

"Don't bother to go to the door with me," I said with a lot more cheerfulness than I felt. "I'll just run in, and I'll let you get home to shave that mustache."

I didn't want to say anything else about the mustache, but the words tumbled out as if I had no control whatever over them. I wanted to help Bob, yet everything I said was wrong.

He looked at me but said nothing. He made no further attempt to get out of the car. I got out and stood for a moment, looking at him. What could I say? What was there left to say?

"What about tomorrow afternoon?" he asked. "Are you free?"

"Sure," I said automatically, too dumbfounded and perplexed to say anything else for a minute.

"I'll see you," he said.

I stared at him. "I hope your mother gets better," I said, finally, and my words sounded inane and senseless as though I didn't mean what I said.

He didn't acknowledge my statement. I watched him a minute to see if he were going to say something else. He turned his head and looked down the street. He made no move to start the engine. I went up the walk to the front steps. Then the full realization of my ineptness overcame me. Remorse and anger at myself was almost more than I could bear. I looked back at Bob.

The last rays of the setting sun shone on the car illuminating his big, ungainly body. His shoulders sagged. He looked beaten. He was staring straight ahead into the empty street.

"I must go to him," I thought. "I don't want us to part like this."

I took a few steps toward the car and stopped. I wanted to go to him, to tell him I loved him as a very dear and valued friend. I wanted to say I needed him. I needed to enjoy his whimsical humor. I needed his help with the books I wanted to write, help he liked to give to people trying to write, even part time. But more than anything else, I needed his friendship.

I couldn't go to him. I didn't know how to tell him. I turned back to the steps. When I reached the top, I looked back. Again, I thought, "I must go to him, try to make him understand I had said the wrong things today because I did not know how to say the right things." I hurried back down the steps.

He started the engine, and so I stood on the walk and watched him drive away.

He did not look at me.

You do what you have to do. He had said something like that many times. Even today. I did what I had to do.

When I walked into the room, Mary Beth looked up and made that silly little gesture of eating out of her hand. I managed a half-hearted laugh. But all I could see was Bob's eyes with their blank expression. I tried to put the picture out of my mind. I could not. I remembered his words: "For life to be worth living, a man must have either a great love or a great cause. I have neither."

Bob, like the rest of us, doesn't make sense either. Why, I wondered, did he ask to see me again tomorrow? To fight with me? He hadn't fought today. To stand me up? If he hated me, why didn't he tell me he'd never see me again?

All during supper, I talked and laughed with Mary Beth and the Hemphill's. I talked glibly of inconsequential things and began to hate myself. I could think, now, how easy it would have been to tell Bob how much his friendship meant to me.

Once the thought came to me that, since I didn't love Bob the way I loved Truett, it was better not to let him speak of love. It was not consoling. The truth was I had not handled a bad situation with the poise and self-confidence I longed to show. I had failed myself as well as a friend. I was terribly sorry; I did not mean to hurt Bob's feelings as I had done.

Tomorrow seemed a long time away. I felt a sense of urgency to set things right immediately. Before I could do anything, even write in my journal, I had to write Bob a letter, asking his forgiveness and understanding.

In the letter, I beat myself over the head in remorse, hoping he would forgive my foolishness. I tried every way to make excuses for the afternoon. I finished the letter and took it to the post office.

"He'll get it before he comes tomorrow," I thought. "It will make things easier for both of us. He's very understanding; he'll realize I am sorry for the silly jokes I tried to make. Maybe he will realize a lot of people need him. His mother is not the only one."

Once, coming back from the post office, I thought about calling Bob and asking him to come tonight, and I would apologize in person. But I didn't really want to see him again today. Besides, the letter was enough. The letter would take care of everything.

After I came back to my room, I was able to write some in my journal. It was not a consoling activity either.

It was worse when I went to bed. Then I could only lie awake, staring at the ceiling. It had been such a hectic day. First, the kids at school rejected everything they should be trying to learn. Then, this afternoon! I had forseen disaster. What I had not forseen was that I would bring about the disaster myself.

If I closed my eyes or opened them, I saw a Bob Howard I had never seen before. Why? Why had it upset me so when he said he had accepted the responsibility of Mrs. Howard—even to the point of changing her nightgown? Why was Bob Howard dejected and beaten? Where was the old Black Irish fight?

What had he meant by: "For a life to be worth living, a man—man or woman—must have either a great love or a great cause; I have neither?"

> *The Nightingale that in the branches sang,*
> *Ah, whence, and whither flown again, who knows!*
> *. . . The Rubáiyat . . .*

We had a short faculty meeting after school. When it was over, I hurried home to Mrs. Hemphill's. No sign of Bob.

That gave me time to go into the house and freshen up a bit. By the time I'd gotten a drink of water, changed my make-up, combed my hair, and he still hadn't come, I got to work on some papers I needed to grade.

It was hard to concentrate on the papers. My mind kept straying to Bob, not because of the date yesterday afternoon, but also to another thing I found odd. The way he disliked Nat Williams, or anyone else whom I liked and admired. I wondered how he felt about Truett now. With all my heart, I hoped they'd gotten to be friends again.

Time passed and Mary Beth came in. "I'm surprised to see you here." she said. "I thought you had a date this afternoon."

I laughed. "I had a date, all right, with a bunch of papers."

I put the papers aside and realized I'd been stood up! So Bob didn't come! He stood me up! Well, so much for that. The funny thing is that I'm neither mad nor glad. The truth is I can't blame him for not coming. But I'm truly sorry to lose Bob's friendship.

Mary Beth is out of the room, and I am free to sit for a few minutes and think about it. I'm a little relieved Bob didn't come . . . that it's over between us. At least, I tell myself that. One thing is certain . . . I don't ever want a date with anybody like the one I had yesterday with Bob. I suppose, too, I must never try to cheer anybody else up. I am calm now and I can forgive myself for my mistakes.

When I write a thing like that down, I remember the day I told Bob I forgave myself for something. He was surprised. He said he'd never heard of such a thing before. I explained the Bible says for us to forgive our brothers, but many times the person who really needs forgiveness is ourself. We need forgiveness for all the dumb things we do and say when we talk without thinking.

Bob agreed with that, and so I finished triumphantly, "Well, then. If we forgive other people for doing dumb things, we ought to forgive ourselves too."

Bob's laugh was pleasant. Then he said that, as crazy as it sounded, it made sense after all. Then he reached his hand over and tangled my hair and said, "If anybody can figure out something like that, you're the one."

I'm sorry for the silly things I said yesterday, trying to cheer Bob up, but I forgive myself. I wish he could too.

But one thing still bothers me. If I have forgiven myself, why do I feel like crying?

And now, pain and anger . . .

If I had gone to the post office yesterday afternoon, instead of coming straight home and waiting for Bob, I might have received this letter from him. In which case, I would have been angry, not sad. Being stood up would have been an act of mercy.

From some of the things in the letter, I think he must have gone home Monday afternoon, thought about our date for a while, wrote this letter and took it with him to Marlin and mailed it from there. By doing it that way, he would have a chance to try to hurt me by standing me up.

The letter makes me realize I hurt his feelings very much. For that, I'm sorry. The letter is a rough one. But it doesn't say a word about the things he said. Not one word did he say about wanting to know whether I loved him or not.

He ignored everything except the jokes I'd tried to make. He ignored completely the things he'd said about wanting to live and to love. Why?

The letter is sharp, blunt, and to the point. It has no date. I think Conan must have written it.

Dear Novalyne:

I'm sorry but I won't be able to keep the date this afternoon. I've got to take my mother to a hospital in Marlin. I suppose you'll find this subject for more criticism, but I can't help it. When I get settled in Marlin, I'll drop you a card, so you can write me if you care to do so. Whether I ever return to Cross Plains depends a great deal on whether my mother recovers or not.

I have thought a great deal about our date yesterday (to which I had eagerly looked forward to as to the bright spot in the otherwise somber pattern of the last few days,) and the memory is much like a fantastic dream. It seems incredible that I, in the blackest hours of my life, should have occupied half an hour in a childish squabble over a mustache! I looked forward to that date; I didn't want you to feel sorry for me, or even approve of me. All I wanted was for you to give me a chance to relax and forget my troubles, to enjoy your company to the fullest. You said I didn't seem to enjoy the date. How could I? What chance did you give me to enjoy it? I was already punch-drunk with grief, worry and trouble; but, with my mother's life ebbing away before my eyes, with my father breaking and aging before me with the worry and strain we both labor under, and I myself faced with the wreckage of all my life's plans and labors, and the utter ruin of my career—I found myself, in the brief period I had stolen in the vain hope of forgetting my miseries for a little while, forced into the same petty altercations. My God, arguing over a mustache when my whole life is crumbling to powder under my hands! The triumph of the inconsequential—the flaunting of the abysmally trivial in the face of black tragedy. Why must we always squabble over unimportant trifles? I can't understand you. Knowing as you did, that I was half frantic already with strain and worry and a load of trouble I can hardly carry, still you did not spare me; you never showed me any kindness or consideration, but it looks like you could have let up on your eternal fault-finding for that one hour, at least. You must be totally incapable of the slightest sensation of human sympathy.

Well, I didn't intend to say any of the things I've said when I started out, but suddenly a flood of pent-up words broke over the dam when I remember all the futile, wasted hours we could have spent in pleasant association and enjoyable companionship, and which, instead, we squandered in everlasting squabbles over trivialities—they were not of my seeking; all I ever wanted was to be allowed to enjoy your company, and I always did, when you gave me any kind of a chance.

Your friend,

Bob

I read the letter twice. Then I went into the bathroom, sat down and cried with anger and frustration. He did a beautiful job of blaming me for being foolish and mean when his life was breaking up around him! I admit I handled the situation badly! Should I write to tell him I loved Truett and that it nauseated me to death to hear him say about his mother: "I changed her gown and bed three times last night." I think that is his dad's job. Not Bob's.

I don't know why that upset me so, anymore than I know why I tried to make jokes and wound up saying all the wrong things.

I can't accept what he said about his father aging before his eyes! That burns me down too. His dad is doing a lot better standing up under the "ordeal" than Bob is doing. I'd go for his dad two to one. That old man may bark at you, glare at you, and argue with you, but, by the Eternal, he is a man!

That line about whether he ever returns to Cross Plains depends upon how his mother gets along! He's always talking about going traipsing all over the world, an adventurer seeking his fortune in strange and sensuous lands of the East. Is that what he's planning?

But after I took the time to think about it, cry, and get angry enough to brain him, I asked myself some questions. Did I handle a bad situation well? And I answered honestly, "No. I panicked and said all the wrong things." When I saw him, there was something different about the way he looked, and all I could think of was to make jokes and cheer him up. I didn't cheer him up with jokes; I only made him angry. Why?

He could not understand because I didn't say the things he evidently wanted me to say. It is human nature which made Bob think about Monday afternoon, get angry, and want to hurt me!

Then I asked myself the big question: since those were the words of an angry, hurt man, facing a problem he can't handle with his fists, did his words harm me? I must answer, "No. His words angered me." Actually, he was no fairer to me than I'd been to him. But I had to face my own ineptness. Every time he said a word, I tried to make a joke and brought up his mustache.

He, too, can use words to wound, but they will not cause me to lose my job or make it easier. In the final analysis, his words relieved him of his anger. If I were to tell Truett about them, which I will not, Truett would understand how I feel.

Why, after this letter, can Bob think I'll answer his card? Why would he ever want to say anything else to me or see me again?

Poor Bob. I'm sorry for him. I'm sorry his mother is ill and his career is in ruins. That's a terrible cross for any man to bear.

> *You are the light eternal—*
> *Like a torch I shall die.*
> *You are the surge of deep music,*
> *I but a cry!*
>   *. . . Akins . . .*

Bob is back in town. He and his mother didn't stay two weeks in Marlin.

The friendship, the good times, the riding around the countryside, talking of fantastic yarns and all the other things we talked about, is ended. I suppose it is always a tragedy when a friendship ends.

But the biggest tragedy of all, it seems to me, is that a man's spirit dies. It is a tragedy when a man will not struggle against the tide. Bob's adventurous spirit is only an echo of music played once and heard no more.

The day after he mailed that letter to me from Marlin, he wrote me a card, a fairly cheerful card, saying his mother seemed to be doing well, and he, too, was feeling better. I didn't answer. I wasn't ready to say anything else to him. I had already written him a letter, trying to excuse myself for the silly things I'd said. In some ways, I chickened out and said I was unhappy.

Now, I think it would have been better that afternoon just to have told him exactly how I felt about him and Truett. But even if I had, I could not have told him how it upset me when he said what he did about his mother. Since that day, I've gone over that statement a hundred times, and I am less upset about it.

But I do think Bob has tried to take over his parents' lives. He said once that parents and children change places in life. When parents become old and sick, you take care of them as you would a child. My trouble, I suppose, is that Mammy will be seventy-nine years old next July, and she can take care of herself with no *ifs* or *buts* about it; consequently, I don't understand Bob.

It surprised me to get his card from Marlin. If he hates me, why does he keep hanging on? He gave me his address if I "cared to write him." Why didn't I? The answer is simple. I was still sorry for the way I'd acted, trying so hard to be cheerful, but I wasn't sure I would not act the same way again under the same circumstances.

Today, after school, I went to the post office. I had another letter from Bob in my box. It made me feel panicky again. I didn't open it at once, for I was going to the drugstore.

While I was in the drugstore, I saw Dr. Howard, and he told me Bob had brought his mother home. He said Mrs. Howard seemed improved; however, he was still worried about her. He also said he and Robert had hired some nurses to help take care of her!

He stressed that. He said Robert had been devoting all his time to taking care of his mother, and to give him some relief, they'd hired some nurses!

While we were talking, Bob's car stopped at the post office. He got out, and I probably gaped at him. *He'd shaved his mustache!* He was nicely dressed, too, and *he'd shaved his mustache!*

Neither Dr. Howard nor I said a word about Bob just as if he hadn't stopped right across the street in front of us. When Bob drove away, I said good-bye to Dr. Howard, came home, and read my letter.

Cross Plains, Texas
March 5, 1936

Dear Novalyne:

I just now read the letter you wrote me Monday, February 24th. None of my mail had been forwarded to me at Marlin and this letter was with the rest I got out of the post office this morning. I'm sorry I didn't get it before I left. If I had, I wouldn't have written you in quite what must have seemed like such a bitter strain, though I did not mean it that way. I can't blame you for not answering the card I wrote you from Marlin. It's hard, in the last analysis, to blame anyone for anything. We are all caught in a mesh of circumstances we cannot break.

I am sorry for your unhappiness with life—so much so that I am moved to say one more thing—breaking my habit of not giving advice. This isn't advice, though I realize it is unforgivable presumption to hand out unasked for comments about other people's business. But I feel that the main source of your unhappiness lies in the very point you brought out in your letter, when you said you are always trying to change things. You cannot change things or people, and you only make yourself miserable when you try. Life is necessarily a continual series of compromises. No one is perfect, nor is anything perfect nor can anything or anyone be perfect. If one is to live at all, one is forced to accept the faults of life along with the virtues. In judging the desirability of anything, we do not discard it because it is not perfect, because nothing can be perfect. We weigh the good points and the bad; if the bad outweigh the good, we discard it; but if the balance is anywhere near even, we, as a general rule, keep or use it for the good points and ignore or try to put up with the bad points. It is a simple matter of reasonable tolerance. If we demand perfection in all things, and try to bend all things into our particular pattern of belief, we only hurt ourselves. You cannot change people, because they cannot change themselves; they were cast in an inflexible mold of heredity and circumstances, long before you ever saw them. You beat against an iron wall and hurt yourself and embitter your life.

But enough of that, I had no business or right to say any of these things, and they were prompted only by my deep sympathy for you, and my sorrow at seeing an artistic nature wrecked by an unfortunate course. You have everything it takes to succeed—skill, determination, education, ambition, intellect, talent, vitality—all except the fluid quality of adapting yourself to the twisting mazes of human faults instead of trying to destroy them. It is useless. If Jesus Christ failed to bring any changes in men's nature, how could you or I hope to succeed? You hurt yourself by demanding too much; no writer or artist was ever satisfied with his masterpieces, but he did not destroy them because they were not perfect. He gave them to the world, and the world overlooked their faults, and enjoyed their points of excellence. Weeds grow in the orchard of life; but happiness is possible only when we can be content that the fruit trees outnumber the weeds.

Your friend,
Bob

At times, I feel a hurt too deep for tears. But I hurt for Bob, not for myself. I read his letter several times. It's good advice is definitely something for me to think about. But his letter is also fatalistic. I see in it a man who will accept whatever life gives him, and who will not raise his arm to ward off a single blow.

Not me. I want to fight. When things go wrong, I want to try to change them. I believe people can change themselves. William James will back me up on that. As a teacher, am I not committed to try to help students change their behavior if it keeps them from the goal they want to attain?

I don't know, but I do know this: If you don't try, you won't do anything.

I was unhappy the day I wrote that letter to Bob. I was sorry for the silly jokes I'd tried to make. But doesn't he remember I am usually happy and laughing. At times, he has gotten angry at me for laughing so much. I'll answer this letter. I'll write a cheerful note and tell him I'm glad his mother is better.

After that, if he wants to come see me again and talk, okay. One thing is sure now: He'll never ask me again if I love him. It's evident from his letter, he doesn't love me or anyone else either. Probably not even his mother.

Something else occurs to me for the first time! Several times when Bob and I have been together, he has asked me if I loved him. I usually make a bright remark and make jokes. But although Bob has asked me that, never . . . never has he said he loved me.

Bob is a strange man. He seems to want to be loved, but does it never occur to him that a person needs to give love as well as to receive it? Music, to be enjoyed to the fullest, must be shared.

And if the well runs dry? What then?

When Bob came back to Cross Plains from Marlin, I was afraid the friendship between us was over, and I cried. I don't know now whether it is over or not, because I've seen Bob a good many times.

He must be psychic or something because he drops over, unexpectedly, in the afternoons after school. I'm working on plays at night, but once in a while, I come back to my room, thinking I'll sit down and get my thoughts together. Just as I get in sight of the Hemphill's, Bob's car stops in the front; or else, I get to the door, and there he is stopping at the curb. How he knows the days when I'm not working at school, I don't know unless he's psychic.

Like Truett, I don't understand Bob anymore. From the way he talks, he's making a good many sales to *Argosy,* sales to *Action Stories,* but the thing that seems to upset him is that *Weird Tales* still owes him about a thousand dollars and doesn't pay.

He appreciates Wright for giving him a start in selling stories, but sometimes he calls Wright a two-bit editor; a man who can't recognize anything good; a dyspeptic; a small man who gags at a gnat and swallows a camel. Although he uses such barbed epithets, he really doesn't mean to be malicious.

The trouble with Wright (I take it) is that he seems very concerned with what the readers say or write. He doesn't take into consideration that readers are a fickle lot. "I lose readers sometimes," Bob said. "I admit that. But, damn it, I always gain them back or get new ones. Wright forgets that. It's a damn losing battle."

We haven't had many dates where Bob says ahead of time he'll be over. He did ask me if he could come over a couple of Saturday nights, but that didn't work out. One weekend, I was going to Brownwood. When I told him I was going home, I tensed up expecting him to ask me if I were going to see Truett, but he didn't. I breathed a little freer.

Another Saturday night, he wanted to come over, but on that night, I had a date with Pat Allen.

"Oh," he said. "You're still going with him?"

I am being perfectly honest with him these days. "Yes. Pat and I are going to Brownwood to see a show."

He whirled and looked at me. "Are you in love with Pat Allen?"

That irritated me.

"Oh, for heaven's sakes, Bob," I said. "Sure I am. I have a heart like a hotel, room for everybody."

For the first time that day, he laughed. "Yeah. I know that."

Then, as usual these days, he talked about the crash of his career, and I said it seemed to me he was making sales, some to new markets too.

At that, he became impatient. "Your career falls in ruins when you go on producing, knowing the well is running dry," he said loudly. "How much more time you have to produce before it dries up, you don't know. You've got to watch that, Novalyne, when you start writing full time."

I've quit reminding him I am going to teach school the rest of my life. However, since I do hope to continue to write a little, too, I just try to keep my mouth shut and learn all I can.

"You start in to write," he said one day, "and, at first, you write day and night. Many days, eighteen hours. Sometimes, if things are going right, you may write twenty-four. But the constant production finally gets you. If you try to settle down to eight to ten hours a day steadily, if you devote your whole life to breaking into the writing game, you should be mighty careful that you don't burn yourself out before you write the big book."

Last Saturday night, I was free and Bob and I had a date. When I came home afterwards, I was so confused I didn't know whether I was coming in or going out. I had not intended to get into an argument with Bob again, especially about psychologists and psychological stories, but I did.

I keep worrying about his fatalistic attitude. I said that believing you were trapped by heredity and environment was debilitating. Then I quoted William James. I told Bob that William James said if you wanted to be brave, you should assume the attitude of bravery, and you would become brave.

Bob said that was crazy. He didn't care who said it, William James or who. Furthermore, he didn't care if James had written a thousand books on psychology, that just wasn't true. He said, vehemently, a man couldn't change, because he was what he was by birth and breeding and that was the end of it.

Why didn't I drop the entire subject? I should have. As much as Bob hates people who write psychological stories, I brought up Henry James, the novelist, William James' brother.

"Well," I said, "it seems to me you think pretty much as Henry James did—that a man couldn't or wouldn't change. Why don't you put that in a story?"

After he calmed down, he said, "Can a leopard change his spots?"

I definitely do not believe Bob has burned out or will burn out soon.

Look at Mammy! She's vital and alive and she's almost seventy-nine! She's full of ideas about how to make her farm pay more, how to improve it. If you're working at something you love, isn't that an indication you are still creative? That the well has a deeper spring?

Maybe when Bob's mother either gets better or passes on, he'll get a new lease on life. At least, he said something to that effect tonight. He said that, when his burden was lifted, things might seem different, he didn't know.

I didn't ask what burden he meant.

The tune is the same, but the words are different . . .

Everything Bob hears over the radio or reads in the paper concerns him. As down in the dumps as he is most of the time now, he still reacts to things that are happening in the world and finds relationships that I never think about. He is so much in favor of labor unions for workers I have often talked against them, just to present a different point of view.

One day, when we were talking about big business taking advantage of the poor worker, I said, "Bob, don't you think that now that the workers have the right to form strong unions, they'll be as bad as big business?"

Bob hooted at the idea. He thought the workers had known such trouble and hardships, they would always deal fairly and squarely with each other and with big business.

Today, he drove over to the house after I had just gotten to my room and put my books down. The idea of riding around for a few minutes appealed to me, and I was glad to see him, especially since he was excited about something. These days, that's important.

The minute we got into the car, he began reminding me I had predicted that when labor became strong enough, they would be as bad as industry. He understood that now, and he could see where I was right about it. The dominance of the strong over the weak predominates in nature.

"We've got a couple of goats now," he said. "We thought goat's milk would be better for Mother than cow's milk. Well, those goats have proved something to me."

I didn't have to ask him what it was, for he was so excited he'd tell me anyway.

"One of our goats is bigger than the other one," he said. "I have to watch her closely. She won't let the little one eat. She gobbles up most of her food, then moves over and runs the little one off and begins on her food. It's the nature of animals to dominate the ones they can. I understand that. Human beings are the same way. They dominate the ones they can dominate. Wright won't pay me what he owes me, because he's got the upper hand. His salary is assured; therefore, I can work my guts out, and it doesn't mean a damn to him. He's the dominant one. It's the animal in him. We're one . . . man and animals."

"We're not one with the animals," I said. "We're civilized."

He shrugged that aside. "When one man can dominate another man . . . or dominate a woman, he does it," Bob insisted. "Look at you and Nat Williams. Nat works you to death, won't give you a minute to relax and do something besides teach, doesn't pay you a third of what he makes."

"If you mean Nat's working me to death and not paying me because I'm directing the senior play," I said emphatically, "I just want you to know Nat didn't want me to direct that play."

Bob tried to watch me and the road at the same time. "You probably think you're pleasing him. He let you know if you directed it, you'd get a pat on the back from him."

I laughed. "You're wrong. Nat really didn't want me to direct it. He wanted to get someone . . . Louise or Mrs. Underwood. This year, since Enid isn't here to nag at me about getting things ready for the supervisor, I suppose Nat thinks he has to. He said I worked too hard on plays and things and couldn't grade my papers as I should. He thought I ought to concentrate on getting everything up in order."

"Then, for God's sake, why are you doing it?"

"Because I want to," I said, grinning. "I've got the best cast in the United States: Melvin Placke, Durwood Varner, Dixie Little, and—"

"He let you talk him into it," Bob interrupted.

"He couldn't help himself," I said. "Directing the play was something I wanted to do, and so I did it."

Bob shook his head doubtfully. "You can be pretty determined all right," he admitted. "But my point is that the stronger man or animal dominates the weaker."

"Right," I agreed, laughing. "I was the stronger."

I suppose Bob gave up then. He grinned and spread his hands out in a hopeless gesture.

He began talking about a rabbit drive people were planning. He worried about it. He sympathized with the rabbits, of course. So did I, but I also knew the farmers feel the rabbits are eating up their crops and they have to do something. Bob said it looked awful to him that big men with guns and cars would go out chasing little animals who had no defense at all; couldn't protect themselves. He said the rabbits were victims of man's lust to kill.

I didn't listen to him. I felt sorry for the rabbits and I didn't want to think about them or man's insatiable appetite to kill. One animal may dominate another. Bob's right about that. Labor unions may eventually dominate industry; a man may dominate another man or a woman, but, in my case, there'd be two in the domination game. I wasn't going to worry about it anymore.

After I came home, I kept thinking about Bob and the small philosophical truth he's arrived at by thinking of such a simple thing as one goat dominating another. He doesn't have many friends and the give and take of personal relationships; he is a loner, able to extract truth from little things. Perhaps all writers and philosophers are loners.

> *Ah, my Beloved, fill the cup that clears*
> *To-Day of past Regret and future Fears;*
> *. . . The Rubáiyat . . .*

The play, like the rain, has come and gone. Bob came early on Sunday afternoon; it was a date somewhat like the old days—talk, laughter, a pleasant day, but still with hurt feelings, momentary anger, and unspoken words hanging in the clear air around us. I don't like hurt feelings and bitterness. Friendship, I think, should be stronger than that.

Bob asked me about the play, how it had gone over, and I told him it was a success. With a great cast like the one I had, any play would have been a success, and, to give myself a little credit, with a director like me who would have killed a kid if he'd gotten an inflection wrong or made a wrong move or turn, it had to be good.

Bob grinned. "They tell me you're a slave driver."

I pointed out that perhaps driving slaves had been easier.

Bob's eyes were anxious when he said he wanted to take a pretty long drive this afternoon, if it was all right with me. I told him I thought the idea was great.

"We'll go first to Rising Star," he said, "then a lot farther on. There's an old house on an old country road I want to show you."

I settled back to enjoy the ride and the conversation. It was one of those days you could feel thrilled and happy just to be alive. The sun was shining, the birds were singing, and the trees were a study in different shades of green. Bob seemed in a good humor, too, which made things much better. I ignored the undercurrents.

I thought, "Things must be going right for him. Maybe his mother is better and *Weird Tales* has paid him." They were subjects I didn't want to bring up, but I did say, politely, "How's your mother?"

"She seems better."

I didn't push it, and he didn't say anymore. I hear, though, they still keep the nurses.

I said I was so happy to have the play over I felt that school was out. No matter whether the supervisor came or not.

That started things off well. "Were your things ready when the supervisor came?" he asked. "Were your papers all graded and bound, the way she wants them?"

"Oh, God," I said, nearly keeling over. "No. She came like a thief in the night . . . unexpectedly. I almost died."

Bob laughed and wanted to know what I did when she came.

"I ran down the hall and motioned for Nat to come out of the office. I backed my ears and told him my displays were not ready. I told him that, sure enough, he was right. I hadn't done anything for the last five weeks but work on that play! Oh, man! Talk about being scared! I was trembling."

"What did he say?"

I groaned. "It's when Nat doesn't say anything that he scares you to death. He dropped his head, and his lips sort of turned white around the edges. He looked at me and didn't say a word. I prayed the floor would open up and swallow me. He stood there a minute before he said, 'Well, there's not much we can do now, is there?' If he'd stuck a knife in my heart and turned it a couple of times, I'd have felt better."

Bob threw back his head and laughed. The more he seemed to enjoy my story, the more I embellished it, trying to keep the shadow of another day from coming between us.

"I don't know how I lived through it," I said. "The Lord was with me. Later, I found out that, after Miss Stamford looked through some of the beautiful, well-organized materials the other teachers brought her and was getting ready to visit their classes, she told Nat she had to make a speech in the near future, and she didn't know how to write it. Nat said, 'We'll get Miss Price to write it for you.' Well, there they came down to my room where I was frantically trying to get some themes corrected, and asked me to write the speech."

"Of course you were glad to," Bob said dryly.

"Wrong!" I said. "I wanted to write that speech the way I wanted her to ask to see the English work I was supposed to have gotten ready. I was too upset to write a speech."

"But the boss asked you to write it, and you did," Bob insisted.

"What else can you do when they've got you facing a firing squad?" I said. "I managed somehow. What a day! Miss Stamford would come into my room, sit down, and you could hear yourself breathe, the kids were so quiet. She'd tell me something else she needed to say in the speech; then she'd rush off to visit someone else. Before I could get my head to working, Nat would come in and say, in hushed tones, 'Did she ask to see your English display?' I'd tell him she hadn't; he'd heave a sigh and go on. The whole day was like that. Miss Stamford in. Miss Stamford out. Nat coming in wanting to know what she'd said, heaving a sigh and going out."

Bob was laughing. It was the first time since February I'd see him laugh as if he really enjoyed it. "Did it ever occur to you they may have been pulling your leg?"

"If they were, they pulled it off and hit me in the face with it."

Bob shook his head, still smiling. "What was the final verdict? What did she say?"

"She said the school was great and deserved full accreditation. She thanked me for writing the speech for her."

While Bob seemed interested in all my activities, I sensed a deeper emotion in him. For one thing, he didn't have anything bad to say against Nat or the supervisor. Usually, high school administrators and officials bring out the worst in him. Sunday, he simply enjoyed the fact I'd had a hectic day, but he said he knew that, as usual, I would survive.

He even gave me a sort of left-handed compliment. He said if I could write the way I talked, I'd have no trouble selling my stories. But, then, he ruined that, for he thought probably part of the telling was the animation of face and body, and all the inflections of the voice.

I said, "I love you too."

He stopped the car in front of the house he wanted to show me. It was old, dilapidated, broken, but set in the midst of primitive beauty. All around it was a jungle of tangled vines, bushes, and trees—live oaks and some I didn't know the names of.

"One day last fall," he said, "I was driving down this road and passed this old house. I got by it before I realized what it was. I stopped, backed up, and got out and looked it over. There's a chimney on the side."

He opened the car door for me, and I got out. "This house has known people," he said, talking rapidly. "There are ghosts and yarns here that would make your hair curl."

I looked at him but made no comment.

"A man and woman lived here when the country was first being settled by white people," he went on. "Night after night, the man sat with his gun across his knees, ready, watching that thicket over there where a thief, a gunman, or an Indian might be hiding." He paused; then smiled. "But when I saw this house, I thought of one of Mammy's witch stories."

We walked across the weedy, grassy yard and stepped onto the broken porch. A plank or two had been torn up.

"It's sad when a person dies," I said, "but it is also sad when a house dies but still keeps standing up as if trying to keep on living."

Bob nodded. "This one especially. Come on in."

He pushed open the old door and then had to hold it to keep it from falling.

We walked into a big room which must have served as a living and bed room combined. Little clumps of straw covered the floor. Whoever owned this house now used it to store hay in. I glanced around the room. It was strangely free of cobwebs, and if there were rats about, they were quiet. The fireplace on the west wall contained wisps of hay and briars. Beside the fireplace, there was a crack in the wall two or three inches wide.

"Look," I said, walking to the fireplace. "I wonder how the people kept warm on cold winter days."

"Cracks like that are not uncommon in old houses," Bob said. "That witch story your grandmother tells could have happened right there. The lady could have sat by that fireplace and that crack in the wall and made her incantations: 'Through fire . . . through flood . . .' "

I laughed because the story had made such an impression on him.

"This isn't a log house," he went on, "but I figured it could have happened here. If there were schools for witches in Alabama, there were bound to be witch schools in Texas."

I hadn't thought about that. Mammy had always described Alabama so vividly, I thought those stories of hers could only have happened there.

"I wonder how long this house has been vacant," I said, walking to the door of the small, narrow room adjoining the large one.

Bob shrugged his shoulders. He moved nearer the fireplace and stood with his back to it. "I like the house, and so I thought I'd bring you out to see it. No other reason, I suppose."

I moved about, trying to find my story, as he seemed to want me to do. A long porch, the width of the house, ran across the back. I stepped onto it, and I saw an old water-shelf from the wall of the house to one of the posts that supported the porch roof.

"Look," I called "Here's where they kept the water buckets. They're bound to have had a washpan here, too, so that people could wash their hands. Oh, this is a nice shelf. It's long enough and wide enough for four or five buckets. Did you ever live in a house with a water-shelf?"

Bob leaned against the side of the door. "Sure. We had a gourd dipper to drink out of."

"We only had a tin dipper," I laughed. "But we had an oaken bucket. In the summer, Mammy wrapped wet towels around it to keep the water cool."

"Best water in the world." Bob stepped off the porch into the yard and walked a few steps from the house. "Here's their old cistern. Reminds me of the one at that old house on your grandmother's farm."

I looked at the thick growth of trees and bushes near the house and tried to let my imagination picture the people who had lived here. Bob intended that I should find a particular story here, and that effort on his part interfered with my finding one. All I could see was a big man whose smiles could not hide the dark shadows in his eyes.

Suddenly, Bob began to talk about my stories he had read. He glanced at me now and then, to see if I were listening. Over and over, I had asked him to tell me what was wrong with them. He had written to Kline for me, read them, complimented me as much as some editors did, but he'd never really talked to me about them.

"Last fall, I stood on that porch, leaned against one of the posts and thought about the way you had written up that witch story Mammy tells."

He shifted his weight and leaned, half-sitting, on the cement slab around the cistern. "This is beautiful country, Novalyne, and there are yarns here waiting to be written. You've lived here all your life. Why don't you write about it? You ought to, you know. A person has to write about the things he knows, even when he puts the action in a foreign country."

Quickly, I tried to explain that my stories were laid in this country. He shook his head. "They're not laid anywhere."

I didn't answer.

We heard a cow bell a little distance from us, and both of us turned our faces in that direction and waited. It didn't seem to come any closer.

"You could write about people who lived in this old house," Bob said earnestly. "You've seen it, walked through it, stood on the porch and looked into the same trees and yard some other young woman looked into. You know this house because you've known others like it."

He stooped to pick up a little blue flower, twirled it a moment and then threw it down. "If you have to have a love story, can you imagine getting a drink from one of the buckets on that shelf? Suppose you were a very lonely, beautiful girl, and you came out here to get a drink. While you were drinking, you saw a handsome Indian brave come out of the trees there. Everything in your experience is against such a man-woman relationship. What you decided to do about the Indian would be the yarn you'd write."

I laughed. "I can imagine getting a drink from one of the buckets. I can imagine being lonely, and I can see the handsome Indian stepping out from the trees. If I were lonely and he were handsome, I'd swallow the dipper and chew up the bucket, but that's as far as I can imagine. The story ends there."

"Why in the hell would you stop just as it got interesting?"

I walked to the edge of the porch and sat down. "Because the next thing I would think of would be telling the brave to take a bath, wash off the warpaint, get a good suit of clothes, and go with me to Sunday School."

Bob groaned. "God. Maybe you're right to stick to teaching."

He was silent a minute; then he began to talk of the different people who may have lived here. One, a big, dumb cowboy, so strong he could pull up a young oak by the roots. Bob talked, too, of the real problems men probably faced here. Disputes over land and water rights. Disputes over cattle. Feuds worse than those of the Hatfields and the McCoys. In all the stories he talked about, there was fighting and killing and one man getting the best of a dozen others.

Finally, I interrupted him. "Bob, you keep talking about stories I might write. What about you? Why don't you write all these things you're telling me to?"

He walked impatiently away from the cistern. "I can't write anything anymore," he said harshly. "No time. Never any time. I get started; I have to stop."

He began to pace up and down the yard, rubbing a hand across his forehead. "I'm burned out. You pound out yarn after yarn—sometimes ten or twelve thousand words a day. You work your damn guts out. Finally, you know you're burning out—that the time is coming fast when there won't be anything left. Nothing at all."

I watched him, trying to understand what it must be like. At the pace he'd always gone—no time for relaxing, being part of a town—only a few friends and not much time with them—that fear was inevitable, I suppose.

"Bob, I don't think you're burned out. Why here today, you've talked about a dozen or more different stories. It seems to me all you'd have to do would be sit down at the typewriter—"

He ran his fingers through his hair and began to talk, but I wasn't sure he was talking to me.

"This country is full of yarns—this house—everywhere—" He spread his arms. "I see them, but—No time. They're everywhere just waiting to be written. You've always talked about writing, and you've asked for help. I'm a damn fool, I reckon, but I thought maybe if I pointed some of the things out, you might— Well, hell!"

I was confused and frustrated. I could see great possibilities in the stories he suggested, but I didn't want to write them. I didn't want to hurt and disappoint him again, and so I had to try to explain.

"Bob, I don't want to write about fighting and killing and pulling oak trees up by the roots. You tell me to write of real problems, but some of the problems you tell me are not real to me. I suppose they don't have to be real in humorous tales, but some of the fighting you talk about wouldn't be very funny anyway. The people who lived in this house probably didn't have much fun. They worked hard from sunup to sunset. Even the weather could be a real problem to them."

Bob stopped his pacing a moment. "You're right. The weather we had last week could be quite a problem to people living on this farm."

This was safer ground for me. "Did you ever see anything like it? It rained a week ago Thursday, and before the rain dried off, we had a dust storm! Then before the dust settled, it turned so cold, people are worried about losing their fruit crops. Then beautiful sunshine again. Rain, dust storms, cold and beautiful sunshine—all in the space of a week at the end of April."

"The weather is a problem to farmers, all right." There was indifference in Bob's voice.

I pounced upon his admission. "It surely can be. When I was a kid, one year we had a beautiful oat crop. A few days before the harvest, we had such a hail storm the oats were almost destroyed. Mammy cried."

I sat, remembering how hurt and scared I was when Mammy cried.

Bob shook his head. He stopped his pacing and walked to the opposite end of the porch from me. He put one foot on the porch and leaned his arms on his knees. "Novalyne, you've lived through a lot of problems. You know them first hand, problems such as the people who lived here faced, but in your yarns, your girl never faces real problems. They're just— Well, hell, just nice."

"Why do I get little notes or messages on my stories?" I asked. "Are editors just mean? Do they just pay you nice compliments to make you think you're getting somewhere?"

Bob laughed shortly. "Editors can be lousy, all right, but I think they write little messages to encourage someone they think may eventually make it. I think, myself, you do have talent."

I sighed and stared into the trees.

"I don't mean to criticize you," he said, "but that yarn about witches you gave me to read last spring didn't sound as full of guts and blood as it did when Mammy told it to me. Your story had a lot of good things in it; the first page was real good. It—"

"I learned that from you," I said. "I think your stories are just great the way you begin them."

Bob straightened up and smiled. "Tell a man he does something well, and he eats out of your hand. That's the trick, ain't it?"

"I don't have to play tricks on you," I said. "You do something I think is good and I tell you. It's that simple."

He sat down on the porch, picked up some gravel and flipped the tiny pieces one by one into the yard. He concentrated on flipping the bits of gravel with his thumb as though it were important. I thought, with amusement, that with some men I might be afraid to sit here on the porch of a lonely old house and look at the thick growth of trees. With Bob, I was not only safe, but untouchable. He'd stay so far away from me I'd never get a wrong impression of his intentions. Especially since that date in February.

"What was wrong with the story as I wrote it?" I asked. "I know Mammy could tell it better than I did. I used to listen to those stories of hers, and I couldn't sleep at night I was so scared."

Bob shook his head. "I'm no authority on slick magazines."

"You sell what you write. I get notes. I've sent that story off before and the editor wrote me a note and said, 'You might tighten.' I didn't know what he meant."

Bob nodded. "I think he meant it was too long for his magazine, too long and too rambling. After the first page, you spent the next ten—I counted them—explaining a good beginning. Leave out those ten pages and it would cut the yarn down by about twenty-five hundred words. Give readers a lot of action and explain only as much as you absolutely have to."

I sat for a minute, thinking of the Conan story Bob had liked so much. Funny, his main character in that story wasn't Conan. Another fellow in trouble was the hero. You didn't have time to get bored.

"Another thing," he went on. "Your yarns never have any real conflict. Your girl comes from a good home; everybody loves her; everything's pleasant. She is happy, and, if she wants something, she gets it."

I took a deep breath. He was right. Editors sometimes called my plots thin.

Bob turned suddenly to face me. "What about you, the unwanted child? At least, you think your dad left home because he didn't love you. You felt your stepfather's people put up with you as a sort of necessary evil. You said they wanted your mother to give you away—to your grandmother. Why don't you write about girls with problems like that?"

"I can't. It hurts too bad."

Bob laughed and got up from where he was sitting and walked about the yard, talking, "All of us hurt. We love. We hate. We win. We lose. We have more enemies than friends. Friends become enemies. We see our parents grow old, become sick and suffer pain. When you write about a girl who doesn't have anymore trouble than which man to choose or which dress to wear, then you're writing about something that never was. People don't want to read yarns like that. Hell. Nothing goes right in real life. You try to help somebody and get kicked in the teeth for your pains. With some of us things don't ever go right."

He paused and looked at me. "When I saw this house, I thought of some of the yarns you write, and I thought I'd try to help someway. Life out here wasn't all sweetness and light. Gunmen roamed the countryside. The weather. Every damn thing you can think of happened to them. But it's the blood and guts life itself is made of. Ready to go?"

The question came so quickly and so unexpectedly I got up in a hurry and started around the house to the car. Bob followed. Neither of us said a word. For a while, he seemed so silent and morose I kept still.

Without warning, he launched into one of his stories about gunmen who used to live in this country. "Some of them got respectable jobs and became good citizens. Some even got to be a sheriff."

He told me a long story about Billy the Kid and John Wesley Hardin and talked glowingly about them. "Talk about your lily-livered psychologists of today," he said vehemently. "They are just pale caricatures of psychologists. By damn, the real gunman like John Wesley Hardin was a better psychologist than any of the sophisticated bastards around today. He could read a man's every thought. He could—"

"Bob," I interrupted, "you're always talking about our rotting civilization and foolish psychologists. You abhor the things a lot of men like. Well, I respect your ability to write. I think you're great, but I also think your ideas about civilization are all wrong."

He glared at me. "You're the one who's—"

"Just let me talk," I said firmly. "Your gunmen were a dirty, stinking, lowdown breed of men and not worth a good man's bullet."

When you emphatically contradict Bob, he nearly knocks the steering wheel out of the car, runs his fingers through his hair, and glares at you worse than Dr. Howard does. He did it all when I said what I did. But I was not about to shut up.

"Let me tell you how I feel about them," I said. "If there's anything wrong with America, it's in our perverted sense of making heroes out of the wrong people—people like John Wesley Hardin and John Dillinger."

"John Wesley Hardin was—" he began.

"Listen to what I'm trying to tell you," I said. "Two or three years ago, I read something in the newspaper about a woman who had run a house of prostitution in some big city. She was old. Her house was closed, and she didn't have any money. To make matters worse, she fell and broke her hip. You know how she decided to make money?"

I didn't let him answer. "Well, she decided to open her house like a theatre to paying visitors, and she lectured on the life she'd lived and the girls who'd lived there."

Bob glared at me. "What in the hell has that got to do with gunmen?"

"It has to do with what you call our rotting civilization. I could admire the old woman's ingenuity, but what about the people who went to her house in droves to look it over and to hear her lecture? We Americans have become so interested in the underworld that we admire and make heroes out of rotten gunmen like John Wesley Hardin and women prostitutes. Look at some of the movies. The heroine is a loose woman with a heart of gold. Well, maybe you're right. Our civilization is in a bad way. A very bad way."

"You miss the whole damn point," Bob barked.

I knew he was downhearted, and I appreciated his helping me with my stories, but I was tired of his everlasting holding up bums like John Wesley Hardin as a hero.

"I don't miss the point. You do when you hold such rascals up as heroes."

Evidently, I had hit a raw nerve in Bob. He speeded up the car, and I had to hold on for dear life. Then, of course, my crazy sense of the ridiculous got the best of me. I began to laugh.

Bob looked at me as if I'd lost my mind.

"Bob," I said, when I could get my breath, "I want to tell you something: I did have a good time today, and I want to thank you for telling me what is wrong with my stories."

The car slowed down. "My God," he said hoarsely. "God! Women!"

Which way is Up? Which way is Down?

Bob is an enigma to me. I think, according to things I've read, that women are supposed to be the enigmas. In our case, it's not a contest. Bob is it.

The other Sunday, when we came home, he hurried up to the door with me, turned with a curt "So long," and left me standing there, not knowing whether I'd ever see him again or not. But today, a week and four days later, I came home from school and saw his car at the curb!

He said he had a few minutes and decided he'd come over and talk with me for a while if I cared to ride around. He looked disheveled and distraught, and so, dumb me, I tried to be cheerful.

I hoped we could ride around without my getting him angry. I told myself very firmly that I was going to be pleasant and agreeable with him. Oh, me! I got mad at him and even madder at his mother! Poor sick woman; I became angry at her for something which she may not be responsible for.

Bob asked about school, and I rattled on and on, even when I knew he was only half listening. I thought he had probably come just to hear me chatter about something far removed from his daily life.

His real feelings came out. He'd been able to sell *Argosy* a couple of yarns, and he had two or three other western heroes going to other magazines. There he was, trying to write and getting interrupted every few minutes! It wasn't, he said, that he didn't want to do whatever his mother needed. She came first in his life, but those people they'd hired to help out couldn't turn around without coming in and asking him how to do it. He glared accusingly at me, as if I'd hired them and sent them there.

He said he didn't want to try to write anything but westerns, nowadays, which he guessed would please me. But he was going absolutely crazy the way people interrupted him. His mother never called him in the middle of a scene he was just getting right. She understood that a man has to be left strictly alone when he's trying to write.

I'm not a writer, but I knew how upsetting that was; I sympathized with him about it. People who've never tried to write, just don't know what it's like to be interrupted. His mother is unusual in that respect.

"They don't understand," I said, "and, unfortunately, you can't tell them."

For a moment it seemed to help Bob to find someone who knew how badly he wanted to strangle people who interrupted him. He talked about them and about the rest of the world—damn fools who thought sitting down at the typewriter and pounding your guts out was not the kind of job a man ought to work at. They thought a man ought to get a job!

He whirled on me, suddenly, and barked out, "What about your novel? How's it coming along?"

I had just gotten through being sympathetic with him over the way he was interrupted, and, being a woman, I expected him to have the same understanding of my problems.

"I'm having a hard time with it," I said. "I teach all day, rehearse plays at night, come back to my room and study my lessons. After that I try to write, but having a roommate in the room with me, I just can't get started. It's easier to write a lesson plan, correct a kid's oration, or just write something in a journal, anything that doesn't have a plot or—"

"The trouble with you is that you spend too much time with other people." His eyes blazed at me. "I think, Novalyne, you just can't be by yourself long enough to get anything written."

That made me so angry, I hated him and his mother, too, although I'd have been hard pressed to say why it made me hate her. He kept talking about never trying to give advice to people, for they didn't take it anyway. Then he went right on pouring out advice by the buckets full. Before I got too mad to hear what he was saying, I realized he had some excellent ideas.

He thought, since I was so close to the teaching situation which I was trying to write about, too involved with Nat and the students, it might be a good idea to lay the ground work for the novel and perhaps dozens of other stories about school teachers in small Texas towns. I could plan to write them later.

He suggested that instead of trying for a real town I think of a number of towns, study them, read about them, read their histories, then create a town that was a composite of several towns. I would need to write about the people in the town—write the histories of several families. Write the story of the main character from the time of her birth, give her a real background and family, see her faults, her strengths and her weaknesses. Go on with my diaries of things that happened at school, not only this one but at others where I might teach, keep those records for several years. At that time, I'd be able to write a dozen novels. I also needed to write backgrounds of teachers with whom my main character was involved.

That made sense to me. He had told me of his doing something similar to that before he began his Conan yarns. He wrote about the land where Conan lived, the age in which he lived and the people he'd known, the sorcerers he'd met.

"You're right," I said enthusiastically. "You know, in a way, I started doing something like that when I was in high school. I started a diary then, and I also had a book I called 'Vanity Fair' after Thackeray's. I put into it descriptions of people I met and talked to. I wrote up hints for the study of character which I found in magazines, and I wrote down incidents and scraps of conversation."

I was carried away with the idea he had suggested, and I knew how easily I could make Vanity Fair into an essay such as he had written about Conan's world. At that moment, I was in love with him again, ready to go over and run the nurses off and take care of his mother myself in order to spare him the troubles he had. But was my sympathy justified? He's a man, isn't he?

"I can't say much for Thackeray's *Vanity Fair,*" he said shortly. "It's not worth a damn. I don't think you've got the idea at all. I know I'm a damn fool for making any suggestions about your writing or anybody else's. I know, when I stop to think, that every person has to work out his own way of doings things. Your way with diaries and scraps of conversation, and character descriptions is probably as good as any. Just forget what I said. I'll keep my mouth shut in the future."

I was too flabbergasted to get my breath or swear. He talked on about the country around here, the farmers, the thousands of yarns that were here, if a man could only have a fair chance to write them.

It was while he was rattling on and on that I got furious at his mother. I could give her credit for understanding him and his writing. But that very thing made it impossible for him to deal fairly with other women. She had impressed upon him, someway, somehow, that she was the only person who understood him, who loved him and who could help him. She had helped him, of course, but in the helping, she had fused him to her.

When we got back to Mrs. Hemphill's, I was wrapped up in my own thoughts. At the steps, Bob said with more cheerfulness than he'd shown all day, "How about tomorrow night? Think you'd like to ride around a while?"

"I have a date with Pat Allen tomorrow night," I said bluntly. I was mad and hurt, and still determined to tell him the truth about any date I had. "We're going to Brownwood to a show."

I'd almost swear Bob's eyes crossed with surprise. "Oh, well—Pat Allen—"

"Yes. Pat Allen."

Bob gulped. "Well—That's fine. Hope you have a nice time at the show."

"Thank you," I said.

"Well—I'll be seeing you."

"I'll look forward to it," I said.

He walked down the steps, and I quit hating him and felt sorry for the way his shoulders drooped, and the way he shuffled along. A young man. Chained. Old before his time with the responsibilities that flayed his ambition.

Had his mother worried about that? Was it his own dispositon that had trapped him?

The day was over, and I wondered why I couldn't have been more understanding and helpful. I had become angry at him, but I was sorry now. He was a big man, but I was the stronger of the two.

> *Tomorrow—Why, Tomorrow I may be*
> *Myself with Yesterday's Sev'n thousand years.*
> *. . . The Rubáiyat . . .*

The last time I was with Bob, I honestly thought I'd never see him again; but he came over today. For two weeks I haven't seen him or heard a word from him. Then he appears, happy-go-lucky, back in my life. At the wrong time or at the right time. I wasn't sure which.

Things hadn't gone too well at school, and I was down in the dumps. I was walking down the street toward Mrs. Hemphill's, enjoying feeling sorry for myself, and I looked up and saw Bob's car stop at the curb. For some reason, it upset me even more than I was. But when he got out of the car, smiling broadly, and stood leaning against the open door, watching me trudge home, I even smiled back!

I got in the car and we started on a drive—toward the peaks and Coleman. Bob was in a rare, friendly mood.

Things were going well, he said. His mother was doing fine. Naturally, I didn't tell him that yesterday Dr. Howard told me he was very uneasy about her and thought she might go any day. I just let Bob paint his glowing pictures. If he realizes his mother is seriously ill, he must be so worn out he's cheerful. That convinces me that when it's all over and the grief eases a little, he'll really begin to live.

He wanted to tell me how the westerns were going, and though he'd used the peaks in his yarns a dozen times, putting them in various parts of the state, he wanted to look them over again to see if there was something new around them.

I laughed. Then I laughed again when we passed them, and he didn't notice because he was so busy talking about what a fine man Byrnes, editor of *Argosy,* was. He hadn't sent Wright, at *Weird Tales,* a yarn in several months, and Wright still owed him a lot of money. The little man and the little writer didn't have a chance in this rotting world we live in. He was in such a happy mood today, it didn't bother me to hear him talk like that. Let him berate civilization if he wanted to!

He asked me when school would be out, and I told him in a couple of weeks. Then he wanted to know when I was going to Louisiana State University.

"The first week in June," I said. "I can hardly wait."

He seemed so interested that I told him everything I knew about LSU. I'd had several letters from Dr. Wise and I knew what subjects I was going to take: speech correction which I'd never had a day of, and also a modern drama course which was THE course as far as I was concerned.

We drove almost to Coleman, talking and laughing happily. Then he brought me back to Mrs. Hemphill's. He walked to the steps with me; he took hold of my hand and held it tight enough for me to remember always.

"Now, you be sure to write to me," he said. "You have my address: old Lock Box 313, Cross Plains, Texas. I ain't likely to be anywhere else for a good while yet."

I said I'd be sure to write, and I'd tell him all about school and the things I found in Louisiana.

"Now, look," Bob laughed, "Don't get into trouble with some of your ideas down there, and in case you run into any voodoo stuff, you get some of the Catholics to hold a cross and say a prayer for you. Then you write me quick. I'd sure like to go down there and run into some old voodoo magic. There used to be some old Southern homes down in Louisiana, too. We lived down there a short time when I was a kid. My mother and I went through several of those old plantation homes. If you see any of them, you take a good, close look for me. Maybe someday, we'll both make a trip down there and look them over."

All that friendly chatter made me forget about being down in the dumps. I promised to write the minute I got to Louisiana, and the minute I heard of any voodoo magic, I'd be sure to write.

"Now, don't forget," he said lightly. "Write me."

To my surprise, he leaned over and kissed me lightly on the cheek. Right there in broad daylight, in front of God and everybody! I didn't faint. I just thought about it. I felt good and all excited. The day had started wrong, but it was ending on a high note. Things were all right between Bob and me again. We were friends again. Just good friends.

I like it better that way. It's not yesterday that counts. It's tomorrow that counts. All our tomorrows.

Ah, yet, ere I descend to the grave
May I a small house and large garden have;
And a few friends, and many books, both true,
Both wise, and but delightful too!
                                        . . . Cowley . . .

I'm the one who ruins things! I never keep things right between Bob and me.

Last Saturday, Mother came to take me home to Brownwood, and I began hurriedly to pack my things. Before I realized what I was doing, I packed all my books in the big suitcase but left out the history book Bob had given me a short time ago. Mother and I were putting things into the car when Mrs. Hemphill found it. "What are you going to do with this book?" she asked, wanting to be sure I didn't leave anything this time.

"Oh, goodness, another big book," Mother said, as if it weighed a ton. "You've got more books now than we've got space for."

"It belongs to Bob," I said quickly. "I forgot to give it to him the last time I saw him."

"What are you going to do with it?" Mother asked, looking at the clock. "Where does he live? Do you want to take it to him?"

Mrs. Hemphill spoke up again. "It might be easier to take it by Dr. Howard's office. You go right past it on your way home."

Mother looked interested. "Wouldn't that be all right?"

I didn't want to. I wanted an excuse to go by the Howard's house and give it to Bob. I wanted to see him again before I left town.

"It won't take long to run by his house," I insisted.

"Well," Mrs. Hemphill said. "Dr. Howard's office is right there on the main street. You go right past it."

That's what we did. We stopped in front of Smith's Drug Store, and I ran in and gave it to Dr. Howard. He wished me a good summer, and said, heavily, that Mrs. Howard was not any better. I hurried out to the car and Mother and I came home.

I put up my things, got ready for my date with Truett, and began to help Mother get my things ready to go to LSU. Truett came, and I was happy. I did think of Bob now and then, and I hoped things were as good for him as they were for me. It didn't occur to me that I'd done anything wrong until I got this short note from him today:

Cross Plains, Texas
May 27, 1936

Dear Novalyne,

You needn't have bothered about returning the book. I intended for you to keep it, if you wanted it. I hope you enjoy your vacation, and that you'll find Louisiana all you hope it to be. I'm sure the courses of study you're taking will be interesting and helpful. With the best wishes for your health, prosperity and success, I am, as I always was,

Your Friend,
Bob

The note was short . . . so different from the way he had talked the last time I was with him. There was only one way to explain it. I had hurt his feelings by returning the history. I hated it bad enough to cry. And, too, I wanted the history because Bob had said it was good. I didn't want to hurt him again either. Why didn't I just bring it home with me? Why did I let Mrs. Hemphill influence Mother?

I read his note again. My throat was tight and my eyes burned. There was only one thing left for me to do. Tomorrow, I promised myself, when I finish packing for LSU, I'll write Bob a friendly letter—one that will make things all right between us again.

I want them right.

New things . . . New surroundings . . .
A new beginning . . .

Louisiana State University is so big! I've heard there are fifteen hundred people here this summer, all of them had to register at the same time. It was a madhouse. It's as if everybody in Cross Plains had come to the high school gym and tried to fill out a long personal history.

I still haven't written Bob! But so many things keep happening! And I can't write him today because I have to try out for a part in a play. But I'll be sure to write tomorrow and tell him what a madhouse registration was. I've never seen anything like it. He's right about schools. They control you.

Registration took place in an enormous gym. You stood in long lines, listening to old friends greet each other, and, sometimes, you wished you knew somebody to greet.

Novalyne Price

This photograph of Miss Price was made at the time of her friendship with Robert E. Howard.

I met Dr. Wise, the chief man in the speech department, and Dr. Gray, who has a magnificent voice. They're wonderful and very nice. They introduced me to everybody. I met the two professors I'll be taking courses from this summer—Dr. Claude Kantner, speech correction, and T. Earle Pardoe, modern drama and a couple of workshop courses.

I loved Dr. Wise and Dr. Gray. They made things easy for me. Kantner is nice looking as well as nice. Pardoe was nice enough, but he seemed to want to let me know, even before we went to class, that he is an authority on drama. Okay. I wouldn't be here if I were an authority on drama.

My room is in an enormous dormitory with rooms, rooms, and rooms like a hotel. On the first floor, as you come in the front door, there is an office where the receptionist, a very friendly young lady, greets you, gives you messages, and tells you where to find the post office, or a place to eat. They tell me she has a book for the young college kids to check in and check out. Graduate students don't have to sign in and out.

The entrance hall is large and well furnished. Behind it is a living room, larger than our high school gym. It has a grand piano in it and divans, chairs, tables, lamps.

Just off the entrance hall are the "date" rooms, nicely furnished, small living rooms with no doors. You can use them when you have a date or a conference with somebody.

There's a basement to this building too. They have a desk there, where a girl works. You can order things from nearby drugstores, and young Negro boys bring your order there. The girl at the desk telephones you, and you go down and pick up your order. When I write Bob, I'll describe it in detail.

This is going to be a great summer!

My days are in the yellow leaf;
The flowers and fruits of Love are gone;
The worm, the canker, and the grief
Are mine alone . . .
. . . Lord Byron . . .

June 15th, and I had not written to Bob.

It was still new, this attending a university in another state! Exciting! Though the weather was a problem. Coming from dry Texas, I couldn't get used to the hot and muggy Louisiana weather. Heavy, blue-gray clouds threatened rain any minute. But then the sun glared out from behind the clouds and the earth steamed. Perspiration rolled off me, and I found myself thinking of our front porch at home where it is always dry and a cool stiff breeze blows. I longed to be there with Truett.

I put Truett out of my mind and reminded myself to write to Bob. Every day it became even more important to me to make things right with him again. In my mind, I planned the letter; but still, each day, I put it off.

Why is it so hard for me to write to Bob? I have written several letters since I came here. I have written Mother. Truett. I also wrote a short note to Nat, telling him how wonderful it was that I was going to learn so much this summer! Always let the boss know you're good and getting better!

It was June fifteenth, and I still had not written to Bob! The time had come! I promised myself I'd run to the library to do some research and then go back to the dorm and write that letter to him.

In the library, I worked for a while at my carrel near the drama and theatre books. I found the play that Pardoe had been talking about: *The Silver Cord* by Sidney Howard.

In a way, it was a horrible play. While I was reading it, I thought of Bob's mother. Knowing her, I could not read such a play without drawing some comparison between her and Mrs. Phelps—the possessive mother in the play. I closed the book and thought about it for a few minutes.

Then I looked at my watch. Almost two o'clock. At two-thirty, I'd go back to the dorm to write my letter to Bob. Now, I had just enough time to look up another play Pardoe had mentioned. He often mentioned plays, didn't discuss them, but because he had mentioned them, he expected us to know them.

In the stacks, I put my purse down in someone else's carrel. Some other hardworking graduate student trying to keep up with a couple of classes that moved too fast, I thought with a grin. Whoever used this carrel was studying Shakespeare. He or she had left a volume of his plays open. I could not resist the impulse to see what he was studying.

Macbeth. My eye ran down the page to one of Macbeth's speeches:

I have lived long enough: my way of life
Is fal'n into the sear, the yellow leaf;

Bob's words. But not from Byron. I read the lines again.

I have lived long enough: my way of life
Is fal'n into the sear, the yellow leaf;
And that which should accompany old age,
As honour, love, obedience, troops of friends,
I must not look to have;

I could not work any longer. This minute, I was going to my dorm and write to Bob! I gathered up my books and hurried out into the sunshine. The oppressive heat almost stifled me.

As I walked into the dormitory, I smiled and waved to the receptionist, who seemed always on the job. She got up and came to the door of the little office. "Miss Price," she called after me. "Miss Price."

I stopped. She came toward me. "I have a telegram and a letter for you."

"A telegram," I said blankly, "and a letter?"

"The letter is a special delivery. You should have gotten it yesterday. But the telegram—Well, Miss Price, the man at the Western Union wants me to apologize to you. This telegram came several days ago, but, for some reason, they couldn't find you. They didn't call us, that's for sure. And this letter is addressed to you in care of Smith Hall; it should have been delivered yesterday, but it wasn't until this morning . . . late."

She handed me the letter and the telegram. The letter was from Truett. I glanced at it, but I began to open the telegram. The receptionist was still apologizing for the delay in delivering it, saying something about the man at Western Union.

The telegram was dated June 11, 1936, and it was from Pat Allen. It read: "Bob Howard killed himself this morning. His mother very low."

My books fell to the floor. The receptionist picked them up and grabbed my arm. "Miss Price," she said over and over. "Miss Price, it's bad news. I know it is. I'm sorry, Miss—"

I stared at her. I had never seen her before. Her words were meaningless. "Miss Price, sit down. Can I do something? It's the Western Union man's fault. Miss Price—"

"They should have found me," I shouted hoarsely. "They should have found me. Neither the Western Union nor the post office—"

The strange girl was pale and very nervous. "Can I help you to your room, Miss Price? Oh, I'll get someone to carry your books. Here. Here are your books. I'll— Are you all right?"

Automatically, I reached for my books. "I'm all right," I said. "I'm all right." I kept trying to tell her that I must write the letter that I hadn't written, saying something about Bob. And about Truett.

"You don't look or sound all right." The receptionist was beginning to cry. Other girls and women were stopping to ask questions and to try to help.

"I'm all right," I said sharply. "Tell—"

But I forgot what I was trying to say.

I ran up the steps that led to the long hall toward my room. Someone tried to stop me to say something. I didn't stop. The hall stretched endlessly. In a moment, I told myself, I'll turn the corner near my room.

Suddenly, anger spread over me. Anger that shook me. I stopped and leaned against the wall. I brushed my hand across my forehead to wipe away the sweat. I gritted my teeth. I hated Bob! I wanted to grab him and shake him. I wanted to hit him. I swore at him savagely. "You dirty, sniveling coward," I said to him. "You did it. You really did it. You lily-livered, yellow coward. You—"

Another picture of Bob flashed across my vision. It was February twenty-fourth. I saw Bob sitting slumped in his car. I could see his eyes, fear-filled, pleading with me. I could hear his words. "I think I might live if you cared." And I heard my silly answer, "Shave your mustache and I'll talk to you about it."

Nausea welled up inside me. "I hate myself," I mumbled. "I should do what he did. He is good. I am the foolish one."

The nausea was getting worse. I had never felt so sick. Never.

I leaned my face against the cool wall. Whirling, conflicting thoughts: "I hate Bob. I hate him." "No. No. I hate myself." "If only I had written—" "Thinking . . . crying won't erase last February twenty-fourth." "Go on. I must try to go on."

Hannah, one of the Jewish girls who roomed next to me, came around the corner to me. She grabbed my arm. "What is it? What happened? They called me on the telephone—Are you all right?"

I straightened up. I came back to reality from some dark place. I looked at Hannah. She was kind. I didn't want to offend her. I would try all the rest of my life never to offend people. But I wanted to be left alone. I reached my hand toward her.

"The telegram—" I began and stopped.

She took it, opened it, and gave a short cry. "Oh, my God. No. Oh, that boy in the picture? Oh, my God. He was so good looking—"

"Not Truett," I said, "the other one, Bob Howard, the one in the profile photograph. The writer."

"Oh, the writer. Oh, my God. Here. Let me help you."

I knew I was going to be sick, that I could not get myself under control. But if I allowed the nausea to control me, where would it end? I would not give up. I would not give in to my own weakness.

"Hannah," I said, "I have to be alone for a few minutes. Please. Take my books to my room . . . my telegram . . . and the letter."

I managed to smile at her, lifted my head high and went into the bathroom to wash my face. The nausea had given way to a sharp, excruciating pain around my heart. It throbbed there. I could not stop it.

I dreaded going back to my room. Girls were always dropping in. Even here, girls were surging around me when I desperately wanted to be alone. I leaned against the wall for a minute, but someone asked me if something was wrong. I shook my head and smiled. I retreated into one of the stalls and closed the door. My mind was going round and round in a senseless jumble. *I must write a letter—an important letter. If only I could talk with Truett—Why? Why, for God's sake, Bob? Why?*

Something was wrong, but I could not grasp the meaning. *Bob didn't want to die. He'd said, "I want to live. I want to live."* There in the steamy bathroom, I could hear his husky, strangled voice. *"I want to live."*

I may have spoken aloud. "Oh, God, why? Why, Bob? Why?"

Leaning against the wall, through my confused disordered thoughts, one thing became clear to me: I had to try to find answers that would satisfy me. Other people would find easy answers. Easy answers. People right there in Cross Plains would say: "He loved his mother so much he could not live without her." Standing on the street corners, one would say to another: "Did you hear about Robert Howard? Killed himself because he loved his mother so much."

Why, Bob? Wait. I must think.

Dr. Howard himself had said things that would contribute to the myth. One afternoon last spring, Dr. Howard came into the drugstore, put his little black bag down, opened it, and put something inside it. I tried to ask him about Mrs. Howard, but I said what was on my mind, "How is Bob?"

Dr. Howard looked at me, and his eyes were dull. He looked tired. "He's having a hard time trying to take care of his mother and write at the same time."

Anger spread through me; I wanted to ask him why he and the nurses couldn't take care of Mrs. Howard and let Bob work. He must have read my thoughts. "Robert is very devoted to his mother. Very devoted."

He seemed to think that was an explanation. I had to grit my teeth to keep from telling him what I thought.

But people in Cross Plains were not the only ones who would believe that. Maybe, even Clyde too. Before he introduced Bob to me, Clyde said, "Bob's trouble is that he's so attached to his mother—the Oedipus complex." Did Clyde believe that?

If I listened to the words Bob said and didn't hear the emotion behind them, I might have agreed with all the rest. One night in early spring, he had come to see me, without a date. He had been upset. "I'm trying to make new markets; Byrnes at *Argosy* is asking for more westerns. I'll try to get something to him, but, damn, I can't get anything written anymore. Damn it to hell, my time is so goddam taken up with housework and caring for my mother, I can't write. I don't have time to write."

He was distraught, but I could not be very sympathetic then. "I thought you hired some nurses to take care of your mother."

He whirled on me. "I did, damn it," he said loudly. "What you don't understand is they can't give her the kind of care I give her. But it's the nights that are bad. I'm up half the night almost every night. Didn't use to bother me, but it bothers me now. I'm getting old."

"Why can't your father take care of your mother some at night?" I asked. "It seems to me it's as much his job as yours."

Bob lunged, beat the steering wheel, and ran his hand through his hair. "I didn't expect to get any understanding from you. You're the most cold-blooded woman who ever lived."

"I didn't ask you to come over tonight," I said coldly. "I certainly didn't ask you to come over and shout at me when I'm trying to be helpful."

He released his breath in a long sigh, wiped his face, and held his hand to his temples. "I'm sorry. I shouldn't take my hell out on you."

Both of us had been silent for a while. Finally, he said, "I guess you'll never understand that life without her isn't worth living."

I asked, then, about *Argosy* to let him talk about something other than his troubles. I knew him, I think, better than anyone else except his mother. Much better than Dr. Howard did. Today, when it was all so clear, I could only think of the deep, rebellious anger I had sensed in Bob. It had almost frightened me, for although I knew he loved his mother dearly, I believed then, and believe now, he hated her as much as he loved her. He had always said a wife would tie a man down, and that a man would hate anyone who tied him down. Did that same hate apply to a mother?

Oh, God, why? Why? I must think of something else. But I could only think of Bob.

If I were right, he could not live with a love that was filled with hate. What had he tried to do? Assuage his guilt? Get the best of her? Well, he had all right. Pat's telegram had said: *Bob Howard killed himself this morning. His mother very low.*

That meant he had died before she did. A senseless laugh was building up inside me. He beat her to it! He went first! He didn't say, "Mother, I'll take care of you until the end." Instead, he said, "I'll beat you to it, Mother. You've been all my life. I owe it to you. I'll give it to you now while you're still alive to take it."

I shook my head. Those were evil thoughts. I must tell myself that what other people said was true. She was the only person who understood him, the one who believed in him when no one else did. After the contacts he had had with me and with other friends his age, he must have been convinced that no other person would ever love him as she did. He could not live without her support.

Sitting there alone, I knew that the pieces of the puzzle did not come together. Some were missing.

One moment, I thought of Bob with tenderness; the next, with anger. I remembered so many things! The Saturday night I had waited for him to come, but he had not come or called. Later, he had told me his mother needed him. But no matter how angry I got at Bob, my thoughts always went back to the afternoon of February twenty-fourth, and I hated myself for my lack of understanding. Bob had been right. His life was in ruins around him, and I had talked facetiously about a mustache! I hated myself more than I hated him! I wanted to say it aloud. I wanted to shout it out for the whole world to hear. I wanted to yell with laughter: He killed himself, and I am sick of living!

"Novalyne!" The sound of my name roused me from hell. It was Hannah. "Novalyne, are you all right? Hadn't you better—It's after three-thirty. Don't you—I mean, don't you have to be somewhere at six?"

"Yes, thank you," I said aloud. I closed my eyes and talked to myself: I will not scream. I will not cry.

"Are you all right?" Hannah said.

"Yes, Hannah. In a minute, I'll come back to my room . . . in a minute."

"Do you need anything—a handkerchief—a wet towel?"

I shook my head, even though she could not see me. She thought I was crying! People got bad news and cried. I had sworn and almost choked with anger and hate, but I had not cried. I would not.

"I don't need anything. I'll be along in a minute."

She waited a few seconds. Then I heard her footsteps move on. I listened to the sounds around me.

There were girls coming into the bathroom, talking loudly; others going out, talking, laughing; some were singing. Talk. Laughter. The sound of a shower and a girl practicing scales. A music student, no doubt.

I took a deep breath, got up, pushed the door open, and walked back to my room, walking straight and tall. My life was not over. I might hate myself and say that I should kill myself, but I would not.

I was in my room when Hannah and her sister came in. Did I need anything? Rachel held a book toward me, shyly. "Here is a book of prayers," she said timidly. "When things go wrong in my life and I cannot pray, I get this book out and read these prayers. It—it seems to help."

I took the book. "Thank you so much," I said mechanically. "I'm sure I'll find it very helpful."

She smiled and joined Hannah at my desk. They looked at the pictures: one of Truett, one of Bob. I saw Rachel point to Bob's picture and Hannah nodded.

I turned on my roommate's fan and sat down on my bed. Hannah had put my books and the letter on the desk. I glanced at it. I would read it later when they left. Now, I wanted to sit quietly and get cool. In a few minutes, I must take a bath, get dressed, eat supper, and be at play practice by six.

Eat. Go to play practice. Routine. I would go on with all the commonplace things I always did. I would not think of things that caused a deep hurt and pain inside me.

Hannah and Rachel left, and still I sat. My roommate, Patricia, dashed in. She was a library science major and always talking and dashing around. She came in with a long recital about a professor whom she and all the other students hated. She went to the lavatory and got ready to wash her teeth. She turned and looked at me. "What's wrong with you?"

I told her.

"The writer?" she asked.

I nodded.

"Most writers are crazy."

I looked at her. "He was not," I said quietly. "He just didn't want to live."

"Did he kill himself over you?" she asked bluntly, pausing with her toothbrush in midair, the corners of her lips smeared with toothpaste.

I shook my head. "No," I said. My mind went back to a cold February afternoon. All at once, something seemed clear to me. "I could have kept him from doing it."

She finished washing her teeth and left, as always, in a hurry. I stood up. The world moved, and I had to move with it.

I was almost dressed when I heard someone at the door. I looked around. Three girls were standing there, staring at me. One, a tall, brassy brunette, spoke, "Are you the girl whose boy friend killed himself over her?"

I stared blankly at her. I thought: People don't make crazy remarks like that. When I couldn't answer, she tried again.

"We heard there was a girl in this room whose boy friend shot himself because of her. We heard the telegram had been delayed, and when she got it, she almost passed out. Are you the girl? Did he kill himself because of you?"

For a minute, I could not make sense out of her words. I stared at the girls without saying anything. They looked at each other with raised eyebrows. I wanted to scream at them. I wanted to tell them that no one was dead. My words came of their own volition. "He did not kill himself because of me. But I could have kept him from doing it. I could have saved him."

The girls looked at each other, uncomprehending. "What happened?" One of the shorter girls asked.

Suddenly, my control snapped. "Get out!" I shouted. "Get to hell out of here."

I turned my back on them and clung to the lavatory.

A wave of that awful nausea swept over me again, and I said to the empty room. "It's not true. I will not believe it. I will not believe—"

I pressed my fingers against my temples until I could stop shaking. I willed myself to listen to the sound around me. As Bob says, "In sound is reality." I heard sound . . . life around me. Laughter. Singing. Radios blaring. Footsteps now walking, now running in the halls. Phones rang. On the street, cars started and stopped. The late afternoon teemed with sound.

"It has been a long day," I thought, "and I am tired, but I must eat. I must go to play practice."

The radio across the hall was playing one of Bob's favorite songs, "Lazy River."

"Tomorrow," I thought, "I must write that letter."

Letters from home . . .

This morning, before time for either of my classes, I went to the post office to see if I had any mail. I did. Several letters and a copy of an article I'd ordered for a research paper. I went into the field house for a coke, and sat down at the first empty table. A large number of college kids were in there, and the air was heavy with smoke. Above the voices, the laughter, the rattling dishes, a radio was playing.

Although I was glad to receive letters from home, I dreaded to open them! These days, letters had things in them about Bob. I read the words and my mind knew that what they said was true, but in my heart, I could not accept them.

The nicest letter from Cross Plains came a few days ago from Mr. Williams. He's going to the University of Texas this summer, and I hope he will write again soon. He is my tie to Cross Plains and a peaceful life and friendship there.

In his letter, he, too, spoke of Bob. But it was casual, and I could read the paragraph without pain. The paragraph was short.

> It was terrible about Robert Howard and his mother. I am sure that Dr. Howard feels terribly alone. They said that they were buried in Brownwood because Mrs. Howard and Robert were never pleased with living in Cross Plains and were constantly looking forward to the time when they could move to Brownwood.

My first impulse had been to sit down and write Mr. Williams to tell him that even though Bob and Mrs. Howard wanted to live there, for some reason Dr. Howard didn't. But it was too mixed up in my own mind.

I wanted to ask Mr. Williams to write again soon. I needed letters from him so that I could know nothing had changed. He was the boss, and he was looking forward to another school year where we'd win County Meet, and life would go on as it always had. No change.

This morning, I had a letter from one of my students who was a senior when I went to Cross Plains, but, of all my students, she was more of a friend than a pupil.

I opened my other letters, read them, and sat for several minutes before I opened Jennie's. Then I read it slowly, very carefully.

I'm sure you've heard about Robert Howard. Someone told me Pat Allen sent you a telegram and someone else said they had written you. It was so sad. We still talk about it and feel terrible.

That morning he asked the nurse if his mother would ever be any better, and she told him no. He turned and walked away from the bed into the dining room where Dr. Howard was drinking coffee and talking to Mrs. Howard's doctor. Robert said, "They tell me Mother will never know me. What do you think?" Dr. Howard said, "I think this is the end, Robert. She may linger a day or two longer. We can't tell, but the end is near. We must get ready for it." Then Robert asked, "What are you going to do, dad? Where are you going?" Dr. Howard said, "Why, I am going with you, son. We'll go together." Robert smiled at him and said, "Oh, you are, dad? I didn't know."

Then Robert walked out of the back door, raised his arms above his head and began to pray. "Have mercy, God, on my immortal soul. Take me through the valley with you. God, have mercy."

The lady who was cooking for them said that he walked on to his car, still praying. She saw him get in but thought he was going to the post office as he did every morning. She heard the gun and saw him slump over the steering wheel. He lived about eight hours after that.

I read Jennie's letter over twice before I folded it again and put it in my purse. I closed my mind to the things she'd written and sat for a moment listening to the sound of the real world around me.

The radio was playing a plaintive tune. A guitar twanged softly. I heard Bob say, "I like that kind of music, girl."

I thought of Jennie's letter. If she were talking about someone I knew and loved, I would not be able to stand it. The tight feeling around my heart would dissolve, and I would cry.

I would not cry.

Do you, within your little hours of Grace,
The waving Cypress in your Arms enlace,
Before the Mother back into her arms
Fold, and dissolve you in a last embrace.
                    . . . The Rubáiyat . . .

Why does it take me so long to understand? Why did I have to come to Baton Rouge and enroll in a drama course to understand Mrs. Howard? But understanding has only come after I received that telegram.

Since the telegram came, everything has changed.

Sometimes, I wake up at night, suddenly, and I think: A man is dead. But I struggle against thoughts such as that. I must make plans for my future—plans that I know will be carried out. I am coming back to school here next summer and pursue that master's degree. I don't want any doubts about it at all. But there are problems.

One of the first things Bob said when I told him I was coming here was, "I hated school, but I'd go crazy in a big university. I'd hate for some damn bastard to think he had control over me. He would have too, damn him. He'd have power over me because I needed a grade."

He's right. My drama professor has control over me. I need a grade. Speech correction is new to me, yet I don't worry about it. Dr. Kantner's lectures are great. You can make a perfect outline as he talks.

With Pardoe, in modern drama class, which should be a snap for me, it's very difficult. All the students complain about Pardoe's lack of organization. In class, he starts out talking about Ibsen and in two minutes, he's talking about Sidney Howard. That wouldn't be too bad if Pardoe were not always on the defensive, ready to snap at you when you disagree with him. And I do disagree with him.

His wife, a lovely person, comes to class every day. I'm crazy about her. She tells me that Pardoe is very nervous this summer. He had to teach a three-week workshop in dramatics and direct a play in addition to teaching this course. He's here this summer to pass his generals for his Ph. D. It's too big a load for a man to carry.

He has taken a special dislike of me; when I express an opinion, he thinks I'm putting him down. I'm not. I'm trying to understand a lot of things this summer. In drama class, I thought I'd be able to find more meaning in life itself.

My downfall seemed inevitable the morning we discussed Sidney Howard's play, *The Silver Cord.* The truth is Pardoe and the class discussed *The Silver Cord.* I discussed Mrs. Howard and Bob.

All the time Pardoe was talking about the play and what a mean, possessive woman the mother, Mrs. Phelps, was, I thought of Mrs. Howard.

"Sidney Howard's play," Pardoe said, "just misses being a great play. It's good, but it's not great."

Immediately, a student said, "What does it need to make it a great play?"

Pardoe beamed. "In the first place, Sidney Howard can't write a great play." The class laughed. Pardoe played to the audience. "He is no Ibsen. He tried to make Mrs. Phelps into a demon, a woman who seems like a lovely woman, but is a monster who devours her sons. But she is not a great demon. She is just mean. Evil."

I came back to the present from thoughts of Bob's mother. "I agree with you, Mr. Pardoe," I said. "I think Mrs. Phelps is just small and mean, and Bob—uh—I mean, Robin is weak."

I needed to talk about the play, to say what was in my heart. But I had to be careful not to use names, not to tell too much. A time comes when you have to search for truth . . . somewhere . . . in some new place.

Pardoe looked at me without smiling. He said Mrs. Phelps was not a *normal* woman because she tried to own her two sons, body and soul. Own a son? Once, I had said that about Mrs. Howard.

A devilish gleam came into Pardoe's eyes. He wanted to be blasé and shocking. "Mrs. Phelps desired her sons sexually."

He didn't shock me. I could dismiss his words and remember Bob's dislike of Freud. Bob insisted a clean relationship should not be damned with a dirty slur. To Pardoe and the class, I tried to explain that if Mrs. Phelps were evil and couldn't help it, it was another reason the play was not a great play.

Why do we go to the theatre? I answered my own question. "If we go to see the personification of evil without a redeeming trait, then we might as well turn to horror stories which pretend to be no more than that—horror stories. But a good drama pretends more. It pretends to present real people in real life situations."

Pardoe laughed sardonically. "I doubt you could find many women like Mrs. Phelps in real life, but—"

"Oh, yes," I said. "There are a lot of . . . Mrs. Phelps, but they are not entirely evil. They are human. Lonely . . . and . . . just human."

Pardoe spoke crisply, "All right, Miss Price, tell us why and where the play misses the mark."

The class was quiet. Mrs. Pardoe turned in her chair and looked intently at me.

"Mrs. Phelps is not a great woman," I said. "Her marriage wasn't happy, and, in the name of being a good mother, she set out, deliberately, to control her son's . . . sons' lives."

I paused. "There is something innocent about Mrs. Phelps. No mother would consciously *destroy* her son. I see that now. She didn't realize what she was doing when she made herself so necessary to him. Just as Oedipus didn't know he had killed his father and married his mother, so Mrs. How—Mrs.

Phelps did not realize what she had done to her son . . . sons. If she had realized it, then the play would have been her personal tragedy. But in the *play,* the two sons are innocent victims of Mrs. Phelp's mothering. One escapes; one doesn't. The sons are pitiful but not tragic."

I wanted to say that Bob was a tragic character, not a pitiful one. I wanted to explain it, but a moment of panic took hold of me. Mrs. Pardoe was looking me straight in the eyes. Pardoe and the class were quiet. In return for what Bob felt she had given him, he *had* to give her all he had. *His life.*

My mouth was dry, but I went on. "After Mrs. Phelps became a widow, she struggled to make her sons successful, but she made them dependent upon her and tied to her apron strings. She did it consciously and deliberately, without thinking of all the consequences. She hid behind a false sentimentality of the infallible mother. When Christina told her she had failed and that she desired her sons sexually, if she had been innocent of *all* her desires until that moment, she would have been, like Oedipus, completely undone; consequently, she would have been a great tragic character."

Mrs. Pardoe spoke for the first time. "I see what you mean."

Pardoe began to dismiss me, to try to take the class back again. He talked of the author's purpose which needed to be taken into consideration when you analyzed a play. "Mrs. Phelps is a demon," he said again, "but she is not a great demon. That's where the playwright failed."

There were other things I wanted to say, but I kept still. I was riding down a highway between Coleman and Cross Plains, listening to Bob talking enthusiastically about the things a yarn needs to make it go. I could hear his voice, "If you want other people to like your main character, you have to like him. When he bleeds, you bleed."

Bob was right, I thought, and Sidney Howard had also failed because he had not created a Mrs. Phelps he could understand or like. She did not succeed, but she was not defeated. She loses one son, but she keeps one to dominate.

In real life, was Bob Mrs. Howard's triumph or her defeat?

The class ended and I walked out into the hall. My head began to hurt, as I walked to the front of the building. Had I defeated myself in class? I had taken it away from Pardoe; he never really got it back again. Would he hold that against me? I had to have a B in that course.

But the hard part was that I still had some unanswered questions.

I was standing on the steps of the Music and Dramatic Arts building, looking toward the cafeteria when Mrs. Pardoe came by me. She reached out her hand and patted my shoulder.

"You stay in there," she whispered. "You stay in there and keep trying. I think—I think you are right about that play."

She whirled suddenly and walked away. Pardoe came by. "Nice day," he said.

"Yes," I said.

I didn't move. I just stood there. I thought of Bob's mother and innocence. I was sorry for her. In the final analysis, she had not succeeded; she had failed. She had given nothing to the world. Not even an Ervin.

All fled—all done, so lift me on the pyre—
The feast is over and the lamps expire.
                    . . . Lines found in Robert Howard's typewriter . . .

After breakfast, I went to the speech building and walked down the empty hall to the office. No one was there. Dr. Kantner had already told me I had a B in his course. Now, if Pardoe didn't hold my disagreements with him against me, I'd be back next summer to work on my master's. I had to come back!

What time would they be at the office? Maybe if I went back and packed my suitcases, it would give somebody time to get there. Dr. Wise had told me he would contact Pardoe and tell me what my grade would be.

As I started back to the dormitory, I saw Mrs. Pardoe stop her car by the curb and get out. She smiled at me. "You made it!" she called cheerily. "You got a B. I had to come tell you."

Relief spread through me, and I thanked her. I knew she had probably kept Pardoe from giving me a C or even a D. I didn't have to wait to see Dr. Wise. I could come back next summer as a full-fledged graduate student! I'd get that master's degree and maybe do work beyond that! I thanked Mrs. Pardoe again and went back to the dormitory. The bus didn't leave until afternoon. I had plenty of time to pack and get to the bus station.

It was hot and clouds billowed up. All I could think of now was getting ready to go home! I would get home a little after seven the next evening. I wanted to see Truett. That was important to me.

Somehow I'd let Bob know it was worth it to go to school!

At the bus station, I checked my suitcases through to Brownwood, put my ticket in my pocket so that it would be easy to give to the driver. I looked at my watch. I still had time on my hands. I decided to get a coke and sit at the table beside the big plate glass window. I had a few minutes just to dream.

Some little Negro boys were playing in the street with a home-built wagon. One was trying to ride and two others were arguing. I smiled at them. What big problems little kids at that age have! A few drops of rain began to fall, and I looked up at the sky. It was a light rain, but the little boys were hurrying to get out of it.

A line from an old story I had tried to write came back to me. "Once, we walked in the rain together." Suddenly, my mind told me what I had avoided facing all summer: "You will not walk laughing in the rain with your friend again. He is dead. Bob is dead."

It was the first time I had been able to say to myself, "Bob is dead."

My tears, so long pent-up, flowed uncontrollably. I sat, watching the three little black boys struggle to get out of the rain. I watched the rain wash down the window glass and wept.

As I boarded the bus, I held my head as high as I could, refusing to look at the driver or at anybody. The driver made some kind of noise as if to speak of my tears, but my attitude said, "Let me be alone in my grief for my friend." He mumbled and took my ticket. I got on the bus and found a seat near a window.

As the bus moved along, stopping now and then, people were getting on and off, talking, complaining, asking the driver questions. Some sat two or three seats from a companion and talked with him, telling the world what Roosevelt ought to do to get things going again. Sometimes a person sat in the aisle seat beside me, made a move or sound, but I turned my back, faced the window and wept.

I cried, not for my own loss, but for my friend deprived forever of life. The sun . . . the rain . . . green fields . . . trees heavy with leaf in the spring . . . the sear and yellow leaf of fall . . . poems to make cares go away . . . conversations to help the beginning writer . . . All these things Bob could not know again, would not love again.

Books and books and books. Books to write. Books to take people on magnificent, strange, exotic adventures with heroes bigger than life . . . these Bob would not write again. So many things we'd loved. So many things we'd shared. No more. Bob is dead!

It was late when we got to Houston, and the bus for Brownwood did not leave until the next morning. My face was red and puffy from weeping, and I still used as few words as possible. "No, thank you, I don't want a taxi." "Where is the restaurant?" "Where is the ladies' room?"

Beside the rest room, there was a larger room with some comfortable chairs, a couch or two, small tables and a floor lamp or two. I found a good, comfortable chair beside a small table where I could sit and be quiet and still. I took a deep breath and tried to relax. "I will not go to a hotel," I thought. "I'll sit here tonight. This chair is comfortable enough. Why go to a hotel just to stare at a dark ceiling all night?"

I tried to settle down, to take deep breaths, to relax.

Women thundered in and out. They came singly, by twos and threes. The two rooms were filled with women, all talking at once. Some women came dragging children; others came with children running. I closed my eyes and opened them again. I could not relax.

"Maybe if I just watch the people," I thought, "it'll take my mind off the emptiness I'm going back to."

And so I watched the women coming in and going out. A few nice looking, elegantly dressed women came, stayed alone and didn't intrude on your privacy. Others came chewing gum, talking loudly, and managed to ask you a question or two as if resenting your aloneness. Once, when I closed my eyes, a woman shook my arm roughly to ask the time. I told her, turned my back, hid my head in my arms, and wept again.

Things began to quiet down after eleven o'clock. The rooms emptied out, except for a few coming in and out during the early morning hours.

I slept some. Then I waked, not sure whether I had dreamed it or whether I had really seen Bob. I thought of Truett and tried to calm myself by trying to imagine he would say, "Stop crying. Bob did what he wanted to do. He went with his mother."

Yet, again, I wept.

In my mind, I tried to find answers. It seemed to me there were several reasons why Bob deprived himself of the excitement and joy of life. It was not just because he was so tied to his mother's apron strings that he could not live without her. I would never believe that. It was not because I would not let him talk to me of love that day, last February twenty-fourth. In my heart, I knew that. My grief, now, was that I could never get over the foolish way I had handled the situation. If I had been helpful, said the right things, he might have—

I stopped such thoughts. No. Bob could not live in the world as he found it. I had vaguely recognized it, but it was not clear to me until now. He had told me many times when he said, "Life is not worth living in this rotting civilization." He made himself believe it.

Bob was not prepared to stand on the street corners and talk with other men about the rain and the crops and the every day things that men talk about. He was different. He belonged in another century. He belonged in England, in coffee houses where men gathered to talk of the adventures of explorers in the new world, or in Ireland where men were taking part in the adventure of war for freedom.

I was restless. I got up, got a drink of water, and sat back down in my chair. I tried to sleep, knowing I would soon wake up and try to make the pieces of the puzzle fit together.

Two women came in, and I looked at them. But the pain in my heart was renewed in their pain. One was an old, half-crippled Mexican woman with a homemade clothes bag, stuffed full of her possessions. She seemed ill at ease in a strange place. A young girl brought in a tired, crying baby, spanked it to make it stop crying, then hugged it, crying too. I shut my eyes to blot out the sight of her frustration and the old woman's anxiety. My own tears began again, and I wept for all of us in our need and sorrow. I wept for Bob and the book he would never write.

About the middle of May, he had begun to feel pretty good about his markets. "Are you going to try the slicks?" I asked, glad of his progress, glad to see some of the old enthusiasm and exuberance.

He laughed and shook his head. "Naw, probably not. Too many damn sophisticates go for those. My cowherder is just an ordinary, everyday sort of guy."

I doubted that. "What about your novel about the early days of Texas?" I asked.

He sighed and shook his head. "Funny thing about that. I've got a hundred yarns about those adventurers who came looking for gold, but most of them are still in my head. They go away when I try to tie them down."

I looked at him and didn't answer, aware, somehow, that he could not write the book he talked about, the book about those adventurers who rode into Texas to look for gold. Those men were not bigger than life. They might hunt for lost gold mines and stand on lonely roads at night and listen to ghost wagons pass, but they could love a woman for herself; they would not think of her as a goddess to be treated with great deference; neither would they think she was Lilith, a woman who would challenge a man.

Such men as those lonely riders had confidence in themselves as men. They did not need to dream of having the strength of ten men.

"If Bob had been born in some other century, he might have been happy."

I thought that. Then I corrected myself. There were people around Bob who would have appreciated him, but the trouble was he could not believe that this was so. He could not understand that whoever had said, "Why don't you get a real job?" was not the kind of person to accept any writer as a flesh and blood human being next door.

Not even my cousin Enid could believe that an ordinary looking man, like Bob, could write literature, and Bob didn't give her a chance to find out where she was wrong. His actions precluded that. But there were others in Cross Plains who knew Dr. Howard and the family, and who could have been proud of Bob as a writer if he had not acted like an Ervin or that Celtic hero of his who began the line.

William James said you have to believe you are what you want to be. Bob could not believe that. "Life," he had said, "is not worth living unless you have a great love or a great cause, and I have neither." He could not believe in a woman's love, no woman's except his mother's. And how could he find a great cause in a rotting civilization? He turned to books, read them, loved them, and understood them, but he didn't know how to live the common, everyday life he dreamed about.

The night was long. I was glad when it was time to get started for

Brownwood. There were intermittent showers along the way. I managed to sit by a window again. There were occasional tears when I remembered—suddenly—that Bob, my friend, was dead.

Then the weeping stopped. I had cried it all out. I thought of Truett and said to myself. "It is all over between Bob and me. It is over."

It was almost sundown when we got to Lometa and, for some reason, we were going to have a twenty-minute rest stop. My tears were over. I needed to wash my face and put on new makeup before I got to Brownwood.

In the rest room, I saw Mary Hart. My first thought was, "Oh, God, now I won't be alone." But I told myself I didn't need to be alone anymore. I had put everything about Bob out of my mind. The friendship, the understanding, the love—these were over.

I tried to concentrate on life around me. Years ago, I had known Mary, but not well. She wanted to know where I'd been and was surprised that I'd been to school out of state. She told me about her father, Dr. Hart, a former professor of mine.

Outside, the people were gathering around the bus, while the driver was loading and unloading bags. I didn't want to be with the group near the bus. I stepped away from them and from Mary.

Through the trees, I looked at the sky and the sunset. My throat tightened, and I caught my breath. The sky was filled with color. Rose blended into orange and gold. Even the billowing white clouds above the deeper blue were tinged with gold.

As I looked, I heard, as clearly and distinctly, as if Bob had been there beside me. "Now, look there, girl. Look at that sunset. Now that's a beautiful sunset if I do say so myself."

My answer was slow in coming.

"Yes, Bob," I whispered. "I thank you for it. But I know now that it is not over between us, is it? It will never be over. I'll never see a beautiful sunset that I won't hear you say those words."

I took a deep breath and straightened my shoulders. "But tomorrow, Bob, the sun will rise and a new day will begin. There will be laughter, friends, and I will love again."

The colors were beginning to fade to gray as I heard the bus driver call to me.

I had reached an ending . . . a finality. Death had come into my life and claimed a good friend.

I closed the book and put aside the pen.